ENERGY RECOVERY AND SAVING

ENERGY RECOVERY AND SAVING

GIACOMO BISIO, MARCO CARTESEGNA,
AND MARIO GOFFI

Nova Science Publishers, Inc.
New York

Senior Editors: Susan Boriotti and Donna Dennis
Coordinating Editor: Tatiana Shohov
Office Manager: Annette Hellinger
Graphics: Wanda Serrano
Editorial Production: Matthew Kozlowski and Maya Columbus
Circulation: Ave Maria Gonzalez, Vera Popovic and Vladimir Klestov
Communications and Acquisitions: Serge P. Shohov
Marketing: Cathy DeGregory

Library of Congress Cataloging-in-Publication Data
Available upon request.
ISBN 1-59033-454-X

Copyright © 2002 by Nova Science Publishers, Inc.
    400 Oser Ave, Suite 1600
    Hauppauge, New York 11788-3619
    Tele. 631-231-7269   Fax 631-231-8175
    e-mail: Novascience@earthlink.net
    Web Site: http://www.novapublishers.com

All rights reserved. No part of this book may be reproduced, stored in a retrieval system or transmitted in any form or by any means: electronic, electrostatic, magnetic, tape, mechanical photocopying, recording or otherwise without permission from the publishers.

The authors and publisher have taken care in preparation of this book, but make no expressed or implied warranty of any kind and assume no responsibility for any errors or omissions. No liability is assumed for incidental or consequential damages in connection with or arising out of information contained in this book.

This publication is designed to provide accurate and authoritative information with regard to the subject matter covered herein. It is sold with the clear understanding that the publisher is not engaged in rendering legal or any other professional services. If legal or any other expert assistance is required, the services of a competent person should be sought. FROM A DECLARATION OF PARTICIPANTS JOINTLY ADOPTED BY A COMMITTEE OF THE AMERICAN BAR ASSOCIATION AND A COMMITTEE OF PUBLISHERS.

Printed in the United States of America

CONTENTS

Acknowledgment		vii
Nomenclature		ix
Abstract		xiii
Chapter 1	Introduction	1
Chapter 2	First- and Second-Law Analyses of Energy Recoveries in Blast-Furnace Regenerators	9
Chapter 3	Second-Law Analysis of the "Hot Blast Stove / Gas Turbine" Combine by Applying The Parameter "Usable Exergy"	17
Chapter 4	Energy Saving and Improvement of Environment Conditions in Coke Oven Plants	29
Chapter 5	Energy Recovery from Molten Slag and Exploitation of the Recovered Energy	47
Chapter 6	Thermodynamic Analysis of the Use of Pressure Exergy of Natural Gas	59
Chapter 7	Thermodynamic Analysis of Blast-Furnace Top Gas Pressure Recovery Turbines	73
Chapter 8	Combined Helium and Combustion Gas Turbine Plant Exploiting Liquid Hydrogen (LH_2) Physical Exergy	85
Chapter 9	The Possible Utilization of the Thermal Energy Discharged from Sintering Plants of Steel Works	103

Chapter 10	Heat Transfer, Energy Saving and Pollution Control in UHP Electric-Arc Furnaces	117
Chapter 11	Energy Recovery by Evaporative Cooling in Several Plants of the Iron and Steel Industry	135
Chapter 12	Oxygen Enrichment of Combustion Air	145
Chapter 13	Exergy Efficiency and Economic Convenience	153
References		159
Index		173

ACKNOWLEDGMENT

The authors thank Mr. Roberto Martini for his valuable help in the editing of the Figures of this work.

NOMENCLATURE

c_p	$= T \partial_1 s_{Tp}$ specific thermal capacity per unit variation of T at constant p [kJ/(kg K)]
D_c	difference between inlet chemical power of coupled process and that of Cowper system alone of corresponding uncoupled process [kW]
D_u	difference between inlet usable exergy flow of coupled process and that of Cowper system alone of corresponding uncoupled process [kW]
E	(total) energy of the system [kJ]
E_m	mechanical energy [kJ]
E_c	kinetic energy [kJ]
E_p	gravitational potential energy [kJ]
e_r	energy (equal to exergy) recovered as shaft work per mass unit of NG [kJ/kg]
Ex	physical exergy [kJ]
ex	specific physical exergy [kJ/kg]
Ex'	(total) exergy [kJ]
Ex_{ch}	chemical exergy [kJ]
Ex_p	gravitational potential exergy [kJ]
Ex_t	physical and chemical exergy of open system [kJ]
ex_t	specific physical and chemical exergy of open system [kJ/kg]
Ex_c	kinetic exergy [kJ]
$Ex°$	exergy power [kW]
ex_c	specific kinetic exergy [kJ/kg]
ex_{ch}	specific chemical exergy [kJ/kg; kJ/kmol]
ex_{cho}	standard specific chemical exergy [kJ/kg; kJ/kmol]
Ex_p	gravitational potential exergy [kJ]
Ex^*	physical non-flow exergy [kJ]
Ex^*_t	physical non-flow and chemical (or nuclear) exergy [kJ]
$Ex^{*'}$	(total) non-flow exergy [kJ]
Ex_a	actual exergy loss [kJ]
Ex_{rf}	losable (or reference) exergy [kJ]
Ex_{ru}	recovered (and actually usable) exergy [kJ]
Ex_u	usable exergy (referred only to fuel) [kJ]
$Ex_u°$	usable exergy (referred to fuel and to the chosen thermodynamic state of waste gas) [kJ]

ex_u	specific usable exergy [kJ/m³(nTp) or kJ/kg]
$Ex°_u$	usable exergy flow [kW]
$Ex°_{uic}$	inlet fuel usable exergy flow of coupled process [kW]
$Ex°_{uiu}$	inlet fuel usable exergy flow of uncoupled process [kW]
C_{eq}	= equivalent consumption [kJ/h]
G	mass flow rate [kg/s]
G_V	volume flow rate [m³(nTp)/h]
G_V*	specific volume flow rate [m³(nTp)/$t_{dry\ coke}$]
h_r	thickness of cooling pipe [m]
h_s	thickness of solid slag on cooling pipe [m]
I	enthalpy [kJ]
$I°$	enthalpy flow [kW]
i	specific enthalpy [kJ/kg]
i_o	specific enthalpy at T_o and p_o [kJ/kg]
k	thermal conductivity [W/(m K)]
k_r	conductivity of cooling element [W/(m K)]
k_s	conductivity of solid slag [W/(m K)]
LCV	lower heating value [kJ/m³(nTp)]
M	merit factor (referred only to fuel) [dimensionless]
$M°$	merit factor (referred to fuel and to the chosen thermodynamic state of waste gas) [dimensionless]
m	specific mass [kg/t]
P_e	electrical power [kW]
P_t	thermal power [kW]
P_{cic}	fuel chemical power going into the coupled process [kW]
P_{ciu}	fuel chemical power going into the uncoupled process [kW]
p	pressure [bar, MPa]
p_o	environment pressure [bar]
p_l	low pressure [bar]
p_h	high pressure [bar]
Q	heat transfer [kJ]
$Q*$	heat transfer per mass unit [kJ/kg]
Q_o	heat transfer with the environment [kJ]
Q_A	heat flux per unit area [MW/m², kW/m²]
R	ratio of e_r to the exergy decrease per mass unit of NG in an isenthalpic expansion [dimensionless]
R_a	percent fuel reduction [dimensionless]
R_b	percent available thermal energy [dimensionless]
R_c	chemical power saved by means of coupling [kW]
R_u	usable exergy flow saved by means of coupling [kW]
$R_c°$	relative saving of chemical power [dimensionless]
$R_u°$	relative saving of usable exergy flow [dimensionless]
R_f	recovery factor (defined in the paper) [dimensionless]
r_f	exergy ratio (defined in the paper) [dimensionless]
r	enthalpy fraction [dimensionless]
S	entropy [kJ/K]

S_o	entropy at T_o and p_o [kJ/K]
S_s	entropy production [kJ/K]
S_{sa}	actual entropy production [kJ/K]
S_{sai}	actual entropy production of a single process (i) [kJ/K]
S_{srf}	reference entropy production [kJ/K]
S_{srfi}	reference entropy production of a single process (i) [kJ/K]
S_{srfw}	reference entropy production of the whole cycle or pseudocycle [kJ/K]
$S_s°$	entropy production power [kW/K]
s	specific entropy [kJ/(Kg K)]
T	temperature [K, °C]
T°	flue gas exit temperature [K, °C]
T_o	environment temperature [K, °C]
T_{ac}	adiabatic combustion temperature [°C]
T_p	preheating temperature [°C]
V	volume [m³]
V_o	volume at T_o and p_o [m³]
V_f	volume fraction [dimensionless]
v	specific volume [m³/kg]
W	work [kJ]
W*	work per mass unit [kJ/kg]
W'	shaft work (open system) and "useful work" (closed system) [kJ]
W*'	shaft work (open system) and "useful work" (closed system) per mass unit [kJ/kg]
x	dryness fraction [dimensionless]
α	heat transfer coefficient [W/(m² K)]
β	low calorific value fraction of natural gas [dimensionless]
Γ	merit factor of a fuel [dimensionless]
Γ°	ratio of the average lower heating value of all the gas to the thermal energy that is transferred to the hot blast [dimensionless]
δ	= P_e/D_c used fraction [dimensionless]
$δ_u$	= P_e/D_u characteristic parameter of the conversion of chemical power into electrical [dimensionless]
ε	essergy [kJ]
ζ	= Q/(- W') performance [dimensionless]
η	energy efficiency [dimensionless]
θ	= $(Ex_2-Ex_1)/(I_2-I_1)$ exergy factor [dimensionless]
μ	permeability [m⁴/(m² s bar), m²/(s bar)]
μ°	permeation rate [m³/(m² s bar), m/(s bar)]
ν	= $μ(O_2)/μ(N_2)$ oxygen/nitrogen separation factor [dimensionless]
$ξ_α$	thermal efficiency (or effectiveness) of a heat exchanger [dimensionless]
$ξ_β$	electrical engine efficiency [dimensionless]
π'	lower heating-value fraction for the NG [dimensionless]
π"	lower heating-value fraction for the BFG [dimensionless]
ρ	isentropic efficiency [dimensionless]
$σ_r$	relative entropy production [dimensionless]

σ_{ri}	relative entropy production of a single process (i) [dimensionless]
σ_{ri}'	relative entropy production of a single process (i) with reference to the parameter S_{srfw} of the whole cycle or pseudocycle [dimensionless]
Φ	exergy efficiency [dimensionless]
χ_I	enthalpy flow multiplier (dimensionless)
χ_{Ex}	exergy flow multiplier (dimensionless)
Ψ_1	Factor that quantifies, in comparison with the reference system, the different total gas consumption when considering the lower heating value [dimensionless].
Ψ_2	Factor that quantifies, in comparison with the reference system, the different percentage consumption of gases with different merit factors [dimensionless].
Ψ_T	Factor that quantifies, in comparison with the reference system, the different total gas consumption when considering the usable exergy [dimensionless].

ABSTRACT

In this work, the exergy definition and the exergy components are firstly dealt with for the system equilibrium states. Some treatments are made for the non-equilibrium states. Then, one examines energy recovery and saving in several plants. Finally, some elements of exergy efficiency and of economic utility are presented.

ZUSAMMENFASSUNG – Energie Wiedergewinnung und Einsparung - In dieser Arbeit, vor allen Dingen wird die Definition der Exergie und die Bestandteile der Exergie für die Gleichgewichtzustände des Systems behandelt. Einige Betrachtungen werden für die Ungleichgewichtzustände gemacht. Nachher werden die Energie Wiedergewinnung und Einsparung von verschiedenen Anlagen examiniert. Zuletzt werden einige Elemente von Exergie Gütegrad und wirtschaftlichen Nutzen vorgelegt.

RÉSUMÉ – Récupération et économie énergétique - Dans cette pièce, d'abord la définition d'exergie et les composants de l'exergie sont traités pour les états d'équilibre du système. Quelques réflexions sont faites pour les états de non-équilibre. Ensuite on examine le récupération et l'économie d'énergie pour différentes installations. Enfin, on présente des éléments de l'efficacité exergétique et de l'utilité économique.

SOMMARIO – Recupero e risparmio energetico - In questo lavoro sono dapprima trattate la definizione d'exergia e le componenti dell'exergia per gli stati d'equilibrio del sistema. Alcune considerazioni sono fatte per gli stati di non-equilibrio. Si esamina quindi il recupero ed il risparmio energetico in alcuni impianti. Sono infine presentati alcuni elementi dell'efficacia exergetica e dell'utilità economica.

Chapter 1

INTRODUCTION

1.1 HEAT AND WORK TRANSFER

We assume the definitions of heat and work in concordance with those reported by Spalding and Cole (1973). Heat is the interaction between system and environment that occurs by virtue of their temperature difference when they communicate. Work is the interaction between the system and environment, during a given operation, when, if positive, the sole effect external to the system could be reduced to the rising of a weight, if negative, the sole effect internal to the system could be reduced to the rising of a weight: in both cases without transfer of mass.

We can assume also, deriving the idea partly from Huang (1988), that heat is any interaction between the system and environment, without transfer of mass, not accountable for as work.

1.2 SOME REMARKS ABOUT EXERGY

1.2.1 The Origin of Exergy Definition

In each cyclic experiment with closed systems, the ratio of the heat transfer amount to the work transfer amount is a constant. Thus, the consequent mathematical developments have led to a definition of a state function, E, called energy of the system (Faggiani, 1968; Spalding and Cole, 1973).

This has allowed the extension of the principle of energy conservation to the field of thermal phenomena. However, owing to the basic "non operative equivalence" between heat and work transfer, the function E does not mean what is associated to the concept of energy of a system in the common language, more or less clearly: ability to do a mechanical work.

As to the title "What is Energy", McGown and Bockris (1980) answer "Energy is that which makes things go". It is quite evident that the function E does not match these requirements. Indeed, a perfect gas compressed to 100 bar has the same E as the same gas compressed to 1 bar at the same temperature, velocity and height, but a quite different possibility to be utilized.

It is just for putting in evidence the "quality" of energy, i.e. the effects of the second law, that the term "exergy" has been devised; thus it was called by Rant (1956) after having been named in different ways ("available work", "availability", "work capacity" and similar).

The exergy of a system is defined as the amount of work that could be obtained when the system is brought to a state of unrestricted equilibrium (that is: thermal, mechanical and chemical) by means of reversible processes with the environment, having uniformly constant temperature T_o, constant pressure p_o and consisting of substances in thermodynamic equilibrium (Baehr and Schmidt, 1963; Szargut and Styrylska, 1964; Baehr, 1979; Kotas, 1980a, 1980b and 1985; Ahern, 1980; Moran, 1982; Bisio, 1987 and 1989b). No other system (with the exception of the environment) can be altered in these processes (with the exception of the rising of a weight). Therefore, exergy is not a property of the system, but of the system-environment combination, even if one says "exergy of the system" usually for the sake of simplicity.

This definition of exergy entails that the system is in a state of internal equilibrium (uniformity of all intensive properties) and that the environment is in a state of internal equilibrium and its intensive variables do not change during time.

1.2.2 Systems in a State of Internal Non-Equilibrium

The case of a system that is a state of internal non-equilibrium has been analyzed in several papers (Evans and von Spakovsky, 1987a and 1987b; Kouremenos, 1989; Bisio and Pisoni, 1991; Bisio, 1994).

Only internal thermodynamic equilibrium states (quasi-static states in the model of Salamon et al., 1977) can be correctly represented in the various thermodynamic diagrams. Non-equilibrium states can be represented in a conventional way, but only some state functions are meaningful in the various diagrams, while for others functions the diagrams are without any physical meaning.

The concepts of maximum obtainable (reversible) work and the departure of the system state from the environment state are not equivalent, at least in general (contrary to what is said in some books), and are represented, respectively, by exergy, Ex, and essergy, ε. In order to obtain the formulation of exergy, the possibility of reversibility, at least as a limit, is necessary. However, the hypothesis of reversibility cannot be made for non-equilibrium steady states (not even as a limit). For essergy, in the case of a two-variable system, without any reversibility hypothesis, Evans and von Spakovsky (1987a and 1987b) obtained the following relation:

$$\varepsilon = E + p_o V - T_o S, \tag{1.1}$$

where E, V, and S are the system energy, volume and entropy, respectively, and p_o and T_o are the pressure and the temperature of the environment.

This parameter expresses the "distance" of the system state from the environment state. It may be divided into two components. The former, ε_r, expresses the maximum obtainable work (in the case all irreversibilities were eliminated, with the exception of those corresponding to the attainment of the internal equilibrium of the system). The latter, ε_i, does not correspond to any obtainable work. It must be noted that, when the system is not in a state of internal equilibrium, the classic definition of exergy fails. For application purposes, one can refer to the component ε_r of essergy. More particulars can be found in (Bisio, 1994).

The name essergy derives from "*ess*ential en*ergy*".

1.2.3 Environment whose Properties are Varying in Time

The occurrence that the temperature of the environment for some problems is to be considered variable during time was considered in several papers (Fiala, 1981; Bisio and Rubatto, 1988; Bisio, Magrini and Rubatto, 1993). In these cases, it is important to distinguish the surroundings (i.e. everything not included in the system) into two parts. The former is near to the system, it may have heat and work transfers with this system and is called environment. The latter is far away from the system, has no energy transfers with this system directly and is called "rest of surroundings". Generally, the term environment applies to some portion of the Earth and its atmosphere, whose intensive properties do not change notably as the result of any process of the system. However, the properties of the environment can change in course of time (periodically or not), because of interactions between the environment and the rest of the surroundings. E.g., the atmosphere varies its temperature owing to the solar radiation, but not, in an appreciable way, owing to the heat received from any engine.

This topic is meaningful in ice storage plants for room conditioning (the so called "ice-banks"). In a similar way, one can utilize the variable height of the sea in some place to produce electrical energy. In these cases, the variability of the environment operates as if there were "exergy sources" in the "system-environment" combination. In fact, these sources are connected to the decrease of exergy in the "environment - rest of surroundings" combination.

1.2.4 Environment Composed of Substances not in Equilibrium among Them

Most important of all is the fact that in no case one can assume that the environment is composed by substances which are in equilibrium among them, not ever as a first approximation. This remark must be reminded, when a system with chemical reactions for actual applications is analyzed. On the other hand, an environment that is in equilibrium precludes the presence of energy sources and deposit of raw materials, thereby preventing the occurrence of those processes whose exergy efficiency is to be examined.

The exergy of a fluid stream depends upon the choice of the reference environment. This choice, which seems obvious according some authors, is, on the contrary, problematic, since every usual environment is in a chemical state of non-equilibrium. In each actual case, the choice of a suitable reference state is necessary (Szargut, 1980; Kameyama et al., 1982; Morris and Szargut, 1986; Marin and Turégano, 1986; Szargut, 1989; Fratzscher and Michalek, 1989; Munsch et al., 1990; Gallo and Milanez, 1990; Fratzscher and Tetzlaff, 1993; Kirova-Yordanava et al., 1984; Van Gool, 1986, 1992 and 1997).

According to the calculations of Ahrendts (1980), the composition of an equilibrium environment differs distinctly from the real compositions. The equilibrium environment would contain, for example, only a very small amount of free oxygen, insufficient for life, whereas a considerable part of the oxygen would be bound in nitrates.

If a non-equilibrium environment is chosen as reference, parts of this environment possess exergy in respect to one another.

Consequently, several models describing the reference environment have been chosen (Munsch et al., 1990):

(i) an environment in equilibrium,
(ii) an artificial environment,
(iii) a partial environment (Baehr and Schmidt, 1963),
(iv) an environment with reference to the considered process (Bosnjakovic, 1963),
(v) an environment consisting of reference substances of exergy value zero (Szargut, 1989).

All the above-mentioned environmental models enable an exergy analysis within the frame of their material extent. If a model is desired that is suitable for the largest number of processes, but in which the local adaptation of mass composition be dispensed with, the choice of an average mass composition of the environment is convenient. This is applied in the environmental models consisting of reference substances of exergy value zero.

The property of a reference system, consisting of reference substances of exergy value zero and not in thermodynamic equilibrium, although mandatory, is a weakness of this approach. Indeed, the spontaneous conversion of the reference substances produces compounds with a negative exergy, which can be returned to the reference state only by adding exergy. However, negative exergies are not taken into consideration in the definition of exergy (Munsch et al., 1990). Hence, processes giving products with negative exergy values are to be excluded from such analysis. These products include, among others, nitric acid and its salts. Other environment models have been developed for such cases.

A reference state consisting of reference substances of exergy value has been proposed and developed by various authors and in particular by Szargut (1989).

The choice of reference species for chemical exergy does not influence the values of internal exergy losses, but influences the values of external losses remarkably and hence also the values of exergy efficiency. Therefore, the assumption of reference species, present in the actual environment, helps to determine the external exergy losses in a correct way.

The reference species should represent the products of an interaction between the components of the natural environment and the waste products of the process. The most probable products of this interaction should be chosen as reference species. Thus, the products of an interaction with the atmosphere (weathering products), or compounds of the external layer of the earth's crust (e.g., SiO_2, CaO), should be recommended.

1.2.5 Exergy Components

The exergy of the open systems (control volume) in steady state, Ex', can be divided into four main components (Kotas et al., 1987):

(i) Physical exergy, Ex, that is the work obtainable by taking the system, by means of reversible processes, from its temperature T and pressure p to the temperature T_o and pressure p_o, exchanging heat only with the environment, and keeping height and velocity constant, as well as avoiding any chemical reaction or mixing with environment (restricted equilibrium).

To avoid thermal irreversibilities, the system, initially at the state 1, must exchange heat only when it is at temperature T_o, and then, owing to the first law of thermodynamics:

$$Q_{1o} = T_o (S_o - S_1) = W'_o + I_o - I_1 . \tag{1.2}$$

Owing to the definition of physical exergy, if also mechanical irreversibilities are avoided, one has:

$$Ex_1 = W'_{1o} = I_1 - I_o - T_o (S_1 - S_o) . \tag{1.3}$$

Thus, we have only from the two laws of thermodynamics:

$$Ex = I - I_o - T_o (S - S_o) . \tag{1.4}$$

We note that this result is obtained without the use of any mechanical model, contrary to what has been done by other authors.

- (ii) Kinetic exergy, Ex_c, equal to kinetic energy E_c, when velocities are relative to the Earth surface.
- (iii) Gravitational potential exergy, Ex_p, equal to gravitational potential energy E_p, when heights are evaluated upon the sea level.
- (iv) Chemical exergy, Ex_{ch}, that is the work obtainable by taking the system, by means of reversible processes, from the state of restricted equilibrium to the one of unrestricted equilibrium with the environment, so that both the system and the environment consist of the same components always at T_o and p_o (Baehr and Schmidt, 1963; Szargut and Styrylska, 1964; Baehr, 1979; Ahern, 1980).

The system state of unrestricted equilibrium with the environment is named "dead state".

We remark that physical exergy is not a part of physical enthalpy, but its value can be both higher and lower than that of physical enthalpy; strictly speaking, the two parameters have in common only the measure unit (kJ).

The exergy of a closed system, $Ex^{*'}$, is named "non-flow exergy" (Kotas et al., 1987). $Ex^{*'}$ can be divided into four components:

(i) Physical non-flow exergy, Ex^*.

To obtain Ex^*, let us define as "useful work", W', the algebraic difference between the total work exchanged by the system and the volumetric displacement work against the environment (atmosphere) pressure p_o:

$$W'_{12} = W_{12} - p_o (V_2 - V_1) . \tag{1.5}$$

Indeed, $[p_o (V_2 - V_1)]$ can not be technically employed (Klenke, 1978).

To avoid thermal irreversibilities, the system, initially at the state 1, must exchange heat only when it is at temperature T_o, and then, owing to the first law of thermodynamics:

$$Q_{1o} = T_o (S_o - S_1) = W_o + U_o - U_1 . \tag{1.6}$$

Owing to the definition of physical exergy, if also mechanical irreversibilities are avoided, one has:

$$Ex^*_1 = W'_{1o} = W_{1o} - p_o (V_o - V_1) = U_1 - U_o - T_o (S_1 - S_o) - p_o (V_o - V_1) . \tag{1.7}$$

Thus, we have only from the two laws of thermodynamics:

$$Ex^* = U - U_o + p_o (V - V_o) - T_o (S - S_o) . \tag{1.8}$$

(ii) Kinetic exergy.
(iii) Potential exergy.
(iv) Chemical exergy.

1.3 EXERGY EFFICIENCY AND ENTROPY PRODUCTIONS

1.3.1 General Statement

The exergy efficiency Φ for an adiabatic expansion is usually defined as the ratio of the shaft work to the exergy variation of the system:

$$\Phi = W'_{12}/(Ex_1 - Ex_2) , \tag{1.9}$$

from which:

$$\Phi = (I_1 - I_2)/[I_1 - I_2 - T_o (S_1 - S_2)] , \quad \Phi = 1 - T_o (S_2 - S_1)/[I_1 - I_2 - T_o (S_1 - S_2)] . \tag{1.10}$$

Note that Φ is the ratio between two effectively homogeneous quantities concerning the same process. In the expression of Φ the actual entropy production is multiplied by environment temperature T_o independently from temperatures T at which it occurs.

Furthermore, exergy efficiency, as is shown in several papers and books, is applicable to any type of processes: either in the presence of one or more energy transfer, or in the absence of exchanges with the environment, and therefore only with the variations of the exergy components of the system (physical, kinetic, gravitational potential and chemical exergy).

Now, let us consider every kind of processes. We observe that Baehr (1968) examined the possible formulations of exergy efficiency deeply and showed how the various inlet and outlet exergies may be distributed between numerator and denominator. He explained the various possibilities for exergy expressions in a general table; any suitable formula previously proposed by different authors has its place in that table.

However, the exergy efficiency expressions proposed by the various above-said authors cannot fulfill for every process the second requirement that we have pointed out, i.e. Φ

variable between zero (for no useful effect) and one (for no irreversibilities), at least in principle.

To achieve this aim, we think it is suitable to find a definition of the efficiency Φ, for all applications, as the ratio of the recovered exergy to the "losable" one (Bisio, 1987 and 1989b). By the term "losable exergy", we mean the highest "loss" of exergy that can occur owing to the irreversibilities in the selected operation domain. Note that a system can generally achieve the path from initial state 1 to final state 2, in principle at least, in the infinite ways included between the way with the highest useful effect and no irreversibilities (upper limit of operation domain) and the one with no useful effect (lower limit). As reference entropy production, S_{srf}, we choose the one corresponding to the lower limit. Consequently, the product ($T_o\, S_{srf}$) represents the "losable" or "reference" exergy, Ex_{rf}, according to our definition, since it is the highest value that can be lost within the formulated assumptions.

If we indicate the actual entropy production by S_{sa}, ($T_o\, S_{sa}$) represents the actual exergy loss, Ex_a, and ($T_o\, S_{srf} - T_o\, S_{sa}$), as the difference between the losable exergy and the lost one, is the recovered exergy, Ex_{ru}. It follows in all cases:

$$\Phi = (T_o\, S_{srf} - T_o\, S_{sa})/(T_o\, S_{srf}) = (Ex_{rf} - Ex_a)/Ex_{rf} = Ex_{ru}/Ex_{rf} = 1 - S_{sa}/S_{srf} = 1 - \sigma_r\,. \tag{1.11}$$

The parameter σ_r is the relative entropy production. It can obviously vary between zero and one, whereas Φ varies between one and zero. In this way, the second requirement we have formulated above for a meaningful statement of efficiency is fulfilled.

1.3.2 Formulations of Exergy Efficiency for Single Processes as a Part of a Cycle or of an Open Series of Processes

In a process (i) belonging to a cyclic or pseudocyclic series, it does not seem meaningful to consider the relative entropy production σ_{ri} as the ratio of the actual entropy production S_{sai} to the reference entropy production S_{srfi} of the single process. For both conceptual and practical purposes, it seems more valid to consider for every process the relative entropy production σ_{ri}' as the ratio of the actual entropy production S_{sai} of this process to the reference entropy production S_{srfw} of the whole cycle or pseudocycle.

Let us consider the process series 1-2-3-4.... (cyclic or pseudocyclic). One has:

$$\Phi = 1 - \sigma_r = 1 - [\sigma_{r12}' + \sigma_{r23}' + \sigma_{r34}' + ...]\,, \tag{1.12}$$

where:

$$\sigma_{r12}' = S_{sa12}/S_{srfw} = [S_{sa12}/S_{srf12}]\,[S_{srf12}/S_{srfw}] = \sigma_{r12}\,[S_{srf12}/S_{srfw}]\,, \tag{1.13}$$

and then:

$$\Phi = 1 - [\sigma_{r12}\,(S_{srf12}/S_{srfw}) + \sigma_{r23}\,(S_{srf23}/S_{srfw}) + \sigma_{r34}\,(S_{srf34}/S_{srfw}) + ...]\,, \tag{1.14}$$

$$\sigma_r = \sigma_{r12}\,(S_{srf12}/S_{srfw}) + \sigma_{r23}\,(S_{sf23}/S_{srfw}) + \sigma_{r34}\,(S_{srf34}/S_{srfw}) + ...\,. \tag{1.15}$$

It is easy to see that the parameters σ_r' of the single processes give more directly than the parameters σ_r the effect of the irreversibilities of every process on the global exergy efficiency of cycles or pseudocycles.

Kotas (1980b) has remarked that there are parts of plants in which there is no recovery of the losable exergy for intrinsic reason, as, e.g., in the case of throttling valves. For these parts, one has always ($\sigma_r = 1$), and that is usually of poor meaning. If one considers, on the contrary, the whole cycle of which the throttling valve is a part, one has a ($\sigma_r' < 1$), different in each case, which gives a measure of the irreversibility weight of such throttling valve on the global exergy efficiency of the plant.

Chapter 2

FIRST- AND SECOND-LAW ANALYSES OF ENERGY RECOVERIES IN BLAST-FURNACE REGENERATORS

2.1 GENERAL REMARKS

The blast furnace is the main energy consumer in steelmaking. The use of coke, natural gas (NG) or coal dust as fuels has become so expensive that their efficient utilization is mandatory. One approach for this purpose is the arrangement of recuperative or regenerative systems. The Cowper stove is a ceramic counterflow heat regenerator. Its function is to preheat the compressed air (cold blast) for the blast furnace by the exchange of heat with the hot combustion products of blast-furnace gas (BFG) and NG or coke-oven gas (COG). This objective is achieved by cyclically transferring heat through the surface of a heat-storing mass, first from the hot gas to the solid and subsequently from the solid to the cold blast. To obtain a continuous supply of air heated by the system, a minimum of two regenerators is required so that, while one regenerator is supplying heated gas, the other is storing thermal energy from the other gas. In this manner, a constant flow of heated gas is assured, although the periodic behavior of the regenerator is not eliminated. The temperature of the gas supplied by the regenerator system varies cyclically with time in a saw-tooth fashion and with a period equal to the time required for each regenerator to lose heat to the cold gas. It is common practice to smooth out the saw-tooth blast temperature to a practically constant temperature by including a by-pass main in the stove system. A blast furnace with two stoves and a by-pass main is shown schematically in Fig. 2.1. For several years, both the lower heating value and the ratio GJ/(t iron) of blast-furnace top gas have been declining. This change is a direct consequence of reduced fuel consumption per ton of iron yield. At the same time, the temperature of the compressed air at the blast-furnace inlet (hot blast) has been going up. In the past, blast-furnace top gas was the only fuel used for Cowper regenerators. In view of the two specified changes, there have been progressive additions of highly caloric gases (NG or COG) to the BFG. Increased energy prices after the 1973 oil crisis induced the iron and steel industries to consider the possibility of utilizing greater quantities of BFG in conjunction with waste-heat recovery systems and, consequently, of reducing the consumption of NG or COG (Hoffmann and Meyer, 1981; Reinitzhuber, 1981; Voges, 1983; Palz, 1984; Meyer, 1984; Pöttken and Voigt, 1985; Peters, 1985; Molenaar and Otterbach, 1986; Aichinger et al., 1986; Held and Reinitzhuber, 1986; Ehl et al., 1987; Beier et al., 1989; Bisio, 1996a). For this purpose, a rapid CO burn-up rate is ensured by optimizing the flow and mixing conditions on the basis of studies with cold models and hot measurements in an experimental combustion chamber (Kowalski et al., 1990).

One examines the reduction of NG or COG in Cowper stoves while considering total energy savings. Several methods are considered, viz., (i) recuperative heating of the stove combustion gas and/or air by using waste gas, either from the main or from an auxiliary stream in which BFG is burnt, (ii) regenerative heating of the stove combustion air by means of other regenerators which are heated by waste gas from the combustion of BFG in an auxiliary circuit, (iii) combustion-air enrichment by means of oxygen. First- and second-law analyses are applied. Finally, other energy savings are investigated.

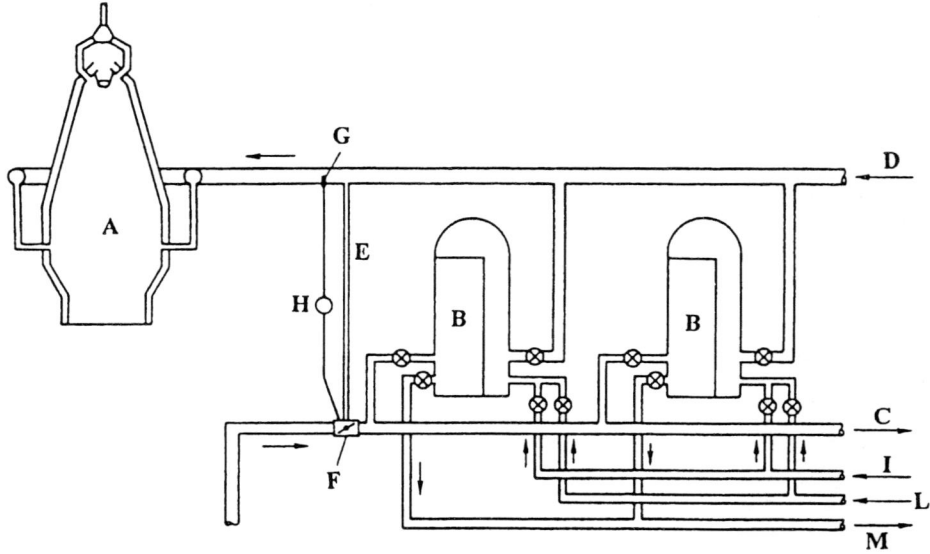

Fig. 2.1. Lay-out of a blast furnace with two Cowper stoves: (A) blast furnace; (B) hot blast stove; (C) cold blast; (D) hot blast; (E) cold blast by-pass; (F) by-pass regulator valve; (G) temperature recorder; (H) valve controller; (I) combustion air; (L) fuel; (M) waste gas.

2.2 METHODS FOR REDUCING VALUABLE FUEL CONSUMPTION IN BLAST-FURNACE COWPER STOVES

2.2.1 Basic System

The basic system of two Cowper stoves used as a reference system is represented in Fig. 2.2A. Neither recuperative nor regenerative preheating of combustion air and fuel are employed.

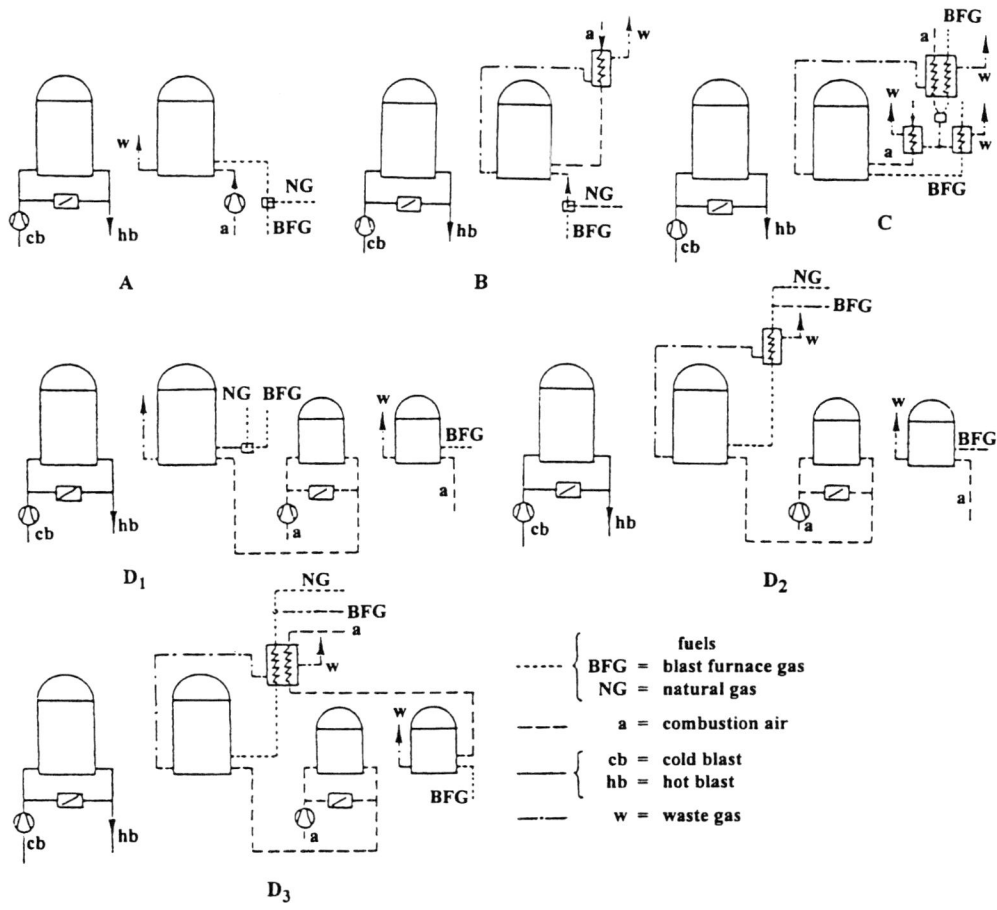

Fig. 2.2. Layout of several methods (A, B, C, D_1, D_2, D_3) for reducing valuable fuel consumption in blast stoves.

2.2.2 Recuperative Preheating of the Cowper Stove Combustion Air by Means of Waste Gas from the Regenerator

The stove waste gas has a temperature higher than 200°C on the average and may be used in a recuperator to preheat the combustion air. The advantages of such a layout (Fig. 2.2B) are:

(a) The total fuel consumption is reduced.
(b) A part of the NG is replaced by BFG with the same mixture combustion temperature.

We refer to (a) as the first-law effect and to (b) as the second-law effect. We propose this last term since replacement of NG by BFG is justified by *usable exergy* savings (and not by *energy* savings); usable exergy measures unavoidable irreversibilities which are notably different among the fuels (see subsection 12.2 and Bisio, 1996a). On the other hand, there are greater exergy losses because of mechanical irreversibilities in the waste-gas and combustion-air channels. These losses are negligible in comparison with the advantages and, consequently, the additional plant expenses are paid off in a short time.

2.2.3 Recuperative Preheating of the Cowper Stove Combustion Air and Fuel

Improved results are obtained by using a more complex system in which fuel and combustion air are recuperatively heated by waste gas from BFG combustion. The gas and air of this auxiliary circuit are preheated, in turn, by stove waste gas. Using this system (Fig. 2.2C), the following results are obtained:

(a) The total gas consumption is slightly increased (first-law effect).
(b) The NG is totally replaced by BFG (second-law effect).

The second-law effect compensates both for the negative influence of (a) and for higher exergy losses arising from mechanical irreversibilities in various fluid circuits. This approach is economically justified in new plants.

2.2.4 Regenerative Preheating of the Cowper Stove Combustion Air

Such a system can be realized in various ways with increasing technical advantages and corresponding plant complexity and costs.

In the more simple lay-out (Fig. 2.2/D_1) a couple of auxiliary regenerators are cyclically heated by means of the waste gas of BFG combustion and, in their turn, heat the Cowper stove combustion air. A recuperative heating of the Cowper stove fuel by means of the waste gas of the main circuit (Fig. 2.2/D_2) can also be added. Finally, such a recuperative heating can be applied for the heating of the combustion air for the auxiliary regenerator too (Fig. 2.2/D_3).

The subsequent results are achieved:

(a) The total gas consumption, with reference to the lower calorific value, is slightly higher for the first layout and slightly lower for the other two (first-law effect).
(b) The NG is replaced by BFG in an increasing amount from the first to the third layout, but never, even in the last, completely (second-law effect).

2.2.5 Combustion-Air Enrichment by Means of Oxygen

The addition of oxygen to the stove combustion air allows progressive and ultimately complete replacement of the NG by BFG. The following results are obtained:

(a) Total gas consumption is slightly reduced whereas energy consumption for producing the necessary oxygen greatly increases total energy use.

(b) The reduction of usable exergy losses, achieved by partial or total substitution of the NG by BFG, is exceeded by exergy consumption for producing the necessary oxygen.

This last statement is well substantiated for combustion with oxygen-enriched (99% O_2) air produced in cryogenic plants. Recently, permselective membranes (i.e. membranes with selective permeation rates) have been developed for oxygen enrichment with greatly reduced exergy consumption (about 1/5 of the value required for cryogenic plants) (Browall and Kimura, 1976; Schell and Houston, 1982). Consequently, (b) may have to be greatly modified when permselective membranes are employed.

2.3 NUMERICAL RESULTS

To verify the significance of a particular analysis, we have performed an evaluation for a Cowper stove for the following conditions: maximum heating-gas temperature = 1450°C, cold-blast temperature at the Cowper inlet = 155°C, hot-blast temperature at the Cowper outlet = 1300°C.

The main results are shown in Table 2.1; the data allow us to highlight advantages and drawbacks of the various layouts by numerical values.

A quantitative comparison shows that system B of Table 2.1 requires the minimum amount of energy, 4.75% less than system A of Table 2.1. In an energy analysis, the possibility of canceling the NG consumption in system C is not expressed by a number that may be compared with the higher total energy consumption (+ 1.38%). On the contrary, the analysis summarized in Table 2.1 expresses the replacement of NG by BFG in terms of numerical values and indicates the preferred solution in terms of two main parameters: global fuel consumption and ratio of NG to total gas. The three factors Ψ_1, Ψ_2 and Ψ_T are utilized. The factor Ψ_1 quantifies the percentage difference for total gas consumption from that for the reference system when considering the lower heating value (first-law effect). The factor Ψ_2 quantifies, relative to the reference system, the difference in the percentage consumption of gases with different merit factors (second-law effect). The factor Ψ_T quantifies, relative to the reference system, the difference in the percentage of total gas consumption when considering the usable exergy (total effect). As shown in Table 2.1, one has $[1 - \Psi_T = (1 - \Psi_1)(1 - \Psi_2)]$. The value of Ψ_T indicates that system D_3 of Table 2.1 is the most convenient technical approach. However, this solution involves the highest plant costs and, therefore, system C of Table 2.1 is usually the most cost-effective. The comparison is valid for a plant that is energy-efficient in the sense that every type of energy is utilized where it is most appropriate to do so (Aichinger et al., 1986). Other authors have shown that energy savings from using waste gases are not economically feasible if the produced steam can be utilized only during a few months of the year. Similarly, the second law shows that higher BFG consumption in Cowper stoves is not desirable if it is necessary to burn a more valuable fuel in the boiler of the thermoelectric station of the same iron and steel plant.

Table 2.1. Primary Numerical Results Obtained for a Cowper Stove.

	A	B	C	D_1	D_2	D_3
π'	68%	59%	--	14,84%	12,09%	11,76%
π''	32%	41%	100%	85,16%	87,91%	88,24%
M	0.6458	0.6305	0,5298	0,5551	0.5504	0.5499
V_f'	15.37%	10.95%	--	1.47%	1.16%	1.12%
V_f''	84.63%	89.05%	69.37%	70.86%	74.26%	74.98%
V_{fa}''	--	--	30.63%	27.67%	24.58%	23.90%
LCV	7008.2	5755.4	2650	3225.2	3086.6	3069.6
LCV'	7008.2	5755.4	2650	3066.1	2979.3	2969.3
LCV''	7008.2	6674.6	7105.2	7158.8	6809.6	6746.7
ex_u	4525.9	3628.5	1404	1816	1716.7	1704.6
ex_u''	4525.9	4208	3764.4	3974	3748.2	3709.8
$\Gamma°$	1.205	1.148	1.222	1.231	1.171	1.160
Ψ_1	--	− 4.75%	+1.38%	+ 2.15%	− 2.83%	− 3.73%
Ψ_2	--	−2.38%	−17.96%	−14.04%	−14.77%	−14.85%
Ψ_T	--	−7.02%	−16.82%	−12,19%	−17.18%	−18.03%

$$(1 - \Psi_T) = (1 - \Psi_1)(1 - \Psi_2)$$

Nomenclature

A   Reference system with neither recovery nor auxiliary preheating (Fig. 2.2A).
B   System with recuperative preheating of the Cowper combustion air by waste gas from this regenerator (Fig. 2.2B).
C   System with recuperative preheating of the Cowper combustion gas and air by waste gas from combustion of BFG, which is recuperatively preheated together with its combustion air by waste gas from this regenerator (Fig. 2.2C).
D_1 System with regenerative preheating of the Cowper combustion air by waste gas from BFG combustion (Fig. 2.2D_1).
D_2 System with regenerative preheating of the Cowper combustion air by waste gas from BFG combustion and with recuperative preheating of the Cowper combustion gas by means of waste gas from this regenerator (Fig. 2.2D_2).
D_3 System with regenerative preheating of the Cowper combustion air by waste gas from BFG combustion and with recuperative preheating of the Cowper combustion gas and of the auxiliary regenerator combustion air by waste gas from the main regenerator (Fig. 2.2D_3).
π' Lower heating-value fraction for the NG.
π'' Lower heating-value fraction for the BFG.
M   Combustion-gas merit factor (see subsection 12.2).
V_f' Volume fraction for the NG.
V_f'' Volume fraction for the BFG.
V_{fa}'' Volume fraction for the BFG of the auxiliary circuit (with reference to the total combustion gas).
LCV Lower heating value of the main circuit gas [$kJ/m^3(nTp)$].
LCV' Average lower heating value of all the gas (main and auxiliary circuit) [$kJ/m^3(nTp)$].
LCV'' Average lower heating value of all of the gas, which is related to a gas volume that transfers as much
ex_u Specific usable exergy of the main circuit gas [$kJ/m^3(nTp)$].
ex_u'' Average specific usable exergy of all of the gas, which is related to a gas volume that transfers as much thermal energy as a volume unit in the reference system [$kJ/m^3(nTp)$].
$\Gamma°$ Ratio of the average lower heating value of all the gas to the thermal energy that is transferred to the hot blast.
Ψ_1 Factor that quantifies, in comparison with the reference system, the different total gas consumption when considering the lower heating value (first-law effect).
Ψ_2 Factor that quantifies, in comparison with the reference system, the different percentage consumption of gases with different merit factors (second-law effect).
Ψ_T Factor that quantifies, in comparison with the reference system, the different total gas consumption when considering the usable exergy (total effect).

2.4 OTHER ENERGY SAVINGS

The waste gases of a plant are usually utilized either to heat the combustion air and fuel of the plant or to produce steam for general purposes. The first use is preferable according to the second law. However, there is also the possibility of using the waste thermal energy of a plant to heat the combustion air and fuel of a nearby plant, as is described by Held and Reinitzhuber (1986). At a blast furnace, the waste thermal energy of the associated sintering plant was utilized to heat combustion air and fuel for the stove. Thermal oil was used as the heat-transfer agent.

A system for large-area district heating was constructed in the Western Ruhr District in 1981 with the goal of saving mostly imported primary energy by utilization of industrial waste thermal energy (Gierig et al., 1983; Held et al., 1985). In order to achieve energy savings and reduced pollution, the system makes use of waste gases from blast-furnace stoves and from pusher-type furnaces (at Thyssen Stahl AG) for water heating.

2.5 FINAL REMARK

In blast-furnace regenerators, it is desirable to reduce the consumption of NG by utilizing BFG without varying the hot-blast temperature. A numerical example demonstrates that minimum *usable exergy* consumption occurs for the solution in which the NG consumption is greatly reduced. This solution is preferable to that achieving minimum *exergy* consumption. In addition to exergy savings, plant and maintenance costs influence the choice of a cost-effective solution.

Chapter 3

SECOND-LAW ANALYSIS OF THE "HOT BLAST STOVE / GAS TURBINE" COMBINE BY APPLYING THE PARAMETER "USABLE EXERGY"

3.1 COMBINED CYCLE PLANT

A particular combined cycle, i.e. an open cycle gas turbine coupled to a hot blast stove of a blast furnace, is examined: the hot blast stove is considered the predetermined facility (Pfenniger, 1960; Heilig, 1969; Cerbe G., 1984; Bisio, 1990b).

The purposes of this analysis are as follows:

(i) Let the electrical and thermal power generated in the coupled process be the same as in the corresponding one with the gas turbine (without waste heat recovery) and the hot blast stove system operating separately. Under this assumption, the fuel saving resulting from the coupling of the hot blast stove with the gas turbine is determined.
(ii) Let the inlet power of the overall system and the useful outlet power of the hot blast stove be equal, both in the coupled process and in the corresponding uncoupled one. Under this assumption, suitable parameters characterizing the merit factor of the conversion of gas chemical power into the electrical one of the turbogenerator are evaluated.

The total process is examined, as in previous section, with the basic aim of annulling or reducing the consumption of high caloric gases, yet utilizing blast-furnace gas with low net heating value and without varying hot blast temperature. Additions of high-caloric value gases (natural or coke oven gas) to the blast-furnace gas are considered only when it is otherwise impossible to attain some basic process parameters.

3.2 LAYOUT OF AN "OPEN CYCLE GAS TURBINE / HOT BLAST STOVE" COMBINE

3.2.1 General Layout

A schematic layout is shown in Fig. 3.1.

The waste gas of an open cycle turbine fed with blast-furnace gas is used as the oxygen carrier for the combustion of the fuel in the hot blast stove and preheater. The solution is similar to the ones proposed, and in some cases already realized, to convert steam plants to combined cycles by means of gas turbines; see, e.g., (Löffel and Thinius, 1985; Rice, 1987a and 1987b; Aluigi et al., 1988; Attig, 1988; Barclay, 1988; Catina et al., 1988; Gurney et al., 1988; Jacobi, 1988; Jäschke, 1988; Negri Di Montenegro et al., 1988; Lozza et al., 1989).

The gas turbine drives both the air and fuel gas compressors and the electrical generator.

Both the blast-furnace gas (combustible) and the turbine waste gas (oxygen carrier) are preheated by means of the combustion of some blast-furnace gas. Turbine waste gas is used as the oxygen carrier for this combustion too.

Furthermore, there is the possibility of utilizing waste thermal energy of other plants for preheating both the turbine combustion air and Cowper fuel (before the preheating mentioned in the previous paragraph). The thermal energy can come, e.g., from a continuous casting (Cerbe, 1984) or from a sintering plant (Held and Reinitzhuber, 1986).

3.2.2 Fuel

Blast furnace gas, after having been refrigerated and filtered, is conveyed by means of a main (C) to the combined system, and there it is divided into three parts. The first part (C11), after two preheatings (first by means of external thermal energy (C12) and then by the combustion of a part of the blast-furnace gas (C13)), is utilized as fuel for the Cowper stove. The second part (C21) is compressed (C22) and fed to the turbine combustion chamber. The third part (C3) goes to the combustion chamber of the preheater.

3.2.3 Oxygen Carriers

The air for the turbine is taken from the environment (A1), compressed (A2), warmed in a heat exchanger by means of energy recovered from a different plant (A3) and, finally, directed to the turbine combustion chamber. Only a part of the air oxygen reacts with the blast-furnace gas here. Thus, the combustion gas (W1) still contains a remarkable quantity of oxygen, which can be used for later combustion (about 16% with reference to mass).

The above combustion gas enters the turbine and leaves it after expansion to a pressure slightly above atmospheric (W2); then, most of this (W3) is warmed in a heat exchanger by means of the waste of blast-furnace gas and goes (W4) to the Cowper stove.

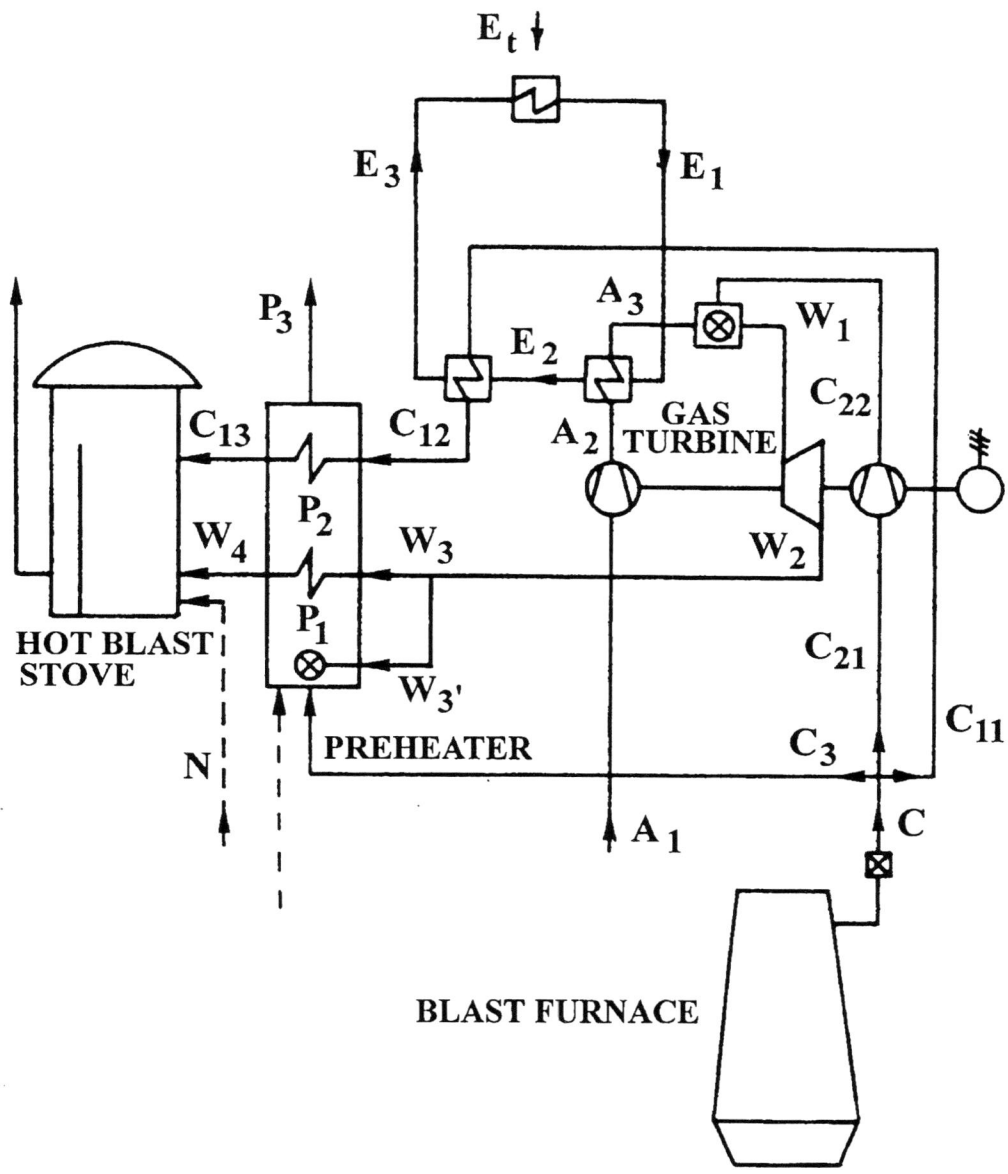

Fig. 3.1. Layout of a coupled (hot-blast stove – open-cycle gas turbine) process.

3.2.4 Combustion

A part of the turbine waste gas (W3') is utilized as the oxygen carrier for the combustion of the blast-furnace gas (C3). The resulting waste gas (P1), after the transfer of thermal energy to the main part of turbine waste gas, (P2), and to the Cowper fuel, (P3), is discharged into the environment.

It is necessary to preheat both the combustible (blast-furnace gas) and the oxygen carrier (turbine waste gas) in order to attain the required combustion temperature. The heating process is so steered that the fuel temperature is pre-established, while the oxygen carrier process is consequently determined. If it were impossible to attain the required combustion temperature with the above layout (e.g., owing to the LCV of the blast-furnace gas being too low as a consequence of advanced improvements in the blast furnace operation), the addition of a valuable fuel (natural or coke oven gas) (N) would be necessary.

3.2.5 Main Parameters

The main parameters to be considered for the plant design are as follows:

(i) the thermal power of the hot blast stove;
(ii) the stove adiabatic combustion temperature;
(iii) the maximum preheating temperature of the fuel and oxygen carrier.

3.3 COMPARISONS BETWEEN "HOT BLAST STOVE / GAS TURBINE" COUPLED PROCESSES AND THE CORRESPONDING UNCOUPLED ONES

3.3.1 General Considerations

Let us consider Fig. 3.2 in which the layout of an uncoupled hot blast stove/open cycle gas turbine process is shown.

In this layout, the blast-furnace gas is divided into three parts.

The first part (C21) is compressed (C22) and conveyed to the turbine combustion chamber. The air for the turbine is taken from the environment (A1), compressed (A2) and led to the turbine combustion chamber. Then, the combustion gas (W1) enters the turbine and leaves it after expansion (W2).

The second part (C11), after two preheatings (first by means of external thermal energy (C12) and then by the combustion of a part of the blast-furnace gas (C13)), is utilized as fuel for the Cowper stove.

The third part (C31) goes to the combustion chamber of the preheater. The external air (B1) is preheated by means of external energy (B2); then, most of this (B3) is warmed and goes (B4) to the Cowper stove, while the remaining part (B3') is utilized for the combustion of the gas (C31).

We intend to compare the coupled system of Fig. 3.1 with the corresponding uncoupled one of Fig. 3.2. This comparison was shown by Cerbe (1984), without the second law analysis exploitation. In this section, the data of Cerbe (1984) are utilized and the concept of usable exergy is applied.

These comparisons are dealt with essentially on the basis of two different questions:

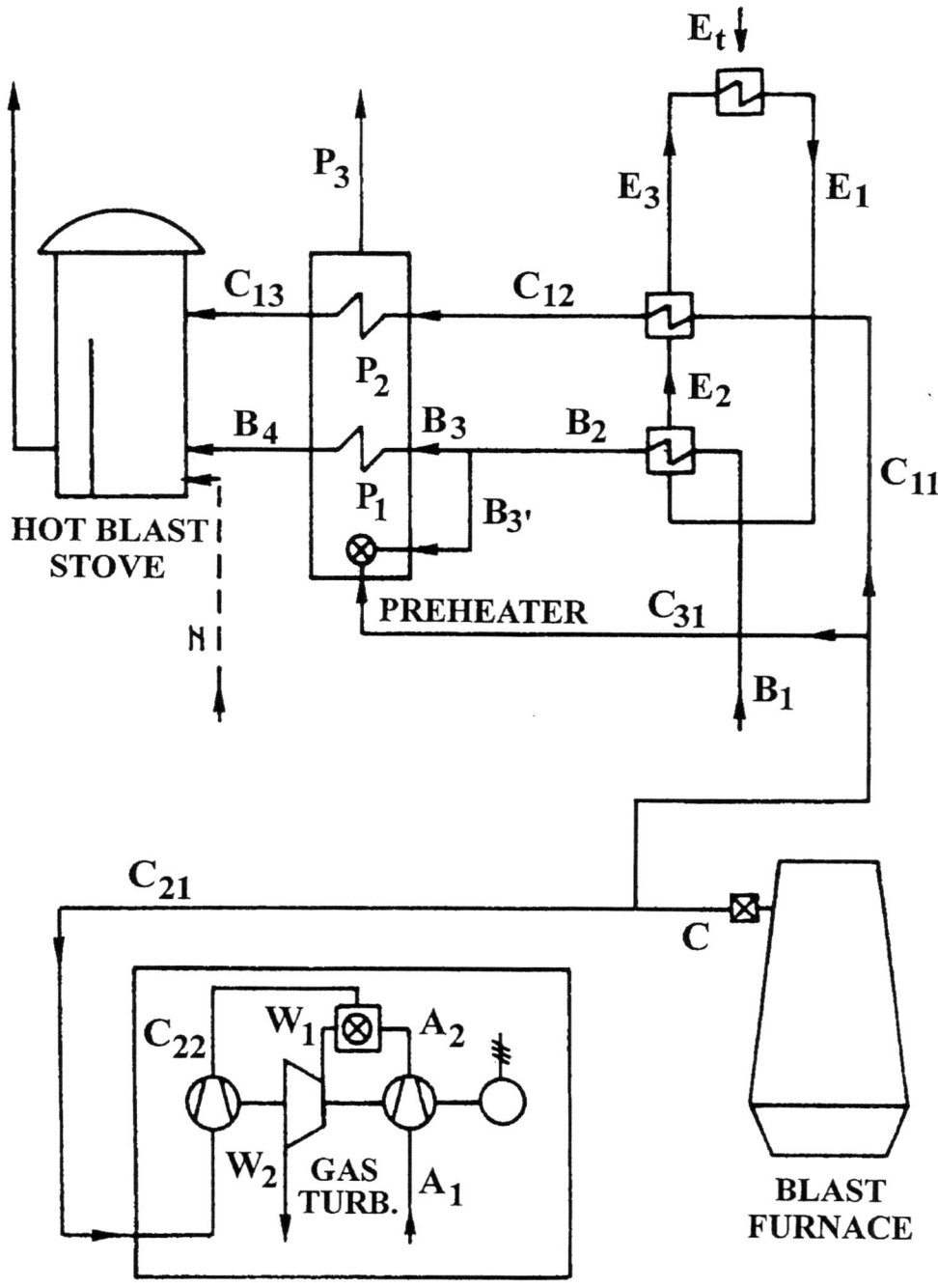

Fig. 3.2. Layout of an uncoupled (hot-blast stove – open-cycle gas turbine) process.

(i) Let the outlet thermal and electrical powers be the same in both processes; in this hypothesis, how much usable exergy flow saving is possible in the coupled process vs the corresponding uncoupled one?

(ii) Let us consider the difference between the inlet usable exergy of the overall coupled process and the inlet usable exergy of the Cowper stove alone of the uncoupled process. Under this assumption, what is the ratio of the turbogenerator electrical power to the above difference? By this analysis, we look for the exergy efficiency of the conversion of chemical into electrical power.

3.3.2 Usable Exergy Saving

Considering the first question, we assume that the Cowper stove outlet thermal power, P_t, and the turbogenerator electrical one, P, are the same in both the coupled and the uncoupled processes.

P_{cic} (expressed by means of LCV) denotes the fuel chemical power going into the coupled process. P_{ciu} denotes the fuel chemical power going into the uncoupled process.

Thus, the chemical power saved by means of the coupling, R_c, is

$$R_c = P_{ciu} - P_{cic} . \tag{3.1}$$

However, the reference to usable exergy flow is more meaningful on the basis of what has been said. The usable exergy flow of the fuel going into the coupled process is denoted by Ex_{uic}, and that going into the uncoupled process is denoted by Ex_{uiu} (for usable exergy, see subsection 12.2).

Thus, the usable exergy flow saved by means of the coupling, R_u, is

$$R_u = Ex_u{}^\circ{}_{iu} - Ex_u{}^\circ{}_{ic} . \tag{3.2}$$

The relative chemical power saved by means of the coupling (with reference to the inlet power of the uncoupled process), $R_c{}^\circ$, is

$$R_c{}^\circ = R_c/P_{ciu} . \tag{3.3}$$

Likewise, the relative usable exergy flow saving by means of the coupling is

$$R_u{}^\circ = R_u/Ex_u{}^\circ{}_{iu} . \tag{3.4}$$

3.3.3 Efficiency of the Conversion of Fuel Chemical Power into Electrical Power

Considering the second question, we assume that the Cowper stove outlet useful thermal power P_t and the inlet chemical power of the overall system are the same in both the coupled and the uncoupled processes. We can consider that the difference between the inlet chemical power of the overall system and that of the Cowper subsystem alone of the uncoupled process, D_c, is utilized for the production of the turbogenerator electrical power in the coupled process. We define the used fraction, δ, of this energy conversion as

$$\delta = P_e/D_c . \qquad (3.5)$$

In this section, this ratio is called used fraction similar to what was made by Faggiani (1968), even if in a slightly different application.

Likewise, denoting the difference between the inlet usable exergy flow of the overall system and that of the Cowper subsystem alone of the uncoupled process by D_u, we define the parameter δ_u, which is more meaningful than D_c on the basis of what has been said, as

$$\delta_u = P_e/D_u . \qquad (3.6)$$

The difference D_c of chemical power is generally obtained by means of blast-furnace gas, but a small quantity of natural gas (or coke oven gas) is sometimes necessary in order to attain the required combustion temperature.

It is to be noted that, with the uncoupled process in the Cowper subsystem, the combustion air and the fuel can be heated up so that it is possible to avoid any addition of valuable fuel. That has been demonstrated in detail in section 2.

The inverse of used fraction represents the quantity of chemical energy (expressed by means of LCV) necessary to obtain a unitary electrical power in a coupled process, when the Cowper outlet useful thermal power and the inlet chemical power of the overall system are the same in both coupled and uncoupled processes. Cerbe (1984) called this parameter "Aufwandsziffer" (expenditure factor).

3.4 SOME NUMERICAL RESULTS

We report some results from Cerbe (1984) with partial modifications that are the consequence of the introduction of the usable exergy concept.

In Fig. 3.3, the natural gas percentage (with reference to LCV), β, is reported in ordinates as a function of the adiabatic combustion temperature, T_{ac}, prefixed in the Cowper stove (abscissae) and of the preheating temperature of the fuel and of the oxygen carrier for the Cowper, T_p, for both the coupled and the uncoupled processes.

The gas chemical power saving of the coupled process vs the uncoupled one, when the useful outlet thermal and electrical powers are the same in both the processes, is shown in Fig. 3.4.

Until there is no need of natural gas in either process, a relative saving a little lower than 16% is obtained with the data reported above. With the increase in the Cowper stove adiabatic combustion temperature and with the decrease in the preheating temperature of the gas and of the combustion air for the Cowper, there is a need for a progressively increasing quantity of natural gas. As the quantity of the necessary natural gas increases, the value of the relative saving rises to a maximum, which is 17.5% for the considered case. Subsequently, the saving R° decreases to about 17%, when it is necessary to add natural gas in the uncoupled process too.

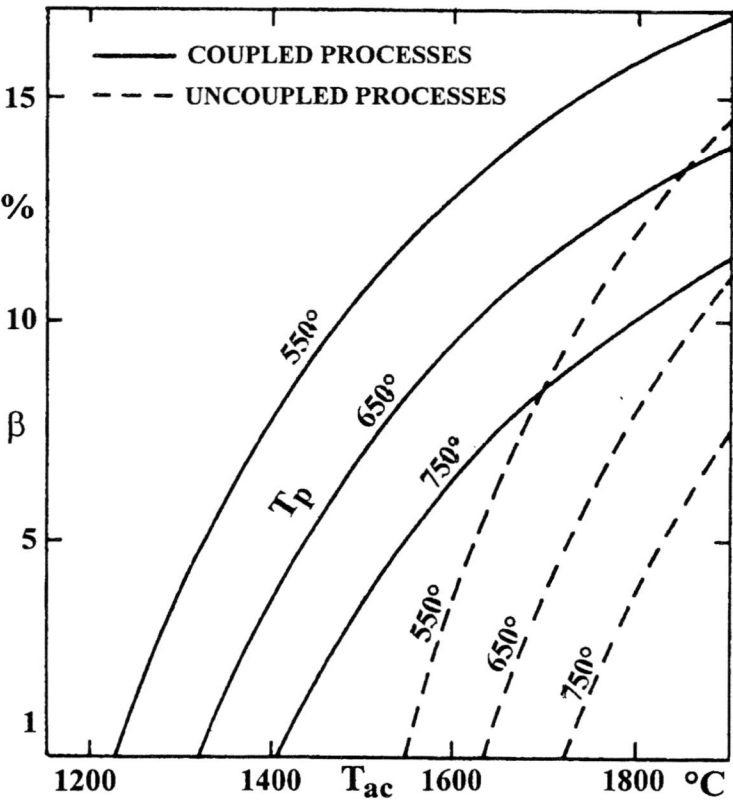

Fig. 3.3. Low calorific value fraction of natural gas in coupled and uncoupled process as a function of the adiabatic combustion temperature T_{ac} and the preheating temperature T_p.

The above is a consequence of the fact that, in the Cowper stove, for equal exit temperature of the combustion gases, the thermal energy loss in these gases is higher for the blast furnace than for the natural gas. Therefore, the chemical energy consumption is lower by as much as the natural gas percentage is higher in the coupled process. This trend is reversed when there is the need to add natural gas in the uncoupled process too.

The fuel usable exergy flow saving of the coupled process vs the uncoupled one, when there are the same useful outlet thermal and electrical powers in both the processes, is represented in Fig. 3.5.

Even in this case, until there is no need to add natural gas in either process, it is possible to obtain a relative saving slightly lower than 16% with the values of the main parameters equal to those of the first comparison. With the rise of the quantity of the natural gas necessary in the coupled process (as a consequence of the increase in the Cowper adiabatic combustion temperature and/or the decrease in the preheating temperature of the gas and of the combustion air for the Cowper stove), the value of the relative saving $R°_u$ goes down to a minimum (13.5% with the assumed parameters). Subsequently, the saving $R°_u$ increases to about 16.5%, when it is necessary to add natural gas in the uncoupled process too.

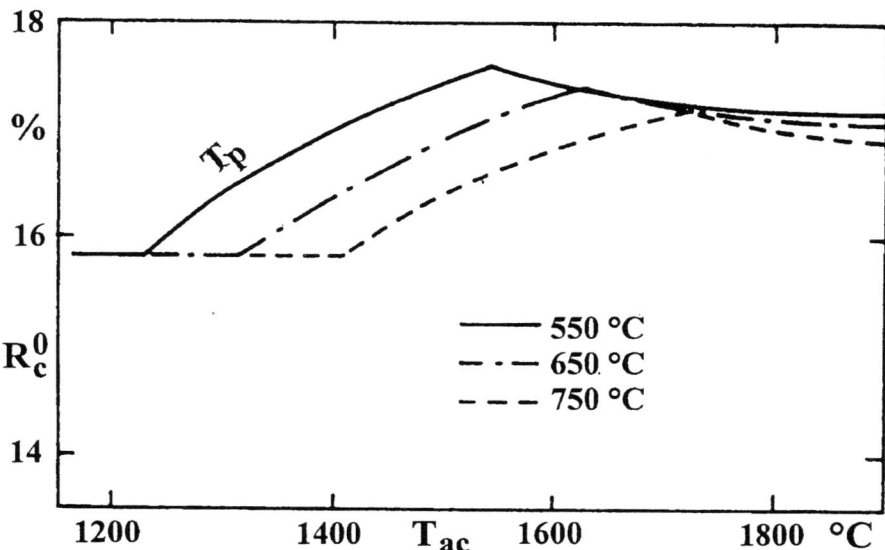

Fig. 3.4. Relative saving of chemical power R_c° of coupled process vs the corresponding uncoupled one.

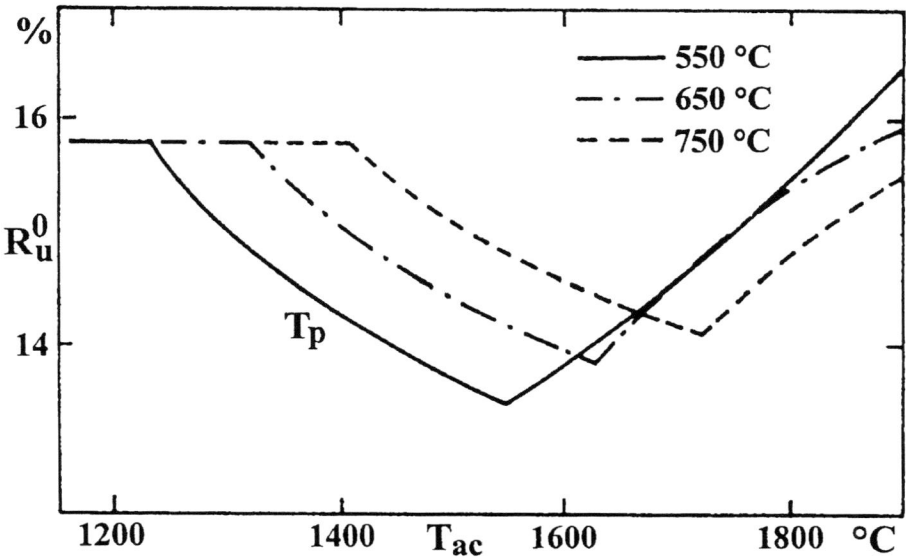

Fig. 3.5. Relative saving of usable exergy flow R_u° of coupled process vs the corresponding uncoupled one.

The diagrams of Fig. 3.5, with reference to the usable exergy concept, reverse some conclusions that can be drawn from the ones of Fig. 3.4 which have been reported from Cerbe (1984) and are based only on first law considerations. From the diagrams of Fig. 3.5, it follows that the coupling of the two subsystems (hot blast stove and gas turbine) becomes progressively less convenient, when the quantity of natural gas necessary in the coupled process increases, without any need of additions of natural gas in the uncoupled process.

The values of usable exergy savings by means of the coupling for up-to-date plants amount to $\approx 14\%$ (see Fig. 3.5 with $T_{ac}=1450°C$ and $T_p=550°C$).

In section 2, examining the possibilities of energy savings in blast furnace regenerators, it is pointed out the technical and economical convenience of attaining a system with no, or little, consumption of natural gas (or of other fuels with high factor of merit), even if, as a consequence, there is a greater total fuel consumption with reference to low calorific value. This result is found again here, and it is shown and emphasized by the comparison between Figs 3.4 and 3.5.

It is to be noted that, in different but analogous cases, some German authors (Hoffmann and Meyer, 1981; Voges, 1983) attain the same conclusions from a qualitative point of view by asserting that the reduction or annulling of the natural gas consumption, in the presence of a greater overall fuel consumption too, is convenient, since it allows the substitution of an import fuel (in great part from politically unstable areas) by means of a home fuel. However, what is drawn in this paper seems to be a result with a greater generality and with the possibility of a quantitative formulation.

The used fraction δ of the coupled process in the case in which the inlet power of the overall system and the outlet useful thermal power of the Cowper are the same in both coupled and uncoupled processes is represented in Fig. 3.6. Until blast-furnace gas alone is utilized in both the processes, a used fraction as: $\delta \approx 0.71$ results. In the presence of natural gas in the coupled process, there are higher values of δ up to a maximum of ≈ 0.85; however, the used fraction goes down to a value of ≈ 0.8 when natural gas is present in the uncoupled process too.

So high values of the used fraction must not be misleading; indeed, they are a consequence of the fact that we have theoretically considered the difference between the coupled process and the uncoupled one, when outlet useful thermal and electrical powers are the same for both processes. Of course, the above values are not attainable with the turbine alone, but are possible only by means of the total improvement resulting from the coupling.

The parameter δ_u of the coupled process in the case in which the inlet power of the overall system and the outlet useful thermal power of the Cowper are the same in both coupled and uncoupled processes is represented in Fig. 3.7. Until blast-furnace gas alone is utilized in both the processes, it follows that $\delta_u \approx 1.33$. In the presence of natural gas in the coupled process, there are higher values of δ_u till a maximum of ≈ 1.53; in contrast, the parameter δ_u goes down to a value of ≈ 1.49, when natural gas is present in the uncoupled process too.

The influence of the presence/absence of natural gas, though it is not negligible and thus makes the diagrams of Fig. 3.7 different from the ones of Fig. 3.6, does not cause the reversals that characterize the diagrams of Fig. 3.5 vs the ones of Fig. 3.4.

In conclusion, the parameter $R_u°$ is the most meaningful for the evaluation of the technical convenience of a coupled process vs an uncoupled one; for economic convenience, obviously, other parameters must be considered in addition to the usable exergy saving (installation, operation and maintenance costs).

The parameter δ_u attributes the whole advantage of the coupling to the production of electrical energy, for an equal efficiency of the Cowper stove in both coupled and uncoupled processes. Thus, it enlightens the attained results from a particular point of view, but does not add further weighty elements in the examination of the convenience of coupling. The parameters R_c and δ, similar to the ones defined by Cerbe (1984), in the opinion of the authors, are less convenient, since they refer only to a first-law analysis.

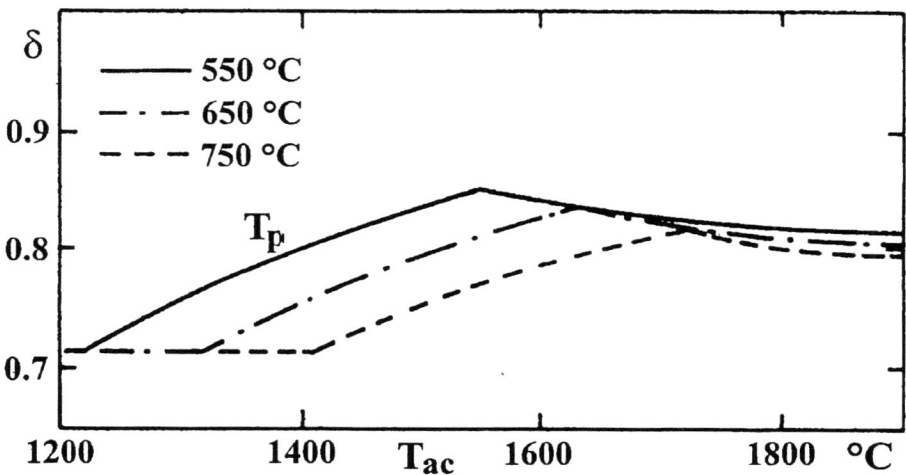

Fig. 3.6. Used fraction δ of coupled process vs the corresponding uncoupled one.

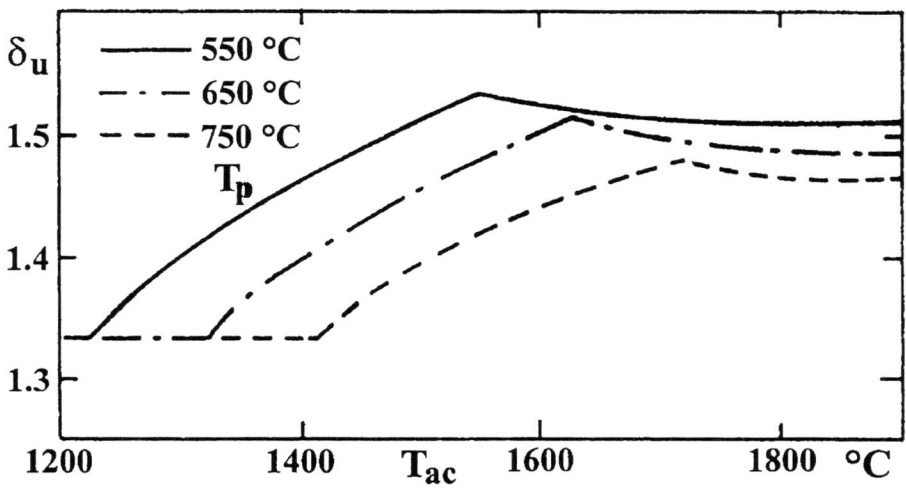

Fig. 3.7. Parameter δ_u of coupled process vs the corresponding uncoupled one.

3.5 FINAL REMARKS

The kind of second-law analysis applied in this section with reference to the usable exergy concept (or to a similar one) has never been used by others, as far as is known by the authors. The main results obtained are as follows.

Let us consider both the gas chemical power saving and the gas usable exergy flow saving of the coupled process vs the uncoupled one, when there are the same useful outlet thermal and electrical powers in both processes; let the values of other parameters (e.g., low calorific values) also be the same.

The reference to the usable exergy concept reverses some conclusions obtainable by means of the only first law of thermodynamics or by utilizing the usual definition of chemical exergy. Among other things, it is found out that the coupling of the two subsystems becomes progressively less convenient, when the quantity of natural gas necessary in the coupled process increases, without any need for additions of natural gas in the uncoupled process.

It must be noted that, in the iron and steel industry, it is very important to save natural gas (or coke oven gas) for high temperature utilizations and to use blast-furnace gas, wherever possible, in order to avoid any blow-off of this gas into the atmosphere.

Let us now refer to the case in which the inlet power of the overall system and the outlet useful thermal power of the Cowper are the same in both coupled and uncoupled processes. Let us consider the parameter δ_u as the ratio of the turbogenerator electrical power of the coupled process to the difference between the inlet usable exergy flow of the coupled process and that of the Cowper subsystem alone of the uncoupled process.

Also in this comparison, the reference to usable exergy concept gives results that are more meaningful but does not reverse the conclusions obtainable by means of only the first law of thermodynamics.

The savings obtained by means of the coupling of a gas turbine with a hot blast stove are similar to those of the best steam/gas combined cycle plants; this result, however, is attained with some plant and operation difficulties.

In our opinion, it is possible to state that the hot blast stove/gas turbine combine is a good solution (as an alternative to other energy saving solutions) at least for new plants.

Chapter 4

ENERGY SAVING AND IMPROVEMENT OF ENVIRONMENT CONDITIONS IN COKE OVEN PLANTS

4.1 GENERAL REMARKS

4.1.1 Coke-Oven Energy Recoveries

The chemical energy of a fuel gas, which is used for a coke oven, amounts to 2500-3200 MJ/$t_{dry\ coal}$. This energy, degraded to thermal energy of various operative values, is discharged from the plant in such forms:

   (i)   Thermal energy of incandescent coke   43-48 %.
   (ii) Thermal enthalpy of coke-oven gas   24-30 %.
   (iii) Thermal energy of waste gas   10-18 %.
   (iv) Permeability, convection and radiation heat from the
         external surface of coke oven, and several losses 10-17 %.

The oil crisis of 1973 created a strong impulse toward a new thinking on the consumption and rational utilization of energy, particularly in the highly industrialized countries with limited indigenous energy resources. At the same time, attention throughout the world was also increasingly focused on environment problems.

The possible utilization of the thermal energy of incandescent coke is dealt with in many papers (Childs and Bridges, 1963; Meckel and Joseph, 1978; Rogan, 1978; Bertling, 1979; Mori et al., 1980; Nashan, 1980; Jablin, 1982; Utsu, 1982; Jung, 1984; Beck, 1984; Baer and Bertling, 1984; Teichert, 1984; Breidenbach, 1984; Beckmann and Gilli, 1984; Bussmann et al., 1985; Aichinger et al., 1986; Breidenbach, 1990; Bertling and Rohde, 1995; Bisio, 1997a; Ameling et al., 1998; Bertling and Stoppa, 1998, Arendt et al., 2000). Usually, in coking technology the coke is cooled by being sprayed with water under special quenching towers. In recent years, the various types of dry cooling plants allow the recovery of nearly 80% of the thermal energy of incandescent coke. The possibilities of utilizing recovered energy are as follows:

   (i)   Production of steam and electricity.

(ii) Preheating of coking coal.
(iii) Room heating.

The thermal energy of coke-oven gas, which is the second largest in the above listing, has so far been rarely utilized. Various studies, however, have been carried out for the possible utilization of this waste energy (Mori and Matsuo, 1983; Aichinger et al., 1986; Breidenbach, 1990; Bertling and Rohde, 1995) and a technique has been recently commercialized in Japan.

The thermal energy of combustion exhaust gas is utilized to preheat both the combustion air and fuel gas mixture through a large-capacity regenerator. Consequently the waste gas temperature is reduced to approximately 200°C. Lately, the further recovery of heat from waste gas has been reported in a few cases using a heat pipe installed in the flue.

The various kinds of heat wasted from the coke-oven external surface have been decreased by the reinforced sealing and better thermal insulation of coke ovens.

In the following subsections, the main types of coke-oven energy recoveries will be considered for a comparison.

4.1.2 Protection of the Environment

As with the problem of energy saving and recovery, the last years have been characterized by increased prevention of atmospheric and water pollution by industrial emissions and domestic wastes. Work to control atmospheric pollution has been carried out in all developed countries. According to Zaichenko et al. (1980), as a result of including measures for environmental protection, the investment and the coking costs are increased by 15%. However, if the calculations included allowance for losses caused by adverse effects of atmospheric pollution on workers health, installation of engineering facilities for maintaining clean air can be cost-effective. In any case, it is obvious that an environmental facility is particularly tempting when, as with coke dry cooling plant, in addition to environment advantages, an energy recovery can be associated, even if the investment costs are higher and not justified only by energy saving.

4.2 COKE DRY QUENCHING

4.2.1 Methods for Energy Recovery and Saving from Coke at the Coke-Oven Outlet

The idea of recovering thermal energy from incandescent coke by means of an inert gas dates back to the early 1900s. The first industrial plants, designed particularly by the Sulzer Brothers (Winterthur, Switzerland) were carried out in the '20s and '30s both in the USA and in Europe (Germany, France, UK, Switzerland) (Childs and Bridges, 1963; Beckmann and Gilli, 1984). However, the greater investment costs of dry quenching plants, in comparison with those of the wet quenching ones, were amortized with difficulty in a period in which energy was very cheap. Consequently, dry quenching plants were given up.

In the early 1960s, a new interest arose: in the USSR (now CSI), dry cooling plants, which basically followed the Sulzer design, were built with the primary aim of preventing the coke from freezing in winter, as happens with wet quenched coke. The plant, constructed in various countries according to the Soviet Giprokoks process (Rogan, 1978), is schematically shown in Fig. 4.1. The red-hot coke, at a temperature of about 1100°C, is pushed from ovens, A, into containers placed on cars. Loaded cars are moved to the dry cooling plant, where containers, B, are lifted by bridge-crane, C, and unloaded through the charging system, D, into pre-chamber, E. Then, hot coke is transferred into cooling chamber, F, in small batches. After leaving the cooling chamber through the discharging system, G, coke runs, at a temperature of about 200°C, onto conveyor belt, H. Coke is refrigerated by a circulating gas, composed mainly by nitrogen and moved by the main blower, I. This gas transfers thermal energy in boiler, N, which produces superheated steam, O, at a pressure up to 100 bar. Before entering the boiler, the gas is scrubbed in the coarse deduster, J, removing coarse particles of coke dust to protect the boiler surface from erosion. After leaving the boiler, the gas streams through the fine deduster, K, where fine dust is scrubbed out.

In 1983, a dry cooling plant, schematically shown in Fig. 4.2, began operation in Germany. Its main characteristic is that 1/3 of the thermal energy is transferred directly from the coke to the vaporizing water and the remaining 2/3 through the inert gas. The advantages are a lower quantity of circulating gas with a corresponding lower consumption of electrical energy by the blower and a greater energy recovery. Refrigerating walls in the cooling chamber represent the critical point of the plant.

In Germany, a combination of the coke dry cooling and coal preheating plant has been developed (Meckel and Joseph, 1978; Nashan, 1980; Beck, 1984; Baer and Bertling, 1984; Teichert, 1984). This system realizes primary energy saving (e.g. gas) instead of energy recovery of lower exergy value (steam) and thus it is thermodynamically to be preferred (see, e.g., Thring, 1963). In addition, the well-known advantages of the single processes with respect to coke quality and increased output have been confirmed. The completely closed system permits significant environmental improvements in the coking plant sector, avoiding the immissions of dust into the atmosphere in a practically complete way.

Jung (1984) considered the convenience of using water gas (H_2 + CO) as the heat transfer fluid. Indeed, water gas has a thermal diffusivity three times that of nitrogen, and thus it allows us to reduce the boiler surface by 50%.

In an anonymous note of "Metal Producing" (1981), it was stated that the most convenient uses of the energy recovered from coke dry quenching (at least in the USA) are the following: the drying of coal and the heating of makeup water for boilers that provide steam in the coke plant per se. Indeed, the energy is available when the coke plant is running, which is of course when it is required. In addition, these quantities of energy match well.

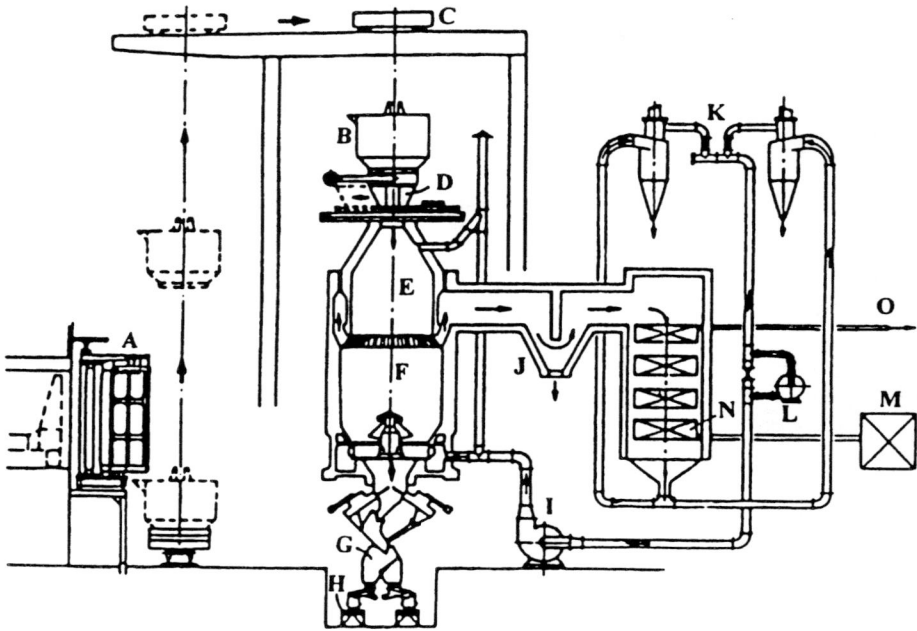

Fig. 4.1. Giprokoks method of coke dry cooling: (A) coke-guide; (B) coke container; (C) bridge-crane; (D) charging system; (E) pre-chamber; (F) coke cooling chamber; (G) discharging system; (H) coke conveyor belt; (I) main blower; (J) coarse deduster; (K) fine deduster; (L) emergency blower; (M) feed water degasser; (N) steam generator; (O) steam outlet.

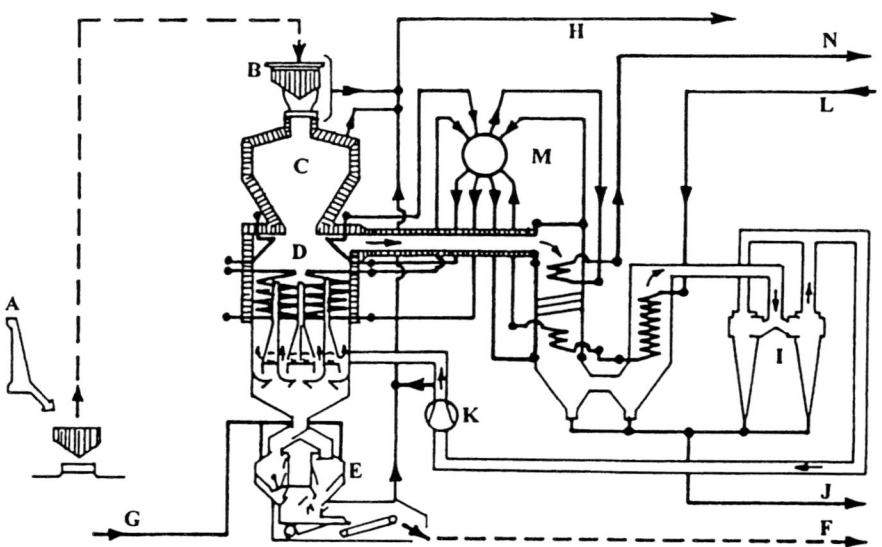

Fig. 4.2. KTK-Process with cooling walls in the coke shaft: (A) coke oven; (B) charging system; (C) pre-chamber; (D) coke cooling chamber; (E) discharging system; (F) coke outlet; (G) inert gas inlet; (H) gas to deduster and atmosphere; (I) deduster; (J) dust outlet; (K) blower; (L) water inlet; (M) steam generator; (N) steam outlet.

4.2.2 Research on the Optimal Temperatures and Pressures of Steam

4.2.2.1 Generalities about Energy and Exergy Analysis

In Fig. 4.3, energy and exergy flow diagrams are reported for a typical coke dry cooling plant with inlet coke temperature = 1050°C and outlet coke temperature = 200°C. Both diagrams are useful; however, only exergy flow is suitable to visualize the operative value of the various energies. From Fig. 4.3 one remarks that with such devices it is possible to recover about 44% of the exergy value of the incandescent coke thermal energy, corresponding to about the 20% of the exergy value of the inlet coal.

Owing to the relatively low value of the exergy efficiency of a coke dry quenching system, it seems interesting to research the optimal values of some parameters, and in particular the characteristics of the steam produced (pressure and temperature) in order to obtain the more convenient plant.

A computer analysis has been made, assuming some input data, experimentally obtained from a recent actual plant. The input data are the temperature and pressure values of the gas flowing through the plant, the mass flow rates of coke at the inlet and outlet of the coke cooling chamber, and at the outlet of the coarse deduster, the mass flow rate, temperature and pressure of steam, the blower isentropic efficiency, and the efficiency in the electromechanical conversion of the electroblower. The fundamental data are:

quenched coke mass flow rate	56 t/h ,	steam mass flow rate	28 t/h ,
inlet coke temperature	1050°C ,	outlet coke temperature	200°C ,
specific volume flow rate of gas	1650 m³(nTp)/t$_{dry\ coke}$.		

By varying the temperature and pressure of steam and/or the gas flow rate, one has determined the variation of the system exergy efficiency, Φ, so defined:

$$\Phi = (Ex_{st} - Ex_{wa} - Ex_e)/Ex_{co} , \qquad (4.1)$$

where: Ex_{st} = steam exergy; Ex_{wa} = boiler feed water; Ex_e = exergy corresponding to the electrical work of the electroblower; Ex_{co} = coke physical exergy (thus, excluding the chemical component of exergy to be utilized in blast furnace).

4.2.2.2 Specific Exergy Dependence upon Temperature and Pressure

Let us consider specific exergy as a function of temperature, T, and pressure, p. In the diagram of Fig. 4.4, the steam specific exergy for an open system is reported as a function of pressure for various values of temperature. It is to be remarked that specific exergy increases always as T increases at constant p (for temperatures above that of the environment), whereas not always ex increases as p rises at constant T. This result seems puzzling and contrary to the concept of exergy.

To justify the topic in a valid way, let consider the definition of specific exergy for an open system:

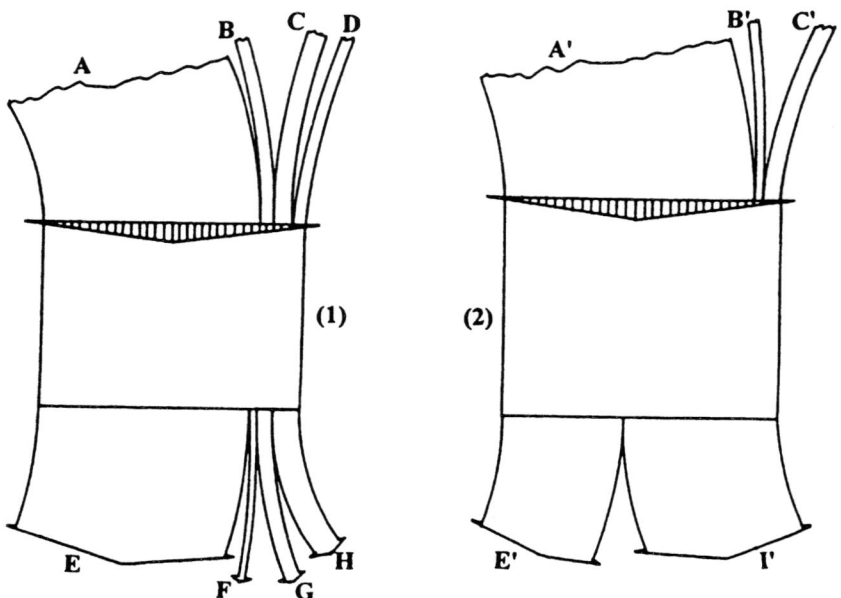

Fig. 4.3. Enthalpy (1) and exergy (2) flow diagrams: (A) inlet coke thermal enthalpy (90.52%); (B) blower enthalpy (2.15%); (C) coke and residual distillation gas combustion enthalpy (5.03%); (D) inlet water enthalpy (2.3%); (E) steam enthalpy (84%); (F) waste gas enthalpy (0.8%); (G) surface losses enthalpy (4%); (H) outlet coke thermal enthalpy (11.2%); (A') inlet coke thermal exergy (89.59%); (B') blower exergy (3.68%); (C') coke and residual distillation gas combustion exergy (6.73%); (E') steam exergy (44.5%); (I') exergy losses (55.5%).

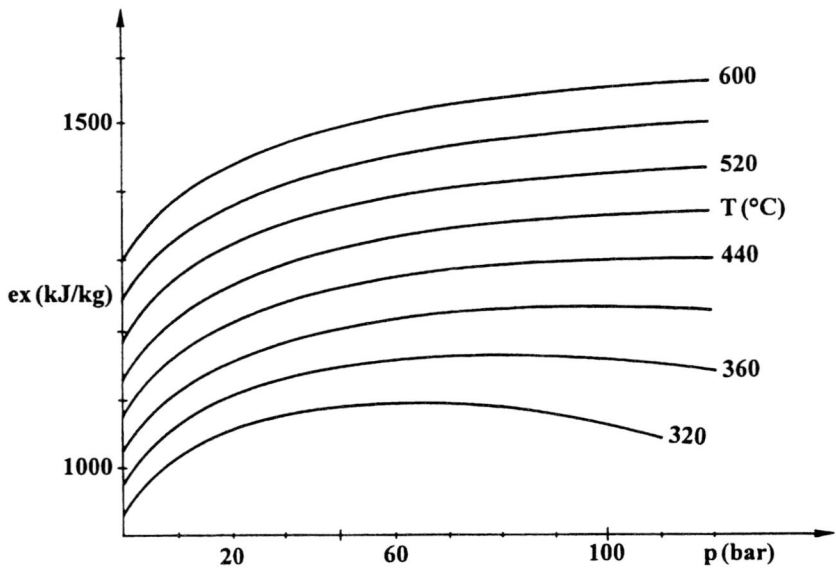

Fig. 4.4. Steam specific exergy, ex, as a function of pressure, p, for various values of temperature, T.

$$ex = i - i_o - T_o (s - s_o),\qquad(4.2)$$

and then

$$dex = di - T_o\, ds,\qquad(4.3)$$

The variation of specific enthalpy, di, and of specific entropy, ds, as a function of T and p can be written as (Bisio and Guglielmini, 1993):

$$di_{Tp} = c_p\, dT + (v_{Tp} - T\, \partial_1 v_{Tp})\, dp,\ \ ds_{Tp} = (c_p/T)\, dT - \partial_1 v_{Tp}\, dp,\qquad(4.4)$$

and then

$$dex_{Tp} = c_p\, dT + (v_{Tp} - T\, \partial_1 v_{Tp})\, dp - T_o\, [(c_p/T)\, dT - \partial_1 v_{Tp}\, dp],\qquad(4.5)$$

$$dex_{Tp} = c_p\, [(T - T_o)/T]\, dT + [v_{Tp} - (T - T_o)\, \partial_1 v_{Tp}]\, dp,\qquad(4.6)$$

$$\partial_1 ex_{Tp} = c_p\, [(T - T_o)/T],\ \ \partial_2 ex_{Tp} = v_{Tp} - (T - T_o)\, \partial_1 v_{Tp},\qquad(4.7)$$

From these relations, one obtains that exergy increases as temperature rises, when ($T > T_o$), and the opposite is verified, when ($T < T_o$), as is well known. About the influence of pressure, one can say that exergy increases as pressure rises, when ($T - T_o$) and $\partial_1 v_{Tp}$ have opposite sign, and, since with very few exceptions ($\partial_1 v_{Tp} > 0$), when $[(T - T_o) > 0]$.

When ($T - T_o$) and $\partial_1 v_{Tp}$ have the same sign, one cannot exclude the possibility that exergy decreases when pressure goes up. This indeed is verified in a range in which the attractive forces are greatly prevailing on the repulsive forces (Gokcen and Reddy, 1996). For the problem that is here considered, this happens for superheated steam not far from the critical point. This analysis justifies that some isothermal curves of Fig. 4.4 have a maximum for a given pressure.

On the other hand, this result could be yet puzzling. Indeed, it is well known that the operative value increases always with pressure. To this purpose, let us compare the following parameters:

$$\partial_2 ex_{Tp} = v_{Tp} - (T - T_o)\, \partial_1 v_{Tp},\ \ \partial_2 i_{Tp} = v_{Tp} - T\, \partial_1 v_{Tp}.\qquad(4.8)$$

From these relations, in the range in which for the steam ($\partial_2 ex_{Tp} < 0$) it follows:

$$\partial_2 ex_{Tp} > \partial_2 i_{Tp},\qquad(4.9)$$

and then it follows that, if exergy decreases as pressure goes down, the decrease of enthalpy is higher and consequently, even if the operative of the mass unit of steam goes down, the ratio of this operative value to the "cost" for obtaining it (i.e. the necessary heat) goes up. This is in agreement with the fact that a higher pressure is technically always more valuable.

4.2.2.3 Analysis Results

"Recovered exergy" has been determined; the numerator of relation (4.1) gives this parameter. As an example, in Figs. 4.5-4.6 the recovered exergy is shown for one value of the specific volume flow rate of gas, alternatively, with steam pressure in abscissae (and temperature as parameter) or with steam temperature in abscissae (and pressure as parameter). One remarks that the recovered exergy goes up almost linearly as the steam temperature increases, and goes up always as the steam pressure rises (contrary to the steam specific entropy), but with negative second derivative.

In Fig. 4.7 the recovered exergy is shown for one value of steam temperature as a function of the specific volume flow rate of gas (in abscissae) for various steam pressures (reported as parameter). To justify the diagrams, it must be remarked that as the specific volume flow rate of gas increases, the heat exchanged in the boiler between the gas and the water-steam increases with negative second derivative. Consequently, for every fixed couple of values of T and p, the steam flow rate and the total steam exergy exhibit the same behavior. On the contrary, owing to the increase of the gas-compression work, the recovered exergy has a maximum in correspondence with a given specific volume flow rate of gas. This maximum, for every temperature value, tends to a higher specific volume flow rate, as the pressure increases. In particular, at (p = 80 bar), the maximum is near to the value $[G_V^* = 1650\ m^3(nTp)/t_{dry\ coke}]$.

The variations of the exergy efficiency, owing to its definition and the constancy of the physical exergy of the incandescent coke, are totally similar to those of the recovered exergy. Thus, only two diagrams for exergy efficiency in correspondence to a specific volume flow rate of gas $[G_V^* = 1650\ m^3(nTp)/t_{dry\ coke}]$ are reported. In Figs. 4.8 and 4.9, exergy efficiency vs steam pressure (with steam temperature as parameter) or vs the steam temperature (with steam pressure as parameter), respectively, is reported.

On the basis of the various diagrams (not all here reported), the specific volume flow rate of gas $[G_V^* = 1650\ m^3(nTp)/t_{dry\ coke}]$ seems to be the more convenient. The very low increase of the recovered exergy (and thus of the exergy efficiency), that can be noted for some values of the couple (T, p) of the steam in correspondence to values of the specific volume flow rate of gas G_V^* slightly higher than $[1650\ m^3(nTp)/t_{dry\ coke,}]$ does not probably compensate the higher plant and maintenance costs.

The temperature rise allows a remarkable exergy efficiency increase. Thus, it seems convenient to choose the maximum temperature consistent with the use of materials that are not particularly expensive. The limit value of (T = 540°C) can be presently chosen.

As the pressure rises, exergy efficiency increases remarkably until a pressure of about 80 bar, and then the increase is progressively reduced. For what is known to authors, the maximum value until now applied is of 103 bar in a steel plant of Japan. Thus, it seems that the more convenient pressure value is of about 100 bar.

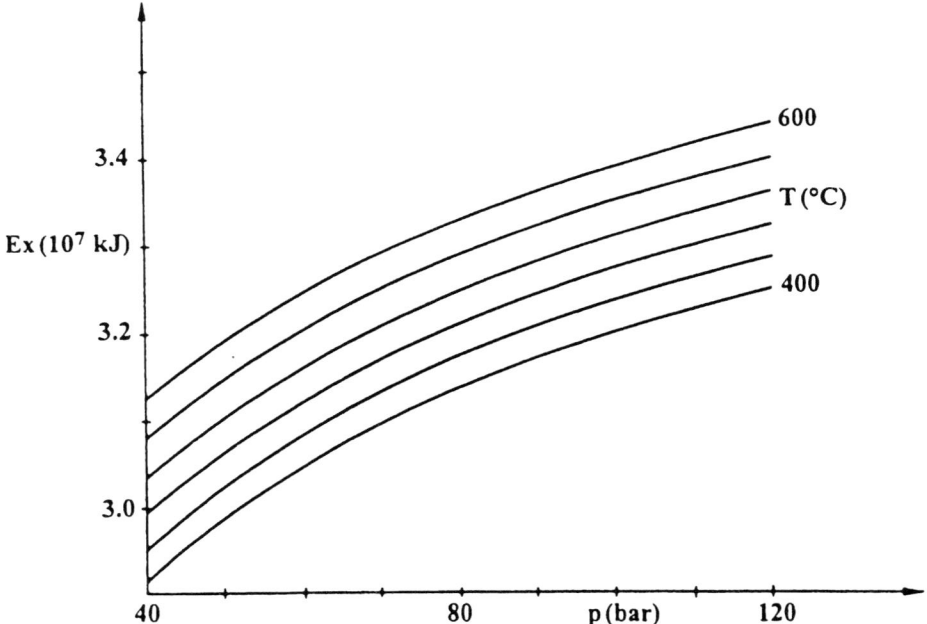

Fig. 4.5. Recovered exergy, Ex, as a function of steam pressure for various values of steam temperature and a specific volume flow rate of gas $[G_V^* = 1450 \text{ m}^3(\text{nTp})/t_{\text{dry coke}}]$.

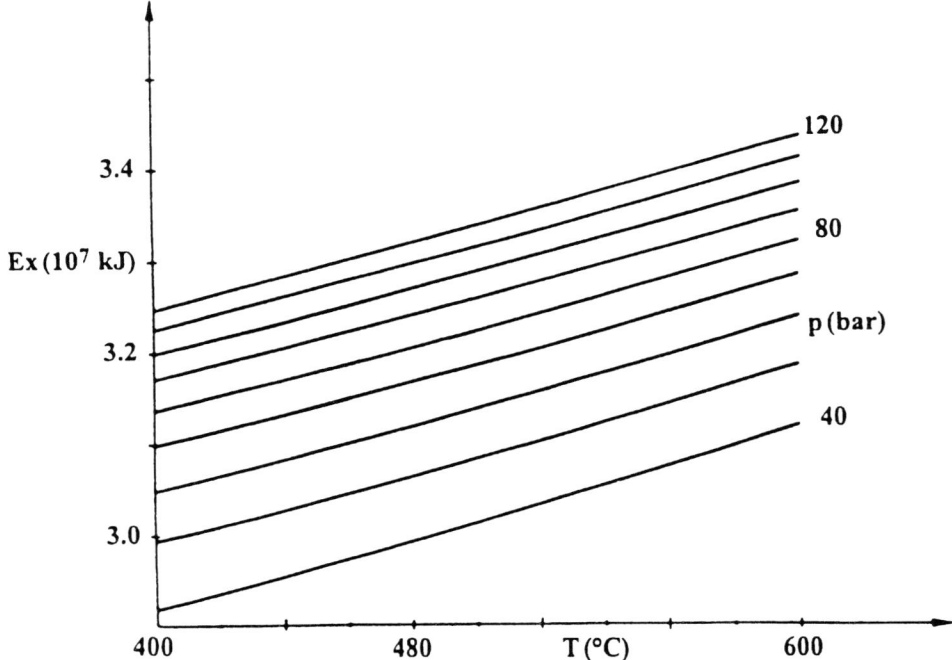

Fig. 4.6. Recovered exergy, Ex, as a function of steam temperature for various values of steam pressure and a specific volume flow rate of gas $[G_V^* = 1450 \text{ m}^3(\text{nTp})/t_{\text{dry coke}}]$.

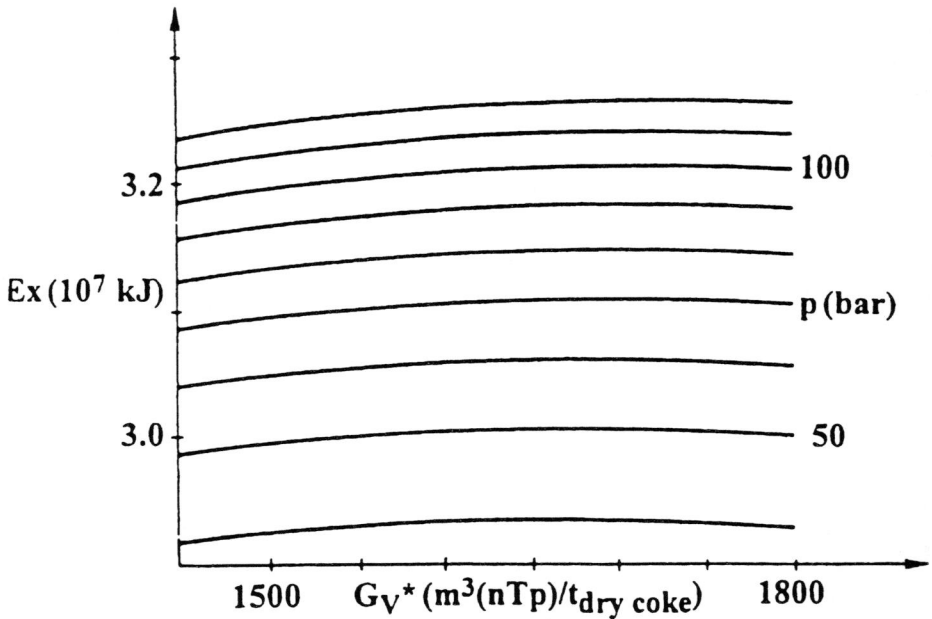

Fig. 4.7. Recovered exergy, Ex, as a function of specific volume flow rate of gas, G_V^*, for various values of steam pressure and a steam temperature T = 520°C.

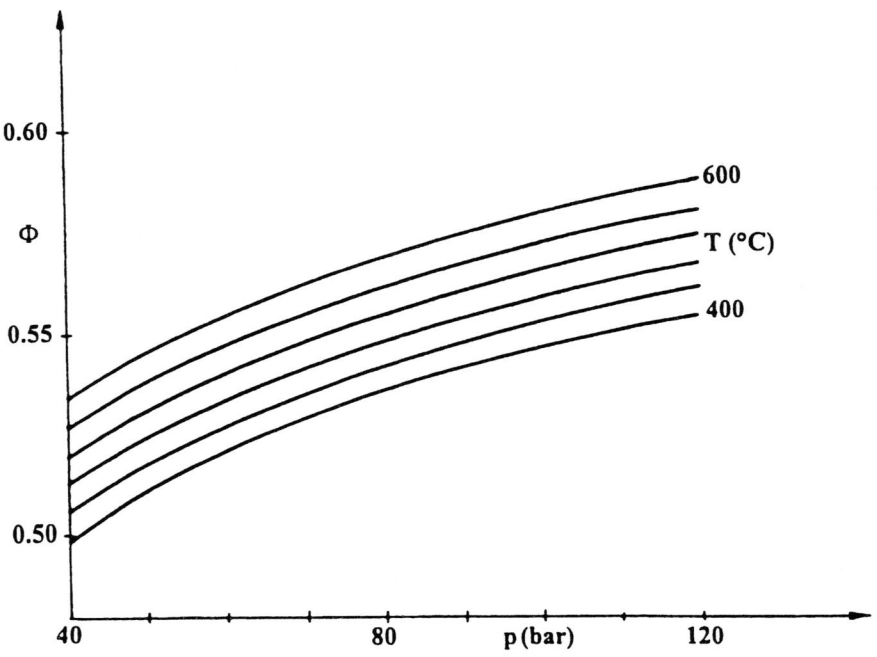

Fig. 4.8. Exergy efficiency, Φ, as a function of steam pressure for various values of steam temperature and a specific volume flow rate of gas [$G_V^* = 1650$ m^3(nTp)/$t_{dry\,coke}$].

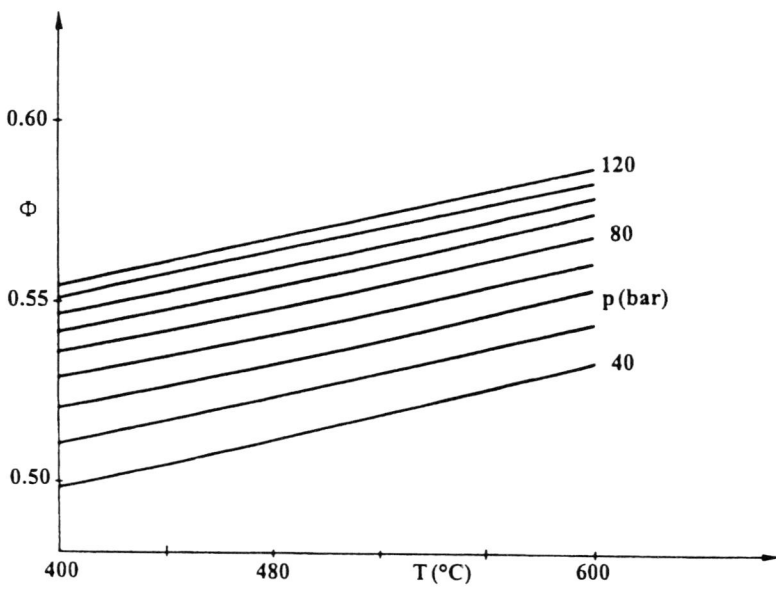

Fig. 4.9. Exergy efficiency, Φ, as a function of steam temperature for various values of steam pressure and a specific volume flow rate of gas [$G_V^* = 1650$ m^3(nTp)/t$_{dry\ coke}$].

4.3 THERMAL ENERGY RECOVERY FROM COKE-OVEN GAS (COG) USING ASCENSION-PIPE HEAT EXCHANGER

The COG temperature at the outlet of coke ovens, though dependent on the coke-oven operating rate and the time elapsed after the loading of the coal, is 650-800 °C. The total COG production is 300-350 m^3(nTp)/t$_{dry\ coal}$ with a thermal enthalpy of about 20.000 kJ/m^3(nTp) or 600-700 MJ/t$_{dry\ coal}$.

Usually the COG, leaving the coal charge, rises through the ascension pipe, is cooled by a spray of ammonia liquor and is further cooled by water in the primary cooler. Thus, the thermal energy of COG is scarcely utilized today. In 1934, a Japanese company installed a boiler on the ascension pipe of a coke oven, but soon had to cease operation of the boiler mainly because of trouble with tar condensates. As the necessity for energy saving was accentuated after the 1973 oil crisis, studies and experiments for the recovery of COG thermal energy were resumed at some steelworks.

When the thermal energy of COG is recovered through a heat exchanger installed in the ascension pipe (Fig. 4.10), the COG temperature decreases and at a critical temperature (about 400°C) tar condenses and is turned into soot on the heat transfer surface, thus impeding heat transfer and the operating performance of the heat exchanger. Therefore, a minimum COG temperature of about 450°C is necessary to avoid such trouble. In this way, about 30% of the total thermal energy of COG can be recovered. Recoveries above this level require the adoption of a particularly accurate technology.

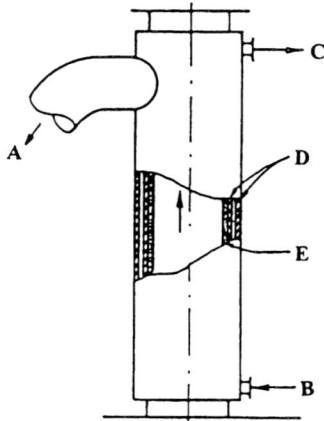

Fig. 4.10. Heat exchanger in the ascension pipe of COG, (A) COG outlet; (B) heat-transfer-medium inlet; (C) heat-transfer-medium outlet; (D) jacket; (E) lining.

Because the ascension-pipe heat exchanger is part of the oven equipment, it is not convenient to stop it for a long time due to regulatory inspection or scheduled maintenance. Hence, instead of a high-pressure steam recovery system, a heat-transfer-medium recovery system, which is capable of being operated at low pressure, is adopted for the ascension-pipe heat exchanger.

In Japan in 1982, the use of the heat recovered through the 16 ascension pipes of a battery of 100 ovens made it unnecessary to use steam hitherto consumed for preheating its fuel gas mixture.

4.4 COMPARATIVE EXAMINATION OF THE VARIOUS RECOVERY KINDS AND FUTURE OUTLOOK

4.4.1 Remarks on the Existing Plants

As above said, the dry coke cooling allows the recovery, as steam at 80-100 bar, of about 20% of the exergy value of the used fuel. The plants that combine the coke dry cooling and the preheating of the coal allow a lower energy recovery; however, since these plants permit a direct saving of primary energy, the total result can also be better.

The ascension-pipe heat exchanger allows a good recovery of the used fuel exergy, but with a very low operative value, therefore also of the heat-transfer-medium recovery system that operates at low pressure. It is to be noted, however, that the recovered thermal energy is usually utilized to save primary energy, preheating either the fuel gas mixture and the combustion air or the coal, even if that is obtained with a developing technology.

The thermal energy recovered from combustion exhaust gas is utilized to save primary energy, either partially or totally.

A new cokemaking technology, the single chamber system, has been recently developed to industrial readiness by the operation of a demonstration plant to improve energy saving (Ameling et al., 1998).

4.4.2 Future Outlook for New Plants

Let us consider the two energy flow diagrams (Figs. 4.11A, 4.12A), derived from (Aichinger et al., 1986), and Table 4.1. The former concerns a plant without coal preheating, the latter refers to a plant with coal preheating; in both, the maximum recovery values with the present technology are shown. In Figs. 4.11B and 4.12B, the corresponding exergy flow diagrams are shown, utilizing the usable exergy parameter (see subsection 12.2). In Table 4.1, the percentages of energy and exergy flow rates are reported.

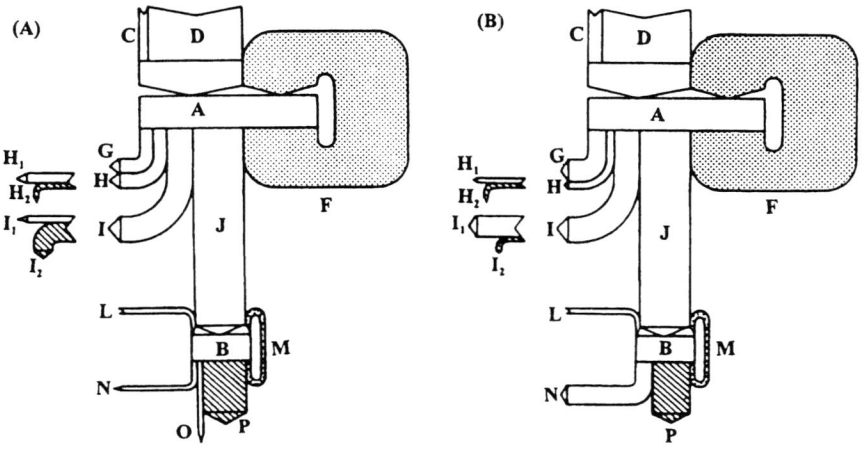

Fig. 4.11. Energy (A) and exergy (B) flow diagram for a plant without coal preheating (see Table 4.1).

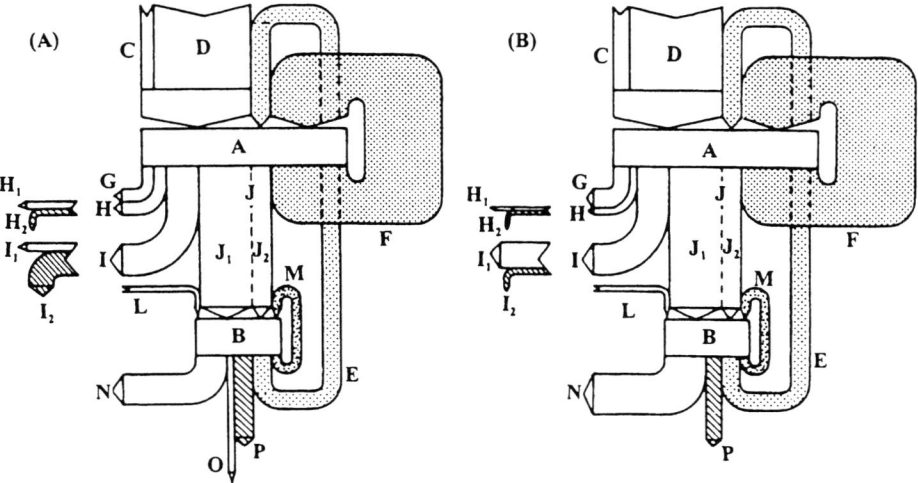

Fig. 4.12. Energy (A) and exergy (B) flow diagram for a plant with coal preheating (see Table 4.1).

Table 1 - Energy and Exergy Flow Rate Percentages for a Plant Without (A) and With (B) Coal Preheating.

	(A)			(B)	
A	Coke-oven battery		A	Coke-oven battery	
B	Coke dry cooling		B	Coke dry cooling	
	Per cent enthalpy values (Fig. 11A)	%		Per cent enthalpy values (Fig. 12A)	%
C	Coal reactions	9.2	C	Coal reactions	11.9
D	Gas combustion (3200 MJ/$t_{dry\,coke}$)	90.8	D	Gas combustion (2330 MJ/$t_{dry\,coke}$)	88.1
			E	Coal preheating (440 MJ/t_{dry})	16.6
F	Gas and combustion air preheating (2620 MJ/$t_{dry\,coke}$)		F	Gas and combustion air preheating (1940 MJ/$t_{dry\,coke}$)	
G	Surface losses and various	13.7	G	Surface losses and various	11.1
H	Waste gas	13.4	H	Waste gas	11.7
H_1	Waste gas (unusable part)	8.0	H_1	Waste gas (unusable part)	7.0
H_2	Waste gas (usable part)	5.4	H_2	Waste gas (usable part)	4.7
I	Coke-oven gas	24.7	I	Coke-oven gas	30.1
I_1	Coke-oven gas (unusable part)	5.2	I_1	Coke-oven gas (unusable part)	7.5
I_2	Coke-oven gas (usable part)	19.5	I_2	Coke-oven gas (usable part)	22.6
J	Incandescent coke	48.2	J	Incandescent coke (J_1=47.1%, J_2=16.6%)	63.7
L	Coke and residual distillation gas reactions	1.8	L	Coke and residual distillation gas reactions	2.4
M	Inert cooling gas	6.1	M	Inert cooling gas	8.1
N	Surface losses and various	3.6	N	Surface losses and various	27.4
O	Dry cooled coke	3.6	O	Dry cooled coke	5.9
P	Steam	42.8	P	Steam	16.2
	Per cent exergy values (Fig. 11B):	%		Per cent exergy values (Fig. 12B):	%
C	Coal reactions	11.8	C	Coal reactions	15.1
D	Gas combustion	88.2	D	Gas combustion	84.9
			E	Coal preheating	16.0

Table 1 continued

F	Gas and combustion air preheating	72.2	F	Gas and combustion air preheating	70.7
G	Surface losses and various; exergy losses	18.4	G	Surface losses and various; exergy losses	13.6
H	Waste gas	5.4	H	Waste gas	4.7
H_1	Waste gas (unusable part)	4.0	H_1	Waste gas (unusable part)	3.5
H_2	Waste gas (usable part)	1.4	H_2	Waste gas (usable part)	1.2
I	Coke-oven gas	23.8	I	Coke-oven gas	28.9
I_1	Coke-oven gas (unusable part)	18.8	I_1	Coke-oven gas (unusable part)	23.2
I_2	Coke-oven gas (usable part)	5.0	I_2	Coke-oven gas (usable part)	5.7
J	Incandescent coke	52.4	J	Incandescent coke (J_1=50.9%, J_2=17.9%)	68.8
L	Coke and residual distillation gas reactions	2.3	L	Coke and residual distillation gas reactions	3.0
M	Inert cooling gas	2.0	M	Inert cooling gas	2.7
N	Surface losses and various; exergy losses	20.2	N	Surface losses and various; exergy losses	42.8
P	Steam	34.5	P	Steam	13.0

It is to be noted that the fuel of the energy flow diagrams of (Aichinger et al., 1986) consists only of blast-furnace gas that is preheated, together with combustion air, only by the waste gas in the regenerators. This preheating, however, is not sufficient, when the lower heating value of the blast-furnace gas is very low, as happens in the most up-to-date blast furnaces with much reduced coke consumption.

The comparison between the energy flow diagrams and the corresponding ones of exergy, though these are only approximate, exhibits the following:

(i) the different operative values of the various energies;
(ii) the expediency of the various preheatings, that allow a direct saving of primary energy;
(iii) the advantage of utilizing all the recoveries chiefly for fuel and combustion air preheating so that the enriching of blast-furnace gas with other fuels, having a greater merit factor, can be avoided;
(iv) the different merit factor of the chemical energy of the combustion gas and of that of coal reactions.

Many authors (e.g., Jung, 1984) point out that it is convenient to do everything possible in order to use blast-furnace gas in coke ovens and keep coke-oven gas (having a higher adiabatic combustion temperature) for hot temperature metallurgical processes.

The result coincides with ours; it is to be noted, however, that the usable exergy method allows quantitative analyses (and not only qualitative), as is particularly done in (Bisio, 1996a).

In the energy and exergy flow diagrams, the thermal energy recovered from COG is not used to save primary energy and, consequently, it exhibits a low operative value. From Figs. 4.11 and 4.12 one notes, e.g., exergy values of 5% and 5.7% in correspondence to enthalpy values of 19.5% and 22.6%.

All the percentages of the recovered exergy would be remarkably lower, if one considered the fuel's exergy instead of its usable exergy.

Let us examine which energy recovery system can be the most convenient for a new plant.

An examination with the energy method would consider all the recoveries to be equivalent and, consequently, the only aim should be that of maximizing the value of the recovered total energy.

The use of exergy methods bears evidence of the convenience of utilizing all the recoveries, within the limits of technical and economical possibilities, for preheating fuel gas, combustion air and coal. In such a way, indeed, the recovered energy (even if of low exergy value) allows, as has been said, a numerically equal saving of chemical energy (of high exergy value). Only the remaining recovery energy must be utilized for steam production or, subordinately, for heating water.

The examination on the basis of usable exergy allows a graduation of the utilization expediency of the various recoveries in the following order:

(i) *Combustion air and fuel gas preheating.* This preheating allows both a reduction in the total fuel consumption and a proportionally greater reduction (and, if possible, the annihilation) in the coke-oven or natural gas consumption. The two last fuels exhibit usable exergy values greater than those of blast-furnace gas for corresponding volumes having the same exergy do. A demonstrative numerical calculation is reported in (Bisio, 1996b) for a different system. The usable exergy saving is greater than exergy saving. When preheating of air and fuel, in order to avoid the use of COG, cannot be carried out only by means of regenerators, it is possible to recover additional energy from COG and waste gas cooling, e.g., according to the scheme of Fig. 4.13.

(ii) *Coal preheating.* In this way, it is possible to obtain a reduction in the total fuel consumption but not a proportionally higher reduction in the coke-oven gas.

(iii) *Production of highest characteristic steam.* This steam can be used for electric energy production.

(iv) *Production of hot water or of low characteristic steam.* These fluids can be used for room heating.

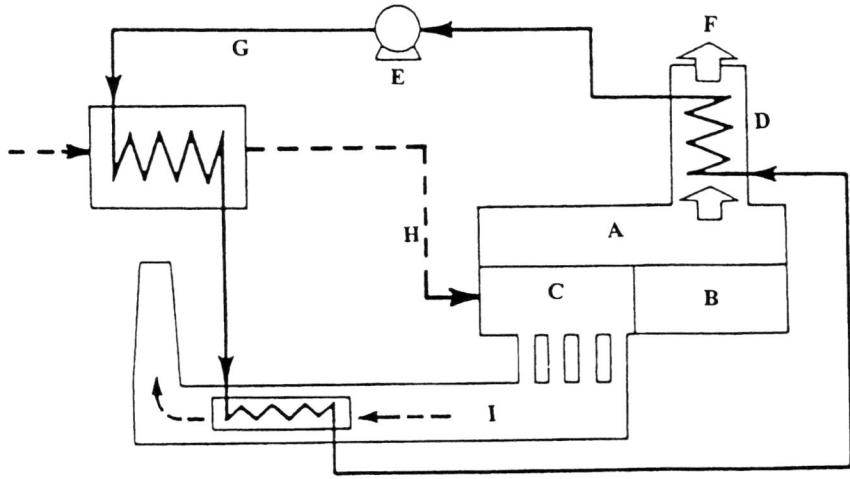

Fig. 4.13. Layout of a system for recovery of additional energy from COG and waste gas cooling: (A) coke oven; (B) combustion chamber; (C) regenerator; (D) ascension-pipe heat exchanger; (E) pump; (F) coke-oven gas; (G) heat-transfer-medium; (H) combustion air; (I) waste gas.

4.5 FINAL REMARKS

The coke-oven energy recoveries are not totally justified on the ground of the actual energy prices, especially in existing plants. However, if one considers the increasingly demands made on the measures for the environmental protection, the indirect advantages as coke quality and productivity as well as a likely increase of energy prices in the medium-long term, an integrated fulfillment of all the possible recoveries in coke-oven plants is completely justified.

Coke dry quenching appears as the most valid system to reduce air pollution allowing at the same time a remarkable energy recovery or saving, especially when it is associated with coal preheating. In addition, dry quenched coke is harder and stronger, and its moisture content is much lower than that of wet quenched coke. To obtain the purpose, some different solutions have been realized or proposed. Even if also energy analysis is useful, exergy analysis is the most valid tool to examine the various alternatives.

On the basis of literature data and of some results of numerical analysis, the following parameters appear to be preferred:

steam temperature	540°C ;	steam pressure	100 bar ;
specific volume flow rate of gas	1650 m^3(nTp)/t$_{dry\ coke}$.		

Obviously, the results do not consider other elements of different kind, which sometimes mandate some parameters. In particular, steam pressure and temperature can be fixed, when steam must be delivered to a power station or a distribution network already preexisting.

It is to be remarked that coke dry cooling is specifically to be applied in the case of a new coking plant. Indeed, antipollution regulations and the need of modifying coking plant capacities in many industrialized countries, justify the replacement of old plants. In these case, modern designs can meet all demands in terms of environmental protection, energy saving and ergonomy.

The thermal energy recovery from coke-oven gas presents various technological problems, in particular tar condensation, and has been so far applied for industrial plants only in the Japanese iron and steel industry which is particularly advanced in energy recovery and saving.

The thermal energy recovery from the waste gas after the regenerators at a temperature of about 200°C has been done only in a few cases using a heat pipe installed in the flue.

The coal preheating allows a reduction of the total fuel gas consumption; the preheating of fuel gas and combustion air allows both the reduction in the total fuel consumption and the proportionally greater reduction (and also annihilation) in the coke-oven or natural gas consumption.

Chapter 5

ENERGY RECOVERY FROM MOLTEN SLAG AND EXPLOITATION OF THE RECOVERED ENERGY

5.1 GENERAL REMARKS

Blast-furnace (BF), converter and electric-furnace (EF) slags represent the last waste energy potential in the high temperature range (1450 to 1650°C) which has had only limited uses. Various pilot plants are being developed both for energy recovery from slags and for reducing emissions of H_2S and SO_2 (Tani and Shinoda, 1981; Tiberg, 1981; Reinitzhuber, 1981; Westin, 1983; Pickering et al., 1985; Gudenau et al., 1986). Slags cause environmental pollution problems when they are poured into slag pits with water as coolant, as is now done at most works. In considering processes for using molten slags, it is important to obtain a commercially useful slag product. All of the blast-furnace slag is sold as a raw material for other processes. Most of the applications are made by the construction industry and involve using the slag as an aggregate or for cement manufacture. Blast-furnace slag can have two solid phases: it may have a crystalline structure produced by cooling the molten slag relatively slowly or it can have an amorphous or glassy structure (which is formed by cooling the slag rapidly, usually by water quenching). The heat released when molten slag is cooled to form a glassy product is about 17% less than the heat released when a crystalline product is formed.

Conventionally, molten slag is quenched in water when a glassy product is required. This product must be dried before it can be used in cement manufacture. This type of slag handling makes it impossible to recover energy. Various utilization procedures for slags are listed in Table 5.1 (Westin, 1983).

Table 5.1. Important Uses of Iron and Steel Slags.

BF slag	Converter slag and EF slag
Air-cooled slag	*Air-cooled slag*
Roads, railway ballast; aggregates for concrete; harbor construction materials; weak soil improvement materials; rubble; raw materials for cement clinkers; silicate-calcium fertilizer; rock wool (slag wool); glass, tile, roofing tile, etc.	Roads; harbor construction materials; weak soil improvement materials; raw materials for cement clinkers; materials for soil conditioning; earth work materials (filling, land preparation).
Rapidly cooled slag (granulated slag)	*Rapidly cooled slag*
Portland & Portland BF slag cement (cement mix); raw materials for cement clinkers; concrete admixtures; autoclaved lightweight concrete; weak soil improvement materials; fine aggregate for concrete and asphalt concrete; stabilization of subgrade and subbase courses, filter layers; silicate-calcium fertilizer; harbor construction materials (lightweight backfill); earth work materials; raw materials for ceramics.	Fine aggregates for concrete; others as for air-cooled slag.
Fairly rapidly cooled slag (expanded slag)	-------
Aggregates for lightweight concrete; lightweight backfill, reclamation materials; heat insulation.	-------

5.2 FUNDAMENTAL PROBLEMS IN HEAT RECOVERY FROM SLAGS

A characteristic feature of most silicate slags is their comparatively low heat conductivity, which creates difficulties in the recovery of energy contained in liquid slag. This topic is illustrated by the fact that a slag ladle left to cool in the air may remain liquid in the center for days. Thermal conductivities of blast-furnace slags were measured in the temperature range from 20 to 1550°C by using the hot-wire method. Results are reported by Goto et al. (1985). As long as the slags are in the glassy phase, the thermal conductivity k increases with increasing temperature from 1 to 2 W/(m - K). However, transition occurs at about 1200°C from glassy to liquid slags and the conductivity decreases rapidly with increasing temperature. In the liquid phase at 1400 to 1550°C, the k values are between 0.1 and 0.3 W/(m - K). On the other hand, values up to 7 W/(m - K) were measured in a crystalline slag.

5.3 INDUSTRIAL SYSTEMS FOR THERMAL ENERGY RECOVERY FROM METALLURGICAL SLAGS

5.3.1 The Merotec Pilot Plant

The liquid slag is fed to granulator B, either directly or via buffer ladle A (Fig. 5.1) at a temperature of about 1300°C (Tiberg, 1981). The Merotec-method involves disintegration of the liquid slag. Fines recycled through the slag-conveyer G and container H are used in the disintegration process and for cooling and protecting the process equipment. The mixture of disintegrated and recycled slag forms the fluidized bed. The thermal energy of the liquid slag is absorbed by the recycled material and by cooling surfaces in granulator B and subsequently in the fluid-bed heat exchanger C. In addition, the recycled fines protect the disintegrated slag from agglomeration. Through elevator D, the granulated slag is moved to screen E, which divides it into two parts according to size 0-3 mm and >3 mm in containers F1 and F2. Two fans I1 and I2 recirculate the air and the slag dust is recovered by two cyclones J1 and J2. The temperature of the granulated slag in the fluid bed is controlled by the ratio of recycled to liquid slag. Typical values are between 500 and 800°C. Energy recovery is about 64% of the slag energy (Gudenau et al., 1986); however, exergy recovery is notably lower.

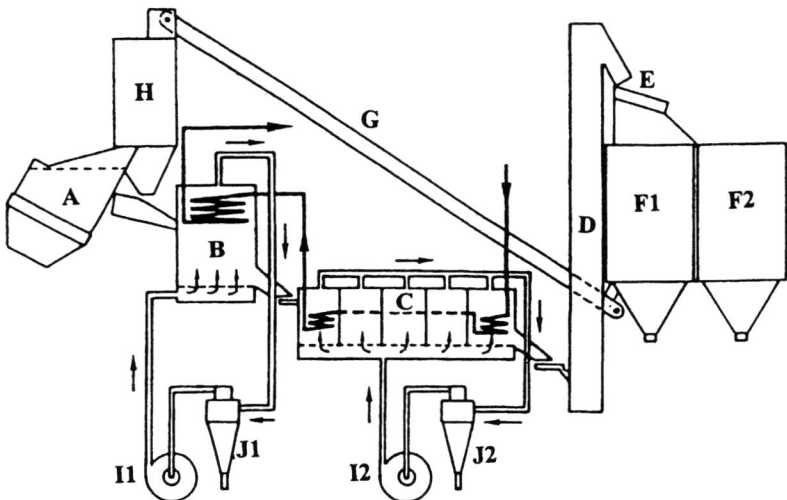

Fig. 5.1. Layout of the Merotec slag granulation plant: (A) liquid slag ladle; (B) granulator bed; (C) fluid-bed heat exchanger; (D) elevator; E, screen; (F1 & F2) granulated slag containers; (G) recycled slag conveyer; (H) recycled granular slag container; (I1 & I2) air fans; (J1 & J2) deduster cyclones.

5.3.2 Japanese Pilot Plants

5.3.2.1 Air Granulation Plant for LD Converter Slag –
Nippon Kokan together with Mitsubishi developed this system, which is schematically represented in Fig. 5.2 (Tani and Shinoda, 1981; Gudenau et al., 1986). The converter slag poured from ladle A is granulated by an air jet (blower B) and blown into hood boiler C. The granulated slag is moved by conveyer D and is added to the granulated slag container E (temperature range = 200-300°C). Heat is recovered as follows: (i) flying slag drops (temperature range 1500-1000°C) transfer heat to boiler pipes by radiation and convection; (ii) hot solid slag particles (temperature range = 1000-300°C) transfer heat to boiler pipes by conduction and convection; (iii) exit hot air (temperature range = 400-300°C) is utilized for drying in drier F. Energy recovery is 40-45% of the slag energy.

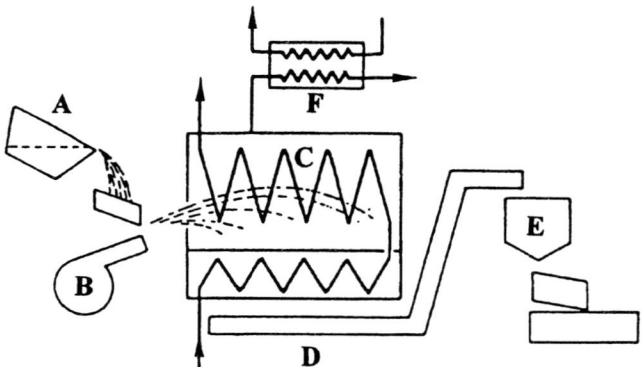

Fig. 5.2. Layout of the NKK air granulation plant for LD converter slag: (A) liquid slag ladle; (B) blower; C, hood boiler; D, conveyer; E, slag container; F, drier.

5.3.2.2 Cooling Drum Process –

The purpose of this plant (Fig. 5.3) is to obtain a rapidly cooled slag with energy recovery (Gudenau et al., 1986). Liquid slag is poured into slag cup A, which is located between two drums that turn, as is indicated in Fig. 5.3. An organic, low-boiling fluid rapidly cools the slag film that develops on the drums; thus, a glassy product is obtained. This glassy slag is removed from the drums by a stripping tool. By means of the heat exchanger C, the recovered heat can be used in a secondary circuit to generate electrical energy.

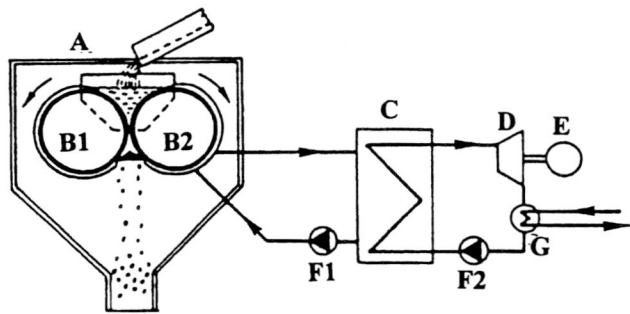

Fig. 5.3. Layout of the NKK cooling drum process: (A) slag cup; (B1 & B2) cooling drums; (C) heat exchanger; (D) turbine; (E) electric generator; (F1 & F2) pumps; (G) condenser.

5.3.2.3 Energy Recovery from Blast-Furnace Slag –

This plant has been constructed by Kawasaki Steel. The liquid slag is granulated to particles smaller than 100 mm in a stirrer, while water pipes are heated by radiation. The granulated slag (temperature range = 1000-1100°C) is cooled in a tower to 250°C while air is heated. This air produces steam in a closed cycle. The steam has the following maximum values: p=50 bar, T=450°C. This steam is utilized to produce electrical power. The basic concept of this plant is similar to that first tested in the USSR for coke dry quenching (Bisio, 1989c). Energy recovery is about 76% of the slag energy, while exergy recovery is slightly lower than 40%.

5.3.3 An English Pilot Plant

The plant is represented schematically in Fig. 5.4. The molten slag enters the heat-recovery vessel A through launder B that is covered to reduce heat loss. The launder delivers the molten slag directly into the rotary-cup air-blast atomizer C located in the center of the vessel. On atomization, the slag particles are projected radially outwards and slightly upwards in a spray and impinge on the vessel wall. The particles do not stick to the cooled vessel wall but fall directly into the primary fluidized bed D, where they are rapidly cooled to a temperature below the devitrification temperature for slag. Subsequently, the slag particle overflow into the secondary fluidized bed E, where more heat is recovered. The slag is then discharged through slag-exit launder F. Tests have shown that the slag particles are cooled fast enough for the product to have a glass content in excess of 95%.

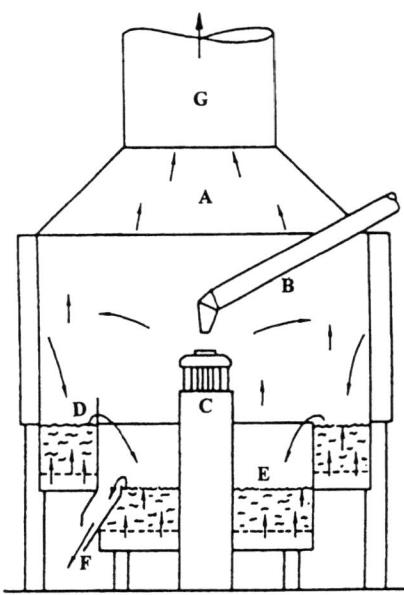

Fig. 5.4. Layout of the BSC granulation plant for blast-furnace slag: (A) heat recovery vessel; (B) slag supply launder; (C) rotary cup air-blast atomizer; (D) primary fluidized bed; (E) secondary fluidized bed; (F) slag-exit launder; (G) hot air exit.

5.3.4 A German Project for the Exploitation of Waste Energy in Metallurgical Slags

Thyssen Stahl together with RWTH developed a process for the utilization of waste energy in metallurgical slags. In first research projects, a small plant was built to exploit the radiant energy of liquid blast-furnace slags. This research led to the following proposals: (i) Heat may be recovered by radiation and convection from a thin layer of liquid slag in the temperature range from 1500 to 1050°C and, consequently, the exergy potential may be exploited to produce steam to generate electrical energy. (ii) Waste energy of solid slag may be utilized according to concepts used in coke dry quenching processes (Bisio, 1989c). The crystalline slag will have a temperature of 950-1050°C at the inlet of the cooling chamber and of 150-300°C at the exit. Air in a closed circuit will produce medium pressure steam.

5.4 MOST CONVENIENT EXPLOITATION OF THE RECOVERED ENERGY

5.4.1 General Considerations

Waste energy can be recovered to produce either steam or heated air and, in some cases, both steam and heated air. The most satisfactory way of utilizing the recovered energy of the blast-furnace slag is to use it in the same blast furnace so that energy does not need to be transported for long distances and the supply of recovered energy will match the blast-furnace demand.

For a large blast furnace (14-m hearth diameter) with a maximum output of 10000 t/d of iron, it is possible to use the two schemes of analysis of Table 5.2. The enthalpy data are taken from Pickering et al who made no exergy examinations (Pickering et al., 1985). In scheme 1A, heat is removed by blowing a large volume of air through the beds. In scheme 2A, a minimum volume of fluidizing air is used and heat is removed by using boiler tubes in the bed to produce steam.

Table 5.2. Schemes of Enthalpy and Exergy Recoveries.

Process	Scheme 1A	Scheme 2A
(a) Recovery from hot air:		
Air flow rate:	18.7 m^3 (nTp)/s T=432°C	8.64 m^3 (nTp)/s T=516°C
Recovered enthalpy flow rate:	10.28 MW	5.76 MW
Recovered exergy flow rate:	3.95 MW	2.45 MW
(b) Recovery from cooled walls:		
Saturated steam flow rate:	1.12 kg/s p=16 bar	2.84 kg/s p=16 bar
Recovered enthalpy flow rate:	3.06 MW	7.75 MW
Recovered exergy flow rate:	1.06 MW	2.68 MW
(c) Total recovery:		
Recovered enthalpy flow rate:	13.34 MW	13.51 MW
Recovered exergy flow rate:	5.01 MW	5.13 MW
(d) Required electric power:	0.75 MW	0.37 MW
(e) Efficiencies:		
Energy efficiency η	0.547	0.571
Exergy efficiency Φ	0.271	0.303

The analysis is done using both the energy and exergy methods with the following environmental values: pressure = p_o=1 bar, temperature = T_o=15°C. For both methods, the recovered enthalpy and exergy are practically equal, while the required electric power is higher in scheme 1A. However, which of the two schemes may be the most convenient to use varies from works to works.

5.4.2 Uses for Steam

Steam may be used on a blast furnace primarily to humidify the hot blast. Using the steam generated by the heat-recovery process to humidify the blast would release steam from this duty at the works power station. More steam would then be available to generate electricity.

5.4.3 Uses for Hot Air

5.4.3.1 On Various Possibilities –

Using the energy recovered as hot air to preheat the cold blast would result in higher temperatures at the bottom of the blast stoves, but this would consequently reduce their thermal efficiency and so there would be little overall saving. Preheating the combustion air for the stoves with the available hot air offers three methods for saving fuel: (a) by reducing the quantity of combustion gas; (b) by reducing the natural gas (NG) or COG enrichment in the combustion gas; (c) by increasing the heat input into the blast.

The results for these methods are compared with those for the base case, using the parameter usable exergy, as defined and employed elsewhere (see subsection 12.2). The results, using scheme 1A, are listed in Tables 5.3 and 5.4. For the base case and the three alternatives, the stove energy efficiency (η), the BFG enthalpy flow ($I°_{BFG}$), the NG enthalpy flow ($I°_{NG}$), the hot air enthalpy flow ($I°_A$), the total inlet enthalpy flow ($I°_T$), the enthalpy flow into blast ($I°_B$), and the lost enthalpy flow ($I°_L$) are shown in Table 5.3. The exergy efficiency Φ and the corresponding usable exergy flows $Ex°$ (instead of the enthalpy flows) are shown in Table 5.4.

Table 5.3. Enthalpy Flows through Hot Blast Stoves (Scheme 1A): A Comparison with the Base Case Method of Three Alternative Methods (a, b, c) of Using Heat Recovered from Molten Slag.

Method	η	$I°_{BFG}$	$I°_{NG}$	$I°_A$	$I°_T$	$I°_B$	$I°_L$
base case	0.780	113.0	43	--	156.0	121.7	34.3
a	0.815	100.0	39	10.3	149.3	121.7	27.6
b	0.780	130.7	15	10.3	156.0	121.7	34.3
c	0.788	113.0	43	10.3	166.3	131.0	35.3

Table 5.4. Exergy Flows through Hot Blast Stoves (Scheme 1A): A Comparison with the Base Case Method of Three Alternative Methods (a, b, c) of Using Heat Recovered from Molten Slag.

Method	Φ	$Ex°_{BFG}$	$Ex°_{NG}$	$Ex°_A$	$Ex°_T$	$Ex°_B$	$Ex°_L$
Base case	0.854	59.9	30.1	--	90.0	76.9	13.1
a	0.913	53.0	27.3	3.9	84.2	76.9	7.3
b	0.919	69.3	10.5	3.9	83.7	76.9	6.8
c	0.897	59.9	30.1	3.9	93.9	84.2	9.7

5.4.3.2 Reducing Combustion-Gas Consumption –

The preheated combustion air may be used to replace some of the mixed combustion gas. The use of preheated air without changing the composition or flow rate of the mixed combustion gas could result in higher flame temperatures and in a greater heat input to the stoves. The heat input can then be reduced to that required by reducing the flow rate of mixed combustion gas. This reduces the volume flow rate of the combustion products through the stove. The higher flame temperatures and lower volumes of the hot gases result in greater stove efficiencies.

5.4.3.3 Reducing NG or COG Enrichment –

For several years, both the lower heating value and the ratio GJ/(t iron) of BFG have been declining. This result is a direct consequence of the reduced fuel consumption per ton of iron yield. At the same time, the temperature of compressed air at the blast-furnace inlet has been going up. In the past, BFG was the only fuel used for the stoves. For these reasons, progressive addition of highly caloric gases to the BFG has become the usual procedure. NG and COG have a greater technical value than BFG and then they must be conserved as much as possible. The use of preheated combustion air in the stoves can considerably reduce the amounts of these gases needed to maintain constant gas temperatures.

5.4.3.4 Increasing Heat Input to Blast –

If the combustion air for the blast stoves is preheated and the same amount of combustion gas is used, then the hot blast temperature can be increased. This can result in savings in coke, but less BFG is produced. This method, however, can be applied only when blast temperatures have not yet reached the superior technological limits.

5.4.3.5 Comparisons –

By method (a), there are the lowest enthalpy losses. However, the lowest losses of usable exergy are obtained by method (b). The exploitation of usable exergy reverses some conclusions attainable by the use of either energy or classic exergy analysis. Furthermore, usable exergy losses for method (c) are higher than for methods (a) and (b). However, for the whole blast furnace process (scheme 1A) we obtain the following: saving in coke enthalpy flow = 21.1 MW, reduction of the enthalpy flow of BFG production = - 11.8 MW, net enthalpy flow saving in blast furnace = 9.3 MW, saving in coke usable exergy flow = 15.2 MW, reduction of the usable exergy flow of BFG production = - 6.3 MW, net usable exergy flow saving in blast furnace = 8.9 MW. Consequently, method (c) that allows a direct saving of primary energy is the most convenient when higher temperatures are applicable in the stoves.

5.4.3.6 Enthalpy and Exergy Multipliers –

We define the multipliers for savings in enthalpy and usable exergy flows as [α_I = (enthalpy-flow savings of fuels)/(increase of the enthalpy-flow of combustion air)] and [α_{Ex} = (usable exergy-flow savings of fuels)/(increase of the exergy-flow of combustion air)]. The following values are obtained for the three cases: case (a) - χ_I = 1.650, χ_{Ex} = 2.487; case (b) - χ_I = 1.000, χ_{Ex} = 2.615; case (c) - χ_I = 0.903, χ_{Ex} = 2.282. By using this analysis, the same results are obtained: the case (a) has the highest χ_I, the case (b) has the highest χ_{Ex}. However, the third case, even if it presents the lowest exergy and energy multipliers, is to be preferred, when possible, since it allows a direct saving of primary energy.

Table 5.5. Schemes of Enthalpy and Exergy Recoveries.

Process	Scheme 1B	Scheme 2B
(a) Recovery from hot air:		
Air flow rate:	18.7 m^3 (nTp)/s T=411.5°C	8.64 m^3 (nTp)/s T=378.3°C
Recovered enthalpy flow rate:	9.76 MW	4.12 MW
Recovered exergy flow rate:	3.65 MW	1.46 MW
(b) Recovery from cooled walls:		
Superheated steam flow rate:	1.12 kg/s (p=16 bar, T=400°C)	2.84 kg/s (p=16 bar, T=450°C)
Recovered enthalpy flow rate:	3.58 MW	9.37 MW
Recovered exergy flow rate:	1.31 MW	3.50 MW
(c) Total recovery:		
Recovered enthalpy flow rate:	13.34 MW	13.49 MW
Recovered exergy flow rate:	4.96 MW	4.96 MW
(d) Required electric power:	0.8 MW	0.4 MW
(e) Efficiencies:		
Energy efficiency η	0.545	0.569
Exergy efficiency Φ	0.265	0.290

5.5 AN ALTERNATIVE SYSTEM THAT ALLOWS US TO OBTAIN SUPERHEATED STEAM FOR ELECTRIC ENERGY PRODUCTION

5.5.1 Kinds and Proportions of the Recovered Energy

Steam may be superheated by means of hot air; in this way, one obtains for the two schemes of Table 5.2 the modification listed in Table 5.5.

5.5.2 Electric Power Obtainable by Means of Superheated Steam

For scheme 1B, the electric power (P_e = 1.12 MW), which is slightly higher than that necessary for operating the system, is recovered. For scheme 2B, one recovers (P_e = 3 M).

5.5.3 Uses for Hot Air

5.5.3.1 Recovery by Means of Scheme 1B –
The results are listed in Tables 5.6 and 5.7. Also in this case, usable exergy losses for method (c) are higher than for methods (a) and (b). However, we obtain the following for method (c): saving in coke enthalpy flow = 20.1 MW, reduction of the enthalpy flow of BFG production = - 11.2 MW, net enthalpy flow saving in blast furnace = 8.9 MW, saving in coke usable exergy flow = 14.5 MW, reduction of the usable exergy flow of BFG production = - 5.9 MW, net usable exergy flow saving in blast furnace = 8.6 MW.

Table 5.6 - Enthalpy Flows through Hot Blast Stoves (Scheme 1B): A Comparison with the Base Case Method of Three Alternative Methods (a, b, c) of Using Heat Recovered from Molten Slag.

Method	η	$I°_{BFG}$	$I°_{NG}$	$I°_A$	$I°_T$	$I°_B$	$I°_L$
base case	0.780	113.0	43	--	156.0	121.7	34.3
a	0.813	100.7	39.2	9.8	149.7	121.7	28.0
b	0.780	130.2	16.0	9.8	156.0	121.7	34.3
c	0.788	113.0	43.0	9.8	165.8	130.6	35.2

Table 5.7 - Exergy Flows through Hot Blast Stoves (Scheme 1B): A Comparison with the Base Case Method of Three Alternative Methods (a, b, c) of Using Heat Recovered from Molten Slag.

Method	Φ	$Ex°_{BFG}$	$Ex°_{NG}$	$Ex°_A$	$Ex°_T$	$Ex°_B$	$Ex°_L$
base case	0.854	59.9	30.1	--	90.0	76.9	13.1
a	0.911	53.4	27.4	3.6	84.4	76.9	7.5
b	0.918	69.0	11.2	3.6	83.8	76.9	6.9
c	0.896	59.9	30.1	3.6	93.6	83.9	9.7

Table 5.8 - Enthalpy Flows through Hot Blast Stoves (Scheme 2B): A Comparison with the Base Case Method of Three Alternative Methods (a, b, c) of Using Heat Recovered from Molten Slag.

Method	η	$I°_{BFG}$	$I°_{NG}$	$I°_A$	$I°_T$	$I°_B$	$I°_L$
base case	0.780	113.0	43	--	156.0	121.7	34.3
a	0.794	108.0	41.1	4.1	153.2	121.7	31.5
b	0.780	120.0	31.9	4.1	156.0	121.7	34.3
c	0.783	113.0	43.0	4.1	160.1	125.4	34.7

5.5.3.2 Recovery by Means of Scheme 2B –

The results are listed in Tables 5.8 and 5.9. We obtain the following for method (c): saving in coke enthalpy flow = 8.4 MW, reduction of the enthalpy flow of BFG production = - 4.7 MW, net enthalpy flow saving in blast furnace = 3.7 MW, saving in coke usable exergy flow = 6.0 MW, reduction of the usable exergy flow of BFG production = - 2.5 MW, net usable exergy flow saving in blast furnace = 3.5 MW.

Table 5.9 - Exergy Flows through Hot Blast Stoves (Scheme 2B): A Comparison with the Base Case Method of Three Alternative Methods (a, b, c) of Using Heat Recovered from Molten Slag.

Method	Φ	$Ex°_{BFG}$	$Ex°_{NG}$	$Ex°_A$	$Ex°_T$	$Ex°_B$	$Ex°_L$
base case	0.854	59.9	30.1	--	90.0	76.9	13.1
a	0.879	57.2	28.8	1.5	87.5	76.9	10.6
b	0.880	63.6	22.3	1.5	87.4	76.9	10.5
c	0.872	59.9	30.1	1.5	91.5	79.8	11.7

5.6 FINAL REMARKS

The relatively new processes for heat recovery from the blast furnace, converter and electric-furnace slags described in this paper yield a dry granulated product with a glass content depending on process details. It can be used for various purposes. In addition, a significant amount of energy can be recovered from both liquid and solid slags. Waste energy can be recovered to produce either steam or heated air. It is proved that the second alternative is preferred for blast-furnace slag when heated air is used for combustion in the blast-furnace stoves. In this way one of these ends can be achieved: (a) reduction of the combustion gas consumption; (b) reduction of NG enrichment in the combustion gas; (c) increase of heat input to blast, and thus reduction of coke consumption and increase of blast-furnace production. Generally, the second end is the most convenient, when heat recovery is applied to an existing plant. Furthermore, slags cause also environmental pollution problems, when they are poured into slag pits with water as coolant. In various works, indeed, the first goal of a slag dry-granulation process is to reduce the environment pollution.

Chapter 6

THERMODYNAMIC ANALYSIS OF THE USE OF PRESSURE EXERGY OF NATURAL GAS

6.1 GENERAL REMARKS

Natural gas (NG) is a fuel that is environmentally unobjectionable, easy to handle and, in addition, is an important raw material for the chemical industry. Its consumption has therefore been steadily increasing for many years. The growth has resulted from several factors, including replacement of coal as a fuel for the provision of space and industrial process heat, the use of NG in making petrochemicals and fertilizers, and strong demand for low-sulphur fuels that emerged in the middle 1960s. As the result, there have been steadily increasing imports of NG into industrialized countries (Western Europe, Japan, and the United States).

For the transportation of NG from producing wells to utilization sites, two approaches are now applied with their relative pros and cons (Szilas, 1975; Harder, 1982; Geist, 1983; Pellò and Vitale, 1984). The first involves NG purification and liquefaction, followed by overseas transport as liquid natural gas (LNG) in tankers and then regasification. The second involves pipeline transportation of NG at high pressure. Obviously, for transport overland and over short distances at sea, the cheapest mode of transport is by pipeline.

The chemical component of NG exergy is by far the most valuable; however, also the physical exergy of NG, due to its pressure (as by pipeline transportation) or to its liquid phase at a temperature of ≈110 K (as in tanker transportation), is not negligible.

Notwithstanding, till now this physical exergy is generally wasted. Indeed, at most receiving terminals, the equipment used to revaporize LNG usually consists of seawater vaporizers, in which all the physical exergy of LNG is destroyed, with additional consumption of electrical energy for the circulation pumps. Similarly, the NG transported by pipelines is usually decompressed in a throttling valve, thereby destroying its exergy pressure with additional consumption of thermal energy to avoid a decrease of temperature.

6.2 COMPRESSOR EXERGY EFFICIENCY

For compression system (Fig. 6.1) so characterized:

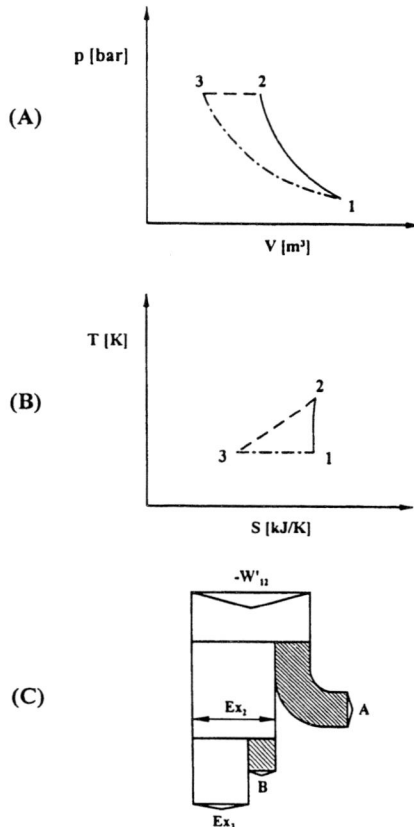

Fig. 6.1. Analysis of compression process: (A) p vs V diagram with 1-3 representing an isothermal process; (B) T vs S diagram; (C) exergy-flow diagram.

$$W'_{12} < 0, \quad T > T_o, \quad Ex_2 > Ex_1, \quad Q_{o12} \leq 0, \tag{6.1}$$

(where Q_{o12} is the heat transfer from or to the environment at T_o temperature), two different efficiency expressions denoted by Φ and Φ' can be considered:

$$\Phi = (Ex_2 - Ex_1)/(-W'_{12}) = 1 - [S_2 - S_1 - Q_{o12}/T_o]/[(I_2 - I_1)/T_o - Q_{o12}/T_o], \tag{6.2}$$

$$\Phi' = (Ex_3 - Ex_1)/(-W'_{12}) =$$
$$1 - [(I_2 - I_3)/T_o + S_3 - S_1 - Q_{o12}/T_o]/[(I_2 - I_1)/T_o - Q_{o12}/T_o], \tag{6.3}$$

where $(p_3 = p_2)$ and $(T_3 = T_1)$.

Actually, the compressor units serve a range of different functions in industrial applications.

In some cases, both the pressure increase and the corresponding temperature rise of the compressed fluid are useful, e.g., compressed air to be used in combustion (Stecco and Manfrida, 1986). In these cases, the exergy value of the final state is quite meaningful and therefore the use of Φ is appropriate.

But often the only purpose is that of obtaining a higher fluid pressure; in fact, the corresponding temperature rise above the value T_o of the environment is either not useful for technical purposes, or it is lost before being used by lack of insulation. The latter occurs, for example, in a compressed air plant for pneumatic tools. In this case, more importance is attached to the expression of Φ' referring to state 3 with pressure p_3 equal to the final pressure p_2 and temperature T_3 equal to the initial temperature ($T_1 = T_o$).

As can be easily seen (Bisio, Goffi and Martini, 2000), Φ' coincides with the formulation of the isothermal efficiency for a compressor. In this way, a definition suggested by practical reasons seems to be fully justified within the general stated concepts.

By Bisio (1989a), the possible advantages of intermediate cooling in the air compression plants for blast furnaces are considered; in these systems, indeed, intermediate cooling involves a higher total energy consumption with a lower work consumption (of greater technical and economical value). For this quite special application, both expressions of exergy efficiency, Φ and Φ', are significant; everyone visualizes a given aspect of the problem. Indeed, two Tables of that paper show that, with the same isentropic efficiency of the single compressor stages, the compressor exergy efficiency Φ is lower and the compressor isothermal efficiency Φ' (alternative expression of exergy efficiency) is higher when an intermediate cooling is applied. The former makes it visible that a greater amount of heat must be supplied to the air by the blast-furnace regenerators and the latter indicates the lower work consumption of the air compressor.

6.3 POSSIBLE UTILIZATIONS OF NG PRESSURE EXERGY

6.3.1 General Remarks

Various processes have been considered in order to employ the physical exergy of NG at the pipeline end, and two alternatives may be envisaged: (a) direct utilization for some specific purpose; (b) indirect utilization in the generation of electric power.

Direct utilization poses some problems and, in particular, it entails coupling two plants with asynchronous characteristics. Indirect utilization in the generation of electric power avoids the problems of direct utilization and generally uses the available exergy in a more efficient way; however, it adds a new step, with its exergy destruction, to the final energy use.

Strictly associated with the indirect utilization in the generation of electric power, there is the possibility of exploitation of the low temperature of NG at the turbine exit. Indeed, if NG is not preheated, the temperature at the turbine exit is low and can be employed for various cooling purposes; however, this is possible only when there is no danger of ice or NG hydrate formation (Glasstone, 1983; Ikoku, 1984; Poettmann, 1984), since NG is sufficiently pure or is purified in a valid way.

It is to be noted that NG hydrates are solid crystalline compounds formed by the chemical combination of NG and water under pressure at temperatures *above* the freezing point of water. In the presence of free water, hydrates are formed when the temperature is below a certain degree (hydrate temperature). Gas hydrate crystals resemble ice or wet snow in appearance, but do not have ice's solid structure, are much less dense and exhibit properties that are generally associated with organic chemical compounds.

Now, let us consider two direct utilizations.

6.3.2 Utilization of NG Pressure Exergy to Compress Recovery Steam

One can say that flash steam, or low-pressure vent steam, is probably one of the largest untapped sources of industrial waste energy. The vent steam is at atmospheric pressure, or slightly above, and consequently it has a large specific volume. Let us consider, e.g., the evaporation of aqueous solutions. In its simplest form, heat is applied to a vessel by means of condensing steam; water is then vaporized and vent off. If the steam enthalpy is not recovered, the operation is thermodynamically wasteful and so expensive. Evaporators are therefore designed to operate in a series of three or more vessels, or "effects". One area of development relating to the use of vent steam is the application of turbocompressors to raise the pressure of the steam vented from one "effect", before its re-use.

It is feasible to use a compressor for recovering vent steam from several processes (Wakefield, 1984). It is to be noted that this steam is commonly not employable in its actual conditions of temperature and pressure (slightly above the atmospheric one). The level at which the steam must be compressed is conditioned by the possibility of finding uses for heating purposes; in addition, only large amounts of vent steam justify the exploitation of such a low level.

Possible utilizations of the steam obtained from the evaporative cooling of metal components of blast furnaces have been considered by Wesemann (1956), Schilcher (1956), Vonnemann (1957), Nolzen (1984), and Bisio (1990a and 1992). As is known, in various works the forced water cooling of metal components at high temperatures of some plant (e.g., slab reheating furnaces, continuous casting machines, electric arc furnaces) has been replaced by evaporative cooling generally at pressures of 20-30 bar (Bredehöft et al., 1986; Andritzke et al., 1987; Brod, 1989). In this way, energy is recovered, the consumption of water is reduced and the service life of the equipment is increased. On the other hand, in blast furnaces, the rated pressure of the evaporative cooling has never been higher than 3-4 bar; in fact, the water-steam pressure should never exceed the blast-furnace interior pressure for safety reasons. Consequently, only few plants of this type have been constructed for blast furnaces due to the difficulty of finding valid exploitations of the recovered energy. Greater possibilities for industrial uses of this energy may result from raising the recovered steam pressure and temperature to higher levels by means of compression.

A layout of a possible application is presented in Fig. 6.2. From the steam-water separator A, the water is delivered by the pump B to the refrigerating elements C of a blast furnace and then returns to the separator only partially vaporized (dryness fraction = 0.04) to avoid any danger of burn-out. The steam is then released in the separator. This steam is compressed in the compressor D (shaft work W') driven by the NG turbine G (with its heater H utilizing low temperature waste heat Q_2) and recycled to the heat exchanger E, where it condenses while giving back heat Q_1 in the temperature interval from T_{1i} to T_{1o} (useful effect). Then the condensed water returns to the steam separator through the throttling valve F.

The exergy efficiency of this system is considered in the next subsection.

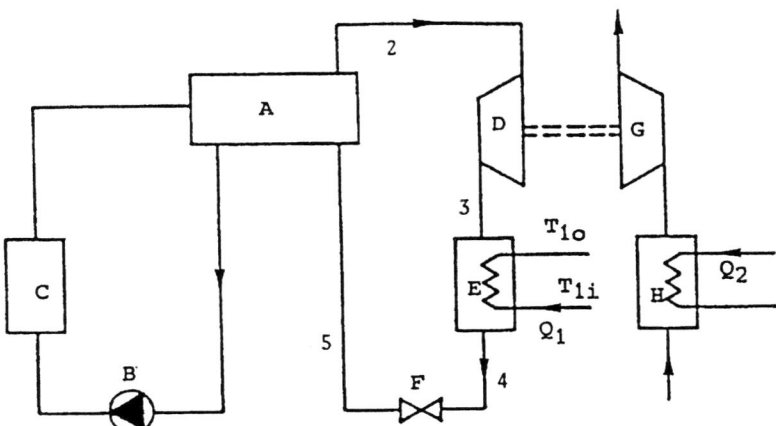

Fig. 6.2. Flowsheet for exploitation of vent steam by compression using NG expansion: (A) steam-water separator; (B) pump; (C) cooling elements of the blast furnace; (D) compressor; (E) heat exchanger; (F) throttling valve; (G) NG turbine; (H) NG heater.

6.3.3 Utilization of NG Pressure Exergy to Compress Air

Another possibility of direct utilization is the employment of the NG pressure exergy to compress air (Gneuss, 1983; Lütge, 1988) and, at the same time, the use of the cooling thermal energy of compressed air to heat NG. In addition, there is in general the necessity of other low-temperature thermal energy to heat NG, and this heat must be derived from "waste energy" owing to economy reasons.

As is well known, in large-size plants (e.g. iron and steel works), there is generally a compressed air network, fed by one or two conveniently located air-compression stations, to reduce the overall pipeline irreversibilities; it is easy to connect the recovery station to the compressed air network. In this way, a drawback of direct utilization can be avoided, since in no case a malfunction of the recovery station can hamper a compressed air utilizer.

In addition, in large-size works, there is a high availability of low-temperature thermal energy and numerous studies have been carried out for actual utilization, e.g. (Gautschi, 1981; Ritter and Jank, 1981; Le Goff, 1979, 1980 and 1982; Hu, 1983).

It is to be noted that, while thermal energy at high and medium temperatures is always exploitable in large works, the thermal energy at low temperatures (< 100°C) is rarely usable.

A layout of a possible system is schematically represented in Fig. 6.3; the corresponding processes of NG (assumed in the calculations as pure methane) and air are described in Figs. 6.4 and 6.5.

The NG flows through the first auxiliary heater A, the first turbine B, the heat exchanger C, the second auxiliary heater D, and the second turbine E. The air flows through the first compressor F, the heat exchanger C (in which air is cooled and NG heated) and the second compressor G.

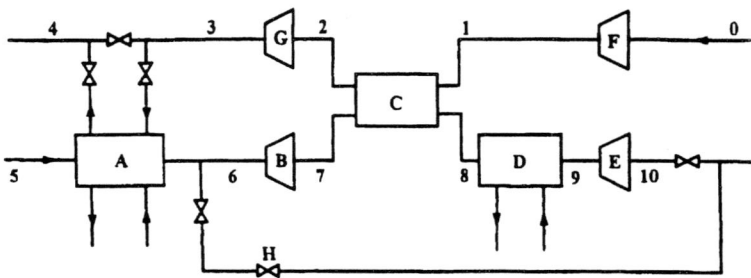

Fig. 6.3. Layout of a system for air compression by means of NG expansion; each one of the two turbines is mechanically connected to one compressor: (A) first auxiliary heater; (B) first turbine; (C) NG/air heat exchanger; (D) second auxiliary heater; (E) second turbine; (F) first compressor; (G) second compressor; (H) regulation valve.

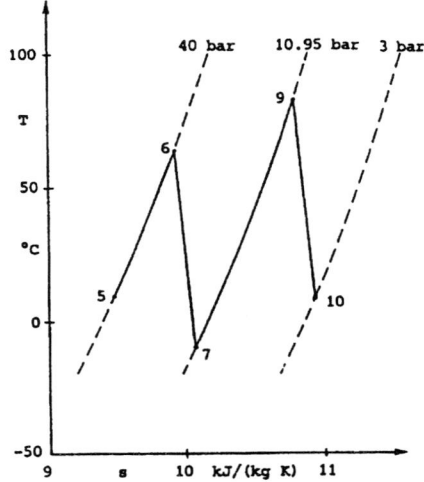

Fig. 6.4. Methane processes in a temperature (T) vs specific entropy (s) diagram.

It is convenient to use a heat pipe exchanger in order to avoid every possibility of explosive mixtures in the case of leaks. After the first auxiliary heater, a by-pass with the throttling valve H is installed to act as a regulator and to assure the supplying of NG to customers in whatever case.

The air at the exit of the second compressor G, after a possible cooling in the exchanger A, goes into the general network of the compressed air of works so that its deficiency is in no case a cause of troubles. Only in particular cases the compressed air can be utilized for a specific plant which is placed in the proximity of the considered expansion-compression system; however, this solution involves, between the above specific plant and the expansion-compression system, various constraints which are hardly-ever consistent with a good operation reliability.

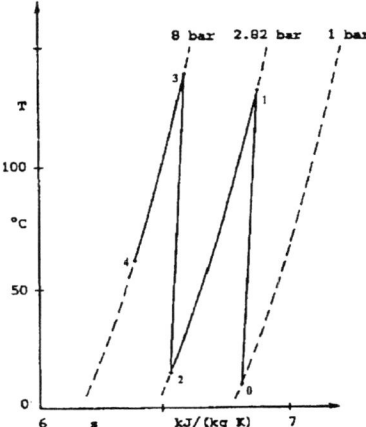

Fig. 6.5. Air processes in a temperature (T) vs specific entropy (s) diagram.

The cooling of the air at the first compressor outlet, by means of the NG at the first turbine outlet, reduces the work of the second compressor and supplies the necessary thermal energy to the NG. The thermal energy obtained from the air cooling after the first compressor is usually not sufficient for the optimal working of the NG turbines. Thus, it is necessary to supply heat in one or both auxiliary heaters; this heat, as mentioned above, must be low-temperature "waste heat", and consequently of low exergy and economic value.

In particular, the thermal energy of the air at the outlet of the second compressor can be used before the introduction into the general network. Obviously, this should not be done when the compressed air is supplied to a plant for which a temperature above that of the environment is profitable (e.g., air for combustion).

In addition, it is necessary to distinguish whether the utilization of the waste thermal energy in the considered system has some technical-economical alternatives or it is the only technically possible use. The presence/absence of alternative uses has a valuable influence on the choice of the optimal solution, as is shown in the following.

It must be noted that, even till now the exploitations of the pressure exergy of NG are very few in industry, the pressure exergy of other fluids has already had various utilizations; this is in particular the case of the top gas pressure in blast furnaces (Flächsenhaar et al., 1981; Caussade, 1982, Hoffmann et al., 1987; Bisio and Simonetti, 1995).

In the next sections, a system for direct utilization of NG pressure exergy for air compression with every possible energy recovery is examined in detail.

6.4 EXERGY ANALYSIS OF A SYSTEM FOR COMPRESSING RECOVERY STEAM

Let us consider the exergy efficiency for the system including separator, compressor, heat exchanger, throttling valve and NG turbine with its heater but excluding the heat exchange in the blast furnace (Fig. 6.2). Indicating by "2" the state of the fluid after its exit from the separator and on its way to the compressor, by "3" the state after the compressor, by "4" the state after the heat exchanger E, and by "5" the state at the inlet of the separator behind the throttling valve, it follows that

$$Q_1 + (I_2 - I_5) = W', \quad I_4 = I_5, \tag{6.4}$$

where: $Q_1 < 0$ (useful effect), $(I_2 - I_5) > 0$ and $W' < 0$ (compressor work).

Let us define the exergy factor θ as the ratio of the variation of the specific exergy of a source (or sink) fluid $(ex_i - ex_o)$ to the corresponding variation of the specific enthalpy $(i_i - i_o)$. The exergy factor can be considered as a "weighted" Carnot factor; it coincides with the usual Carnot factor, $(T - T_o)/T$, in the cases of heat sources or sinks of infinite thermal capacity. Consequently, the heat Q from a source or to a sink is characterized by the exergy factor θ and the exergy transfer $Q\theta$. As is obvious the exergy factor of shaft work is one. When there are two different energies (at the inlet or at the outlet of a system), it is possible to consider a weighted mean exergy factor.

Let us apply the general concepts regarding exergy efficiency, dealt with in section 2, to this particular system.

The actually lost exergy is given by:

$$Ex_a = (\Delta Ex_{ng} + Q_2 \theta_2) + (Ex_2 - Ex_5) + Q_1 \theta_1, \tag{6.5}$$

where: ΔEx_{ng} = absolute value of the variation of the NG physical exergy in the turbine, and $Q_2 \theta_2$ = exergy of the waste heat Q_2

The exergy actually lost can be divided into two parts: the exergy lost in the NG subsystem, Ex_{a1}, and the exergy lost in the steam subsystem, Ex_{a2}. Here,

$$Ex_{a1} = (\Delta Ex_{ng} + Q_2 \theta_2) + W', \quad Ex_{a2} = (Ex_2 - Ex_5) + Q_1 \theta_1 - W'. \tag{6.6}$$

The losable exergy, i.e. the exergy destruction with no useful effect, is given by:

$$Ex_{rf} = (\Delta Ex_{ng} + Q_2 \theta_2) + (Ex_2 - Ex_5), \tag{6.7}$$

The actual entropy production and the reference entropy production are, respectively:

$$S_{sa} = Ex_a/T_o = (\Delta Ex_{ng} + Q_2 \theta_2)/T_o + (Ex_2 - Ex_5)/T_o + Q_1 \theta_1/T_o, \tag{6.8}$$

$$S_{srf} = Ex_{rf}/T_o = (\Delta Ex_{ng} + Q_2 \theta_2)/T_o + (Ex_2 - Ex_5)/T_o. \tag{6.9}$$

Hence, the relative entropy production and the exergy efficiency becomes, respectively:

$$\sigma_r = S_{sa}/S_{srf} = [(\Delta Ex_{ng} + Q_2 \theta_2)/T_o + (Ex_2 - Ex_5)/T_o + Q_1 \theta_1/T_o]/$$
$$[(\Delta Ex_{ng} + Q_2 \theta_2)/T_o + (Ex_2 - Ex_5)/T_o] ==$$
$$1 - [-Q_1 \theta_1]/[(\Delta Ex_{ng} + Q_2 \theta_2) + (Ex_2 - Ex_5)], \tag{6.10}$$

$$\Phi = Ex_u/Ex_{rf} = (Ex_{rf} - Ex_a)/Ex_{rf} = [(\Delta Ex_{ng} + Q_2 \theta_2) + (Ex_2 - Ex_5) -$$
$$((\Delta Ex_{ng} + Q_2 \theta_2) + (Ex_2 - Ex_5) + Q_1 \theta_1)]/[(\Delta Ex_{ng} + Q_2 \theta_2) + (Ex_2 - Ex_5)]$$
$$= [-Q_1 \theta_1)]/[(\Delta Ex_{ng} + Q_2 \theta_2) + (Ex_2 - Ex_5)] = 1 - \sigma_r. \tag{6.11}$$

From the above relations one notes that the exergy efficiency can be derived in the same way either with reference to exergy or with reference to entropy.

In addition, it is possible to consider a coefficient of performance of the compression process, taking into consideration the fact that the compression allows the utilization of an energy that is otherwise useless notwithstanding its valuable exergy value.

One can define the performance ζ in this way:

$$\zeta = Q_1/(-W') = (I_3 - I_4)/(-W') . \tag{6.12}$$

This parameter is significant and useful for the comparisons with the performance of other upgrading techniques.

6.5 EXERGY ANALYSIS OF THE SYSTEM FOR COMPRESSING AIR

6.5.1 Exergy Parameters Considered in the Search for Thermodynamic Optimum Solution

In the search for thermodynamic optimum solution, the following parameters are considered:

(i) The energy (equal to exergy) recovered as shaft work per mass unit of NG, e_r. This parameter multiplied by the mass flow rate gives the power recovered.
(ii) The ratio R of e_r to the exergy decreases per mass unit of NG in an isenthalpic expansion to the same final pressure (in a throttling valve). This parameter is particularly meaningful when the economic value of the auxiliary heat can be judged practically zero since it has no alternative use.
(iii) The classical exergy efficiency, Φ_1. This parameter is the ratio of the recovered exergy, i.e. the shaft work, to the losable exergy, i.e. the decrease of the NG exergy from the system inlet to outlet plus the exergy of the auxiliary thermal energy Q_i with its weighted exergy factor θ_i (see Fig. 6.3), viz.,

$$\Phi_1 = Ex_u/Ex_{rf} = -W'/(Ex_{ng5} - Ex_{ng10} + Q_i \theta_i) , \tag{6.13}$$

with the corresponding relative entropy production:

$$\sigma_{r1} = (S_{srf} - S_{sa1}/S_{srf}) = 1 - (-W'/T_o)/[(Ex_{ng5} - Ex_{ng10} + Q_i \theta_i)/T_o] =$$
$$= 1 - (-W'/T_o)/[(Ex_{ng5} - Ex_{ng10} + Q_i \theta_i)/T_o] = 1 - \Phi_1 . \tag{6.14}$$

(iv) The exergy efficiency Φ_2. Applying this parameter, in accordance with the ideas of subsection 6.2, one considers as not usable the component of the physical exergy of the NG at the second turbine outlet due to the difference (positive or negative) between its temperature and that of the environment. Indeed, this component of the physical exergy is usually lost. It follows that

$$\Phi_2 = -W'/(Ex_{ng5} - Ex_{ng10,o} + Q_i\,\theta_i)\,,\quad \sigma_{r2} = 1 - (-W')/(Ex_{ng5} - Ex_{ng10,o} + Q_i\,\theta_i)\,, \qquad (6.15)$$

where $Ex_{ng10,o}$ is the exergy of the NG at the system outlet pressure and at the environment temperature.

(v) The exergy efficiency Φ_3, ratio of the recovered exergy, i.e. the exergy increase of the air, to the losable exergy, i.e. the decrease of the exergy of the NG from the system inlet to outlet plus the exergy of the auxiliary thermal energy Q_i with its weighted exergy factor θ_i, viz.,

$$\Phi_3 = Ex_{a4}/(Ex_{ng5} - Ex_{ng10} + Q_i\,\theta_i)\,,\quad \sigma_{r3} = 1 - Ex_{a4}/(Ex_{ng5} - Ex_{ng10} + Q_i\,\theta_i)\,. \qquad (6.16)$$

(vi) The exergy efficiency Φ_4, ratio of the usable exergy increase of the air to the usable exergy decrease both of the NG and of the auxiliary heat (for usable exergy, see subsection 12.2), viz.,

$$\Phi_4 = Ex_{a4,o}/(Ex_{ng5} - Ex_{ng10,o} + Q_i\,\theta_i)\,,\quad \sigma_{r4} = 1 - Ex_{a4,o}/(Ex_{ng5} - Ex_{ng10,o} + Q_i\,\theta_i)\,, \qquad (6.17)$$

where $Ex_{a4,o}$ is the exergy of the air at the system outlet pressure and at the environment temperature.

This parameter is particularly meaningful when only the air pressure increase is technically useful, whereas the temperature increase is either not useful or is lost before a possible use.

Also in the case of this system for compressing air, the various expressions of exergy efficiency are derived in the same way either with reference to exergy or with reference to entropy production.

6.5.2 Results Obtained by Computer Analysis

For a plant of the type schematically shown in Fig. 6.3, the influence of various system properties and of other quantities on the defined exergy parameters has been examined by computer analysis.

Some quantities (inlet temperature, inlet and outlet pressures of air; inlet and outlet temperatures and pressures of methane; temperature at the outlet of the first turbine; efficiencies of compressors and turbines) have been considered as independent variables to be fixed for an actual plant. The temperature of the air at intermediate cooling has been linked to some previous quantities by a suitable relation. Pressure drop in the heat exchangers has been linked to other previous quantities by a relation with a variable coefficient to be fixed according to the kind of plant. Finally, other parameters (chemical composition of NG assumed to be pure methane, thermal efficiencies of heat exchangers, mechanical efficiencies of the turbine-compressor groups) have been assumed constant. By means of these assumptions, the auxiliary thermal energies in the heat exchangers are determined. As an alternative, the heat to be supplied in the exchanger D, Q_2, is assumed to be an independent variable, and in this case the final expansion temperature is obtained. An investigation has been made of the dependence of the exergy parameters e_r, R, Φ_1, Φ_2, Φ_3, Φ_4 on each of the above-mentioned quantities, keeping the others constant. In addition, the variations of the above exergy parameters have also been obtained as functions of two or more quantities, assumed with some constraints among them.

It is to be noted that not always it is possible to obtain the assigned temperatures after the expansions, since the auxiliary thermal energies must be necessarily positive (or zero in the limit).

The diagrams of Figs. 6.6 and 6.7 show the variations of the exergy parameters e_r, R, Φ_1, Φ_2, Φ_3, Φ_4 vs various system properties and other quantities; it is to be noted that Φ_2 is represented in the diagrams only when it differs appreciably from Φ_1.

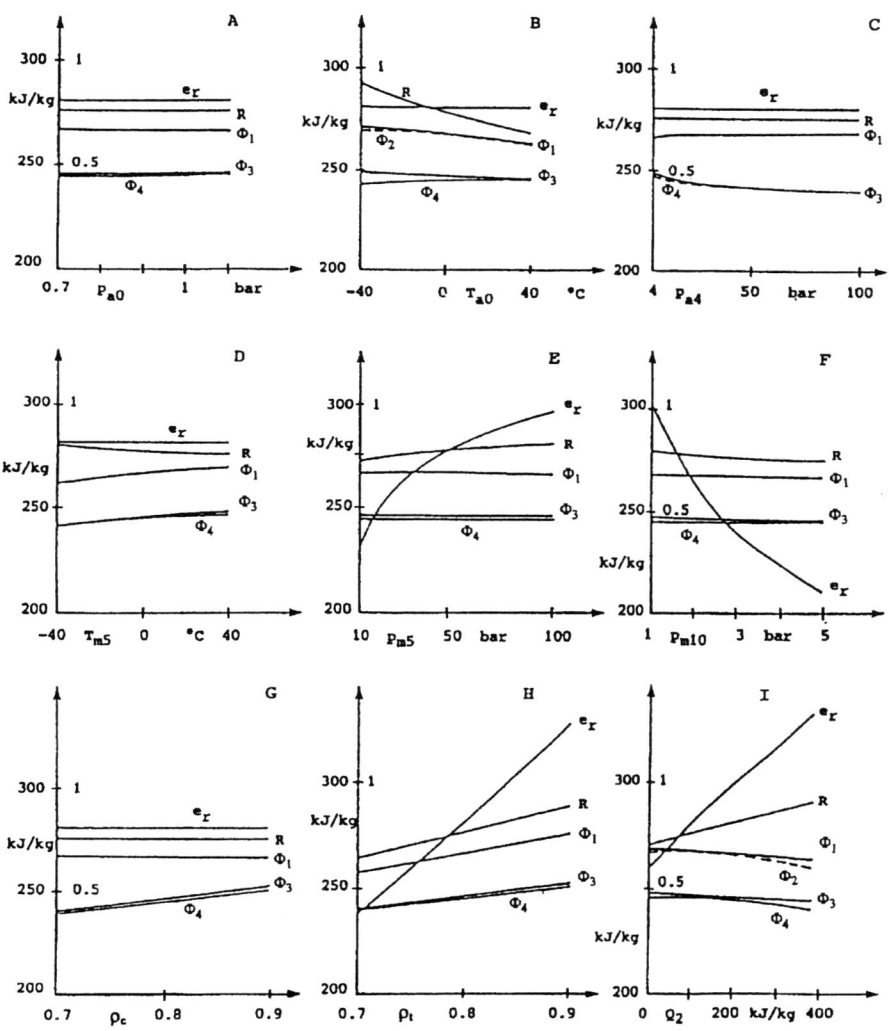

Fig. 6.6. Diagrams with the exergy parameters e_r, R, Φ_1, Φ_2, Φ_3, Φ_4 vs: (A) air initial pressure, p_{a0}; (B) air initial temperature, T_{a0}; (C) air final pressure, p_{a4}; (D) methane initial temperature, T_{m5}; (E) methane initial pressure, p_{m5}; (F) methane final pressure, p_{m10}; (G) compressor isentropic efficiency, ρ_c; (H) turbine isentropic efficiency, ρ_t; (I) second auxiliary heat, Q_2.

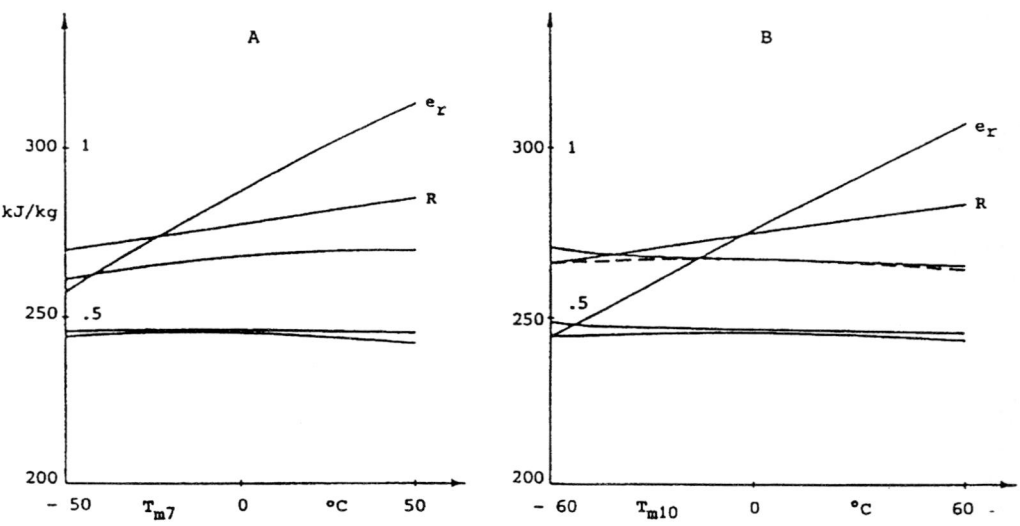

Fig. 6.7. Diagrams with the exergy parameters e_r, R, Φ_1, Φ_2, Φ_3, Φ_4 vs: (A) temperature after first methane turbine, T_{m7}; (B) temperature after second methane turbine, T_{m10}.

6.5.3 Remarks on the Results Obtained

Leaving out what is obvious, the following remarks are made.

In Fig. 6.6B one notes that, as the air inlet temperature increases, there is a slight increase in e_r and decreases in R, Φ_1, Φ_2, Φ_3. This result is verified owing to the fact that, at the methane pressure assumed constant at 40 bar, the methane exergy increases, if the environment temperature rises. To justify this remark, it is to be observed that a reversible adiabatic expansion from a high pressure to the environment pressure causes temperature values lower than that of the environment. Consequently, with same shaft work at different environment temperatures, the remaining operative value (i.e. exergy value) is greater the greater the environment temperature.

The parameters R and Φ_1 show a divergent trend vs various quantities shown in abscissae; this is in relation to the fact that the operative value of the auxiliary heat does not have an influence on R. This phenomenon is particularly evident, with opposing results, in Figs. 6.6D and 6.6I, in which the initial temperature of the methane and the second auxiliary heat, respectively, are reported on the abscissae.

The difference between Φ_1 and Φ_2 is in all cases negligible or very small; this is due to the fact that the non-utilization of the exergy corresponding to the difference between the outlet temperature of methane and that of the environment is of very little importance.

From these results and in a similar way from others not reported here, it appears that the optimum thermodynamic solutions are very different depending on whether the auxiliary thermal energy is practically free (at least during most of the year) or whether it can be used in alternative with other technically and economically valid exploitations.

In the former case, e_r is the most meaningful parameter; this result suggests the maximum utilization of the auxiliary heat, to increase the temperature after the second methane turbine and also after the first turbine until a value is reached that still allows the air cooling after the first compressor. In the latter case, if only the methane is considered (and this would be valid if the turbine were utilized for other purposes different from air compression, e.g., for electric power production), Φ_2 is the most meaningful parameter. The supply of auxiliary heat appears not so expedient: it depends upon its temperature and its possible utilization in other plants. The parameter Φ_2, contrarily to Φ_1, presents a maximum in correspondence to a temperature after the second turbine lower than the environment temperature (about 20°C lower).

If also the air processes are taken into consideration, the parameters Φ_3 and Φ_4 are the most meaningful, respectively, for the cases in which the air final temperature is usable or not. Generally, however, the efficiency Φ_4 is the most significant for the characterization of optimal solutions. Also Φ_4, as a function of the temperature after the second turbine, presents its maximum at a temperature lower than that of the environment; it is, nevertheless, a very flat maximum. Consequently, a temperature not lower than that of the environment can be chosen for other practical reasons.

To carry out in a valid way the heat exchange between the air and methane, it is convenient to choose a methane temperature after the first turbine about -10°C. It is to be remembered that the second compressor work is then lower, as also the temperature of intermediate cooling is. In addition, a high final temperature of the air is generally not profitable. However, it must be remembered that there is always some water vapor in NG. Consequently, it is necessary to choose the lowest temperature after the first turbine that avoids the formation of ice and of gas hydrate crystals safely. It is also necessary to avoid the condensation of higher alcanes (e.g., butane), which are sometimes present in a valuable amount in NG.

With reference to a large integrated iron and steel factory (with an output of 8-10 millions of t/year), a power of 2000 kW can be recovered. This power can be used to compress to 7-8 bar 1/15-1/20 of the mass-flow rate necessary to the works.

6.6 FINAL REMARKS

Exergy analysis, on the basis of the two laws of thermodynamics, is a suitable tool for any kind of energy-saving investigation. In the analysis, it is convenient to assume, as a reference value, the entropy production corresponding to no useful effect; multiplied by the environment temperature, it gives, for the selected operational domain, the maximum exergy loss, a parameter called losable exergy. The ratio of the actual entropy production to the reference one is called relative entropy production. The difference between one and the relative entropy production is equal to the exergy efficiency. One notes that in general the exergy efficiency may be derived irrespective of reference to exergy or entropy production.

However, in the examination of various systems (as in one of this paper) it is expedient to consider different exergy parameters. In the thermodynamic analysis, reference is made to earlier papers about exergy efficiency in general, and regarding compression systems specifically.

Some possibilities for the exploitation of the NG pressure exergy at the end of pipelines before the use of this gas at a reduced pressure in various works are studied in the paper; as well known, the available pressure exergy is generally wasted in a throttling valve. Indirect utilization in the generation of electric power avoids coupling plants with asynchronous characteristics, but adds a new step to the final energy employment. One observes that the study of the optimal connections in large-size works may allow a more economical exploitation of energy resources, even if some links among the various sections of the works are established. Two direct utilizations of NG pressure exergy seem convenient, notwithstanding the above-mentioned links among different plants.

It is feasible to use the NG expansion work in a turbine to raise the recovery steam pressure (particularly from evaporative cooling systems of blast furnaces) to a level at which valid possibilities of industrial uses exist; only in this way evaporative cooling is economically convenient.

The exploitation of the NG pressure exergy in a turbine for the compression of air in large integrated iron and steel works seems a valid solution, since this direct utilization has an advantage which is characteristic of indirect utilizations, as is pointed out in this paper. Indeed, with the connection to the general network of compressed air of the works, in no case a malfunction of the recovery station can hamper a compressed air utilizer.

For this second possible direct utilization, a detailed analysis has been made and the results are reported in the paper. The influence of various system properties and of other quantities is considered, and various exergy parameters are defined to visualize different aspects of the problem.

It is worth to be pointed out that the optimal solutions are very different whether an auxiliary thermal energy is practically free (at least during the most part of the year: e.g., when there is no necessity of space heating) or it results usable in alternative with other technically and economically valid exploitations.

In addition, it is to be noted that the choice of the temperature after the first expansion of NG in the turbine must be made at the lowest value, which grants that any formation of solids (ice or gas hydrate crystals) is avoided.

Chapter 7

THERMODYNAMIC ANALYSIS OF BLAST-FURNACE TOP GAS PRESSURE RECOVERY TURBINES

7.1 GENERAL REMARKS

Blast-furnace gas contains a large amount of chemical and pressure exergy. Since many years, chemical exergy has been utilized for several purposes in all the blast furnaces. In the past, on the contrary, pressure exergy was never utilized and was generally destroyed in septum valve. Since the sixties the blast-furnace top pressure has been increasing until 3.5 bar, while the blast-furnace gas network is usually at a pressure of 1.1-1.2 bar. Some pressure drop occurs in wet (≈ 0.3 bar) or dry (≈ 0.02 bar) cleaning; nevertheless, the pressure existing at the top of modern large-size blast furnaces constitutes an exergy potential that can be used for the generation of electrical energy (or for other purposes) provided the top gas is decompressed in a suitable recovery turbine (Ikeda, 1979; Gordon et al., 1980; Flächsenhaar et al., 1981; Iki, 1981; Saito, 1981; Caussade, 1982; Romagnoli et al., 1982; Asai et al., 1983; Kitamura, 1983; Heller and van Gilst, 1983; Peters et al., 1984; *Steel Times*, 1986; Fisher, 1988; Lao et al., 1992). Up to 50% of the electrical energy required for blast compression can be recovered in this way.

When a turbine for exergy pressure recovery is installed downstream from an existing blast furnace in which the gas is wet cleaned, the turbine takes over from the gas scrubber as the means of controlling top gas pressure. The moving cone of the annular gas scrubber is opened as far as it can be in order to minimize the pressure drop at this point.

A further change must be made in the operation of the gas scrubber. In order to maximize the electrical output from the generator driven by the energy recovery turbine, it is desirable to attain a high enthalpy gradient across the turbine. This is obtained by allowing part of the cooling of the gas to take place during the passage through the turbine. Therefore the gas must have a higher temperature at the outlet of the scrubber than it would have in the absence of an energy recovery turbine: this is achieved by reducing the amount of water sprayed into the gas before it passes through the scrubber.

The gas outgoing from the cleaning plant or from the cleaning plant/turbine system is so utilized:

(i) One part (usually 1/3 - 1/2 of the total) goes to the blast-furnace regenerators at a temperature very near to that of the turbine outlet.

(ii) The remaining part goes to the gasholder and then to the various customers, that use it after a time interval so that its temperature becomes very near to that of the environment.

7.2 REMARKS ON PLANT ELEMENTS TO UTILIZE THE BLAST-FURNACE GAS PRESSURE

7.2.1 Axial vs Radial Turbines

In the sixties the first axial turbines were constructed in the Soviet Union; however, they required a clean, dry and heated gas. In the seventies radial turbines were constructed in Europe and it was thought that this type was the only capable of sustaining a gas flow in saturated state (after wet cleaning) containing both free water and a small amount of dust without suffering damage. However, axial turbines have a higher efficiency than the radial design. In reference (Hoffmann et al., 1987) the values 0.865 and 0.78 are reported for axial and radial turbines respectively at the design point; in addition, the difference is higher when the flow rate is lower. Afterwards, with the benefit of modern materials and design methods axial turbines were constructed with wet and also dry cleaning plants.

7.2.2 Wet and Dry Cleaning Systems

Most top gas cleaning plants are of the wet type and have a pressure drop of 0.25-0.30 bar and a temperature of about 50°C at the turbine inlet. To reduce the exergy destructions due to the temperature and pressure drops some dry cleaning plants have been constructed, firstly with bagfilters and subsequently with electrofilters. With the electrofilters, the pressure drop is about 0.02 bar and the temperature drop is about 10°C.

It is to be remarked that several improvements in blast furnaces have lowered the temperature of top gas (until values lower than 100°C) making dry cleaning less valuable.

On the contrary, the injection of fuel oil and of powdered coal into blast furnace increases the top gas temperature as can be seen from Fig. 7.1, derived from reference (Hoffmann et al., 1987). If the injection of fuel oil is no longer convenient after the oil crisis of 1973, the injection of powdered coal is a technology useful to reduce coke consumption (Gudenau et al., 1994; Peters and Reinitzhuber, 1994). Consequently, the injection of powdered coal make dry cleaning more convenient.

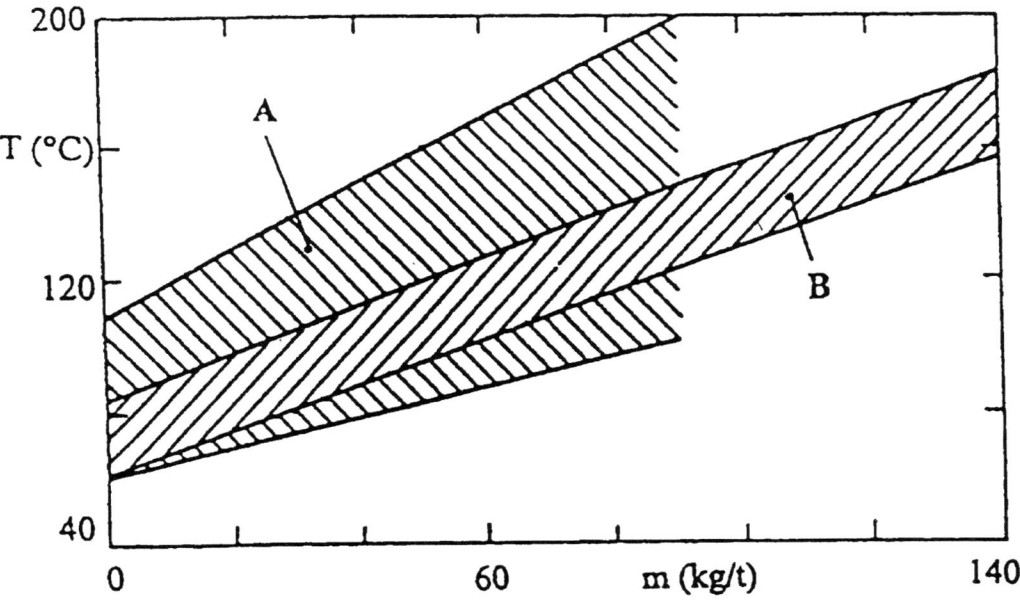

Fig. 7.1. Effect of the specific quantity of fuel injected, m, into the blast furnace on the top gas temperature, T; variation ranges: (A) with injection of fuel oil; (B) with injection of powdered coal.

7.3 EXERGY ANALYSIS

7.3.1 Exergy Power Flows of Wet Cleaning Plants without and with Bottom Expansion Turbine

Table 7.1 - Exergy Power Flows of a Wet Cleaning Plant without Turbine with Inlet Gas Temperature 90°C (See Fig. 7.2.1).

(a) gas exergy power behind the scrubber - $Ex°_1$	100.0
(b) exergy power behind the scrubber – $Ex°_2$	108.8
(c) exergy power destroyed in the scrubber	79.1
(d) exergy power destroyed owing to heat transfer to the environment	0.2
(e) gas exergy power after the scrubber – $Ex°_3$	19.5
(f) water exergy power after the scrubber – $Ex°_4$	10.0
(g) exergy power destroyed in the water pipeline	2.7
(h) electrical exergy power for the pump – $Ex°_5$	1.5
(j) water exergy power behind the scrubber – $Ex°_6$	8.8
(p) exergy power destroyed owing to heat transfer to the environment	4.6
(q) final gas pressure exergy power – $Ex°_8$	14.9

Table 7.2 - Exergy Power Flows of a Wet Cleaning Plant with Turbine with Inlet Gas Temperature 90°C (See Fig. 7.2.2).

(a) gas exergy power behind the scrubber – $Ex°_1$	100.0
(b) exergy power behind the scrubber – $Ex°_2$	109.5
(c) exergy power destroyed in the scrubber	12.7
(d) exergy power destroyed owing to heat transfer to the environment	0.4
(e) gas exergy power after the scrubber – $Ex°_3$	83.5
(f) water exergy power after the scrubber – $Ex°_4$	12.9
(g) exergy power destroyed in the water pipeline	4.0
(h) electrical exergy power for the pump – $Ex°_5$	0.6
(j) water exergy power behind the scrubber – $Ex°_6$	9.5
(m) exergy power destroyed owing to heat transfer to the environment	1.3
(n) exergy power destroyed in the turbine	15.2
(o) recovered mechanical exergy power – $Ex°_7$	51.8
(p) exergy power destroyed owing to heat transfer to the environment	0.3
(q) final gas pressure exergy power – $Ex°_8$	14.9

Top gas at the blast-furnace outlet has a temperature included between 90 and 200°C (higher values take place in the case of the injection of powdered coal in the blast furnace) and its volume, with reference to normal conditions (nTp), is about 1.4 times that of the blast-furnace inlet air. In Tables 7.1 and 7.2 the exergy power flows of two wet cleaning plants are reported; the first without recovery turbine (Table 7.1) and the second with recovery turbine (Table 7.2). The same exergy power flows are schematically represented in Fig. 7.2 too. For both plants the top gas has a pressure $p_1=3$ bar and a temperature $T_1=90°C$. The gas pipeline after the scrubber or the scrubber-turbine system has a pressure $p_8=1.2$ bar. Ones assumes the environment with pressure $p_o=1$ bar and temperature $T_o=15°C$.

Consider a wet cleaning system without turbine (Table 7.1 and Fig. 7.2.1); let, e.g., $Ex°_1=100$ kW. The following values for the losable exergy power and the reference entropy production power are obtained:

$$Ex°_{rf} = Ex°_1 + Ex°_5 = 100 + 1.5 = 101.5 \text{ kW}, \tag{7.1}$$

$$S°_{s\,rf} = Ex°_{rf}/T_o = 101.5/288.15 = 0.3522 \text{ kW/K} \cdot ° \tag{7.2}$$

The actual entropy production powers in the scrubber ($S°_{s\,a1}$), in the water pipeline ($S°_{s\,a2}$) and owing to heat transfer to the environment ($S°_{s\,a3}$ and $S°_{s\,a4}$), and then the relative entropy productions, are given by:

$$S°_{s\,a1} = 79.1/288.15 = 0.2745 \text{ kW/K}, \quad S°_{s\,a2} = 0.0094 \text{ kW/K}, \tag{7.3}$$

$$S°_{s\,a3} = 0.0007 \text{ kW/K}, \quad S°_{s\,a4} = 0.0160 \text{ kW/K}, \tag{7.4}$$

$$\sigma_{r1} = 0.7794, \quad \sigma_{r2} = 0.0267, \quad \sigma_{r3} = 0.0020, \quad \sigma_{r3} = 0.0454. \tag{7.5}$$

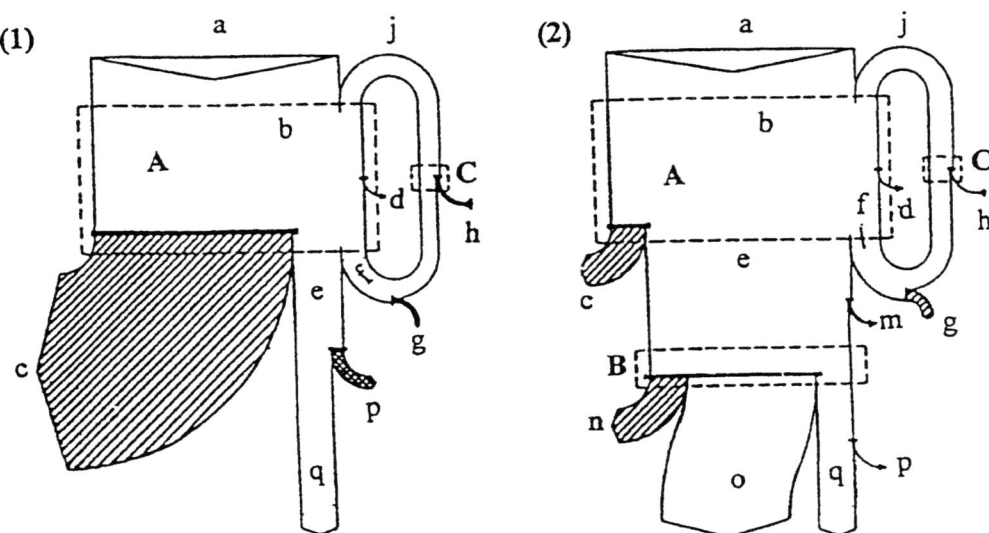

Fig. 7.2. Schema of the exergy power flows of two wet cleaning plants, the first (1) without turbine (see Table 7.1) and the second (2) with turbine (see Table 7.2): (A) scrubber, (B) turbine, (C) pump.

However, it must be remarked that $S_s°_{a4}$ takes place actually only when the top gas goes to gas-holder before utilization; on the contrary, when the gas is utilized in blast-furnace regenerators directly, the corresponding thermal exergy is not destroyed.

In the first case, one has the following exergy efficiency:

$$\Phi' = 1 - \sigma_r' = 1 - (\sigma_{r1} + \sigma_{r2} + \sigma_{r3} + \sigma_{r4}) = 0.1465 \,, \tag{7.6}$$

and in the second case:

$$\Phi'' = 1 - \sigma_r'' = 1 - (\sigma_{r1} + \sigma_{r2} + \sigma_{r3}) = 0.1919 \,. \tag{7.7}$$

In a similar way one obtains:

$$\Phi' = Ex°_u'/Ex°_{rf} = 0.1468 \,, \Phi'' = Ex°_u''/Ex°_{rf} = 0.1921 \,. \tag{7.8}$$

These values are practically coinciding with the previous ones.

Consider a wet cleaning system with turbine (Table 7.2 and Fig. 7.2.2) and let, e.g., $Ex°_1 = 100$ kW. The following values for the losable exergy power and the reference entropy production power are obtained:

$$Ex°_{rf} = Ex°_1 + Ex°_5 = 100.6 \text{ kW} \,, S_s°_{rf} = Ex°_{rf}/T_o = 0.3491 \text{ kW/K} \,. \tag{7.9}$$

The actual entropy production powers in the scrubber ($S_s{°}_{a1}$), in the water pipeline ($S_s{°}_{a2}$), in the turbine ($S_s{°}_{a3}$) and owing to heat transfer to the environment ($S_s{°}_{a4}$, $S_s{°}_{a5}$ and $S_s{°}_{a6}$), and then the relative entropy productions, are given by:

$$S_s{°}_{a1} = 0.0441 \text{ kW/K}, \quad S_s{°}_{a2} = 0.0139 \text{ kW/K}, \quad S_s{°}_{a3} = 0.0528 \text{ kW/K}, \tag{7.10}$$

$$S_s{°}_{a4} = 0.0014 \text{ kW/K}, \quad S_s{°}_{a5} = 0.0045 \text{ kW/K}, \quad S_s{°}_{a6} = 0.0010 \text{ kW/K}, \tag{7.11}$$

$$\sigma_{r1} = 0.1263, \quad \sigma_{r2} = 0.0398, \quad \sigma_{r3} = 0.1512, \tag{7.12}$$

$$\sigma_{r4} = 0.0040, \quad \sigma_{r5} = 0.0129, \quad \sigma_{r6} = 0.0029. \tag{7.13}$$

The gas at the turbine outlet may be at temperatures both higher and lower than that of the environment, T_o, but very near to T_o. The thermal exergy is always positive, but very small. If the gas goes to the gasholder, this exergy is lost. If the gas goes to the blast-furnace regenerators, even if always positive, exergy is useful when the gas temperature is higher than T_o, but it is harmful in the contrary case. Consequently, we consider this exergy always as lost exergy.

Thus, exergy efficiency is given by:

$$\Phi = 1 - \sigma_r = 1 - (\sigma_{r1} + \sigma_{r2} + \sigma_{r3} + \sigma_{r4} + \sigma_{r5} + \sigma_{r6}) = 0.6629. \tag{7.14}$$

In a similar way one obtains:

$$\Phi = Ex°_u / Ex°_{rf} = (51.8 + 14.9)/100.6 = 0.6630. \tag{7.15}$$

This value is practically coinciding with the previous one.

7.4.2 Exergy Power Flows of Wet and Dry Cleaning Plants with Bottom Expansion Turbine

Let examine the influence of the type of cleaning plant (wet or dry) on the overall exergy efficiency of the cleaning plant/turbine system. Otherwise, from the cases considered in the previous subsection, the top gas temperature is 160°C, whereas the other parameters are equal.

Consider a wet cleaning system with turbine (Table 7.3 and Fig. 7.3.1); let, e.g., $Ex_1 = 100$ kW. This system has higher exergy loss than that of Table 7.2; indeed, the inlet exergy has a thermal component higher, but is substantially useless and, on the contrary, it requires a higher work for the scrubber circulation pump.

One has the following values for the losable exergy power and the reference entropy production power:

$$Ex°_{rf} = Ex°_1 + Ex°_5 = 101.3 \text{ kW}, \quad S_s{°}_{rf} = Ex°_{rf}/T_o = 0.3516 \text{ kW/K}. \tag{7.16}$$

Table 7.3 - Exergy Power Flows of a Wet Cleaning Plant with Turbine with Inlet Gas Temperature 160°C (See Fig. 7.3.1).

(a) gas exergy power behind the scrubber- $Ex°_1$	100.0
(b) exergy power destroyed owing to heat transfer to the environment	1.4
(c) exergy power behind the scrubber – $Ex°_2$	118.4
(d) exergy power destroyed in the scrubber	24.5
(e) exergy power destroyed owing to heat transfer to the environment	0.2
(f) gas exergy power after the scrubber – $Ex°_3$	66.8
(g) water exergy power after the scrubber – $Ex°_4$	26.9
(h) exergy power destroyed in the water pipeline	8.4
(j) electrical exergy power for the pump – $Ex°_5$	1.3
(m) water exergy power behind the scrubber – $Ex°_6$	19.8
(n) exergy power destroyed owing to heat transfer to the environment	1.1
(o) exergy power destroyed in the turbine	9.7
(p) recovered mechanical exergy power – $Ex°_7$	43.7
(q) exergy power destroyed owing to heat transfer to the environment	0.3
(r) final gas pressure exergy power – $Ex°_8$	12.0

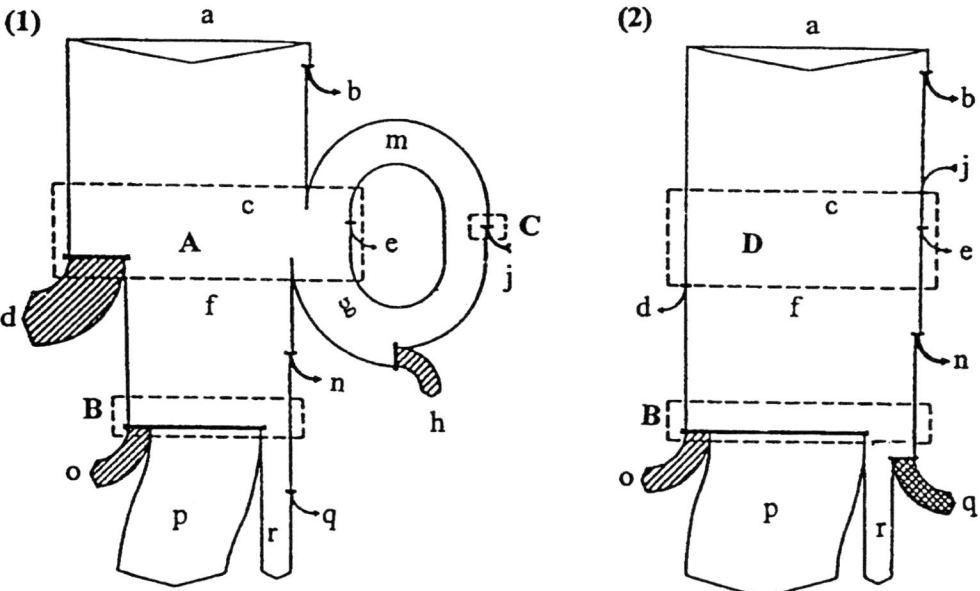

Fig. 7.3. Schema of the exergy power flows of two cleaning plants with turbine, wet (1) (see Table 7.3) and dry (2) (see Table 7.4), respectively: (A) scrubber, (B) turbine, (C) pump, (D) electrofilter.

The actual entropy production powers in the scrubber ($S_s°_{a1}$), in the water pipeline ($S_s°_{a2}$), in the turbine ($S_s°_{a3}$) and owing to heat transfer to the environment ($S_s°_{a4}$, $S_s°_{a5}$, $S_s°_{a6}$ and $S_s°_{a7}$), and then the relative entropy productions, are given by:

$$S_s°_{a1} = 0.0850 \text{ kW/K}, \ S_s°_{a2} = 0.0292 \text{ kW/K}, \ S_s°_{a3} = 0.0337 \text{ kW/K}, \quad (7.17)$$

$$S_s°_{a4} = 0.0049 \text{ kW/K}, \ S_s°_{a5} = 0.0007 \text{ kW/K}, \ S_s°_{a6} = 0.0038 \text{ kW/K}, \quad (7.18$$

$S_s{}^°_{a7} = 0.0010$ kW/K , $\sigma_{r1} = 0.2419$, $\sigma_{r2} = 0.0829$, (7.19)

$\sigma_{r3} = 0.0958$, $\sigma_{r4} = 0.0138$, $\sigma_{r5} = 0.0020$, (7.20)

$\sigma_{r6} = 0.0109$, $\sigma_{r7} = 0.0030$. (7.21)

Thus, one has the following exergy efficiency:

$$\Phi = 1 - \sigma_r = 1 - (\sigma_{r1} + \sigma_{r2} + \sigma_{r3} + \sigma_{r4} + \sigma_{r5} + \sigma_{r6} + \sigma_{r6}) = 0.5497 . \quad (7.22)$$

In a similar way, one obtains

$$\Phi = Ex°_u/Ex°_{rf} = (43.7 + 12)/101.3 = 0.5498 . \quad (7.23)$$

This value is practically coinciding with the previous one.

Consider a dry cleaning system with turbine (Table 7.4 and Fig. 7.3.2); let, e.g., $Ex°_1 = 100$ kW.

The values for the losable exergy power and the reference entropy production power can be written as:

$$Ex°_{rf} = Ex°_1 + Ex°_5 = 100.2 \text{ kW} , \quad S_s{}^°_{rf} = Ex°_{rf}/T_o = 0.3477 \text{ kW/K} . \quad (7.24)$$

The actual entropy production powers in the electrofilter ($S_s{}^°_{a1}$), in the turbine ($S_s{}^°_{a2}$) and owing to heat transfer to the environment ($S_s{}^°_{a3}$, $S_s{}^°_{a4}$, $S_s{}^°_{a5}$ and $S_s{}^°_{a6}$), and then the relative entropy productions, are given by:

$S_s{}^°_{a1} = 0.0007$ kW/K , $S_s{}^°_{a2} = 0.0351$ kW/K , $S_s{}^°_{a3} = 0.0049$ kW/K , (7.25)

$S_s{}^°_{a4} = 0.0007$ kW/K , $S_s{}^°_{a5} = 0.0052$ kW/K , $S_s{}^°_{a6} = 0.0319$ kW/K , (7.26)

Table 7.4 - Exergy Power Flows of a Dry-Cleaning Plant with Turbine with Inlet Gas Temperature 160°C (See Fig. 7.3.2).

(a) gas exergy power behind the scrubber - $Ex°_1$	100.0
(b) exergy power destroyed owing to heat transfer to the environment	1.4
(c) exergy power behind the electrofilter – $Ex°_2$	98.8
(d) exergy power destroyed in the electrofilter	0.2
(e) exergy power destroyed owing to heat transfer to the environment	0.2
(f) gas exergy power after the electrofilter – $Ex°_3$	98.4
(j) electrical exergy power to electrofilter – $Ex°_5$	0.2
(n) exergy power destroyed owing to heat transfer to the environment	1.5
(o) exergy power destroyed in the turbine	10.1
(p) recovered mechanical exergy power – $Ex°_7$	65.6
(q) exergy power destroyed owing to heat transfer to the environment	9.2
(r) final gas pressure exergy power – $Ex°_8$	12.0

$\sigma_{r1} = 0.0020$, $\sigma_{r2} = 0.1008$, $\sigma_{r3} = 0.0140$, (7.27)

$\sigma_{r4} = 0.0020$, $\sigma_{r5} = 0.0150$, $\sigma_{r6} = 0.0918$. (7.28)

However, it must be remarked that $S_s°_{a6}$ takes place actually only when the top gas goes to gas holder before utilization; on the contrary, when the gas is utilized in blast-furnace regenerators directly, the corresponding thermal exergy is not destroyed.

In the first case the exergy efficiency formulation is given by:

$$\Phi' = 1 - \sigma_r = 1 - (\sigma_{r1} + \sigma_{r2} + \sigma_{r3} + \sigma_{r4} + \sigma_{r5} + \sigma_{r6}) = 0.7744,\qquad(7.29)$$

and in the second case:

$$\Phi'' = 1 - \sigma_r = 1 - (\sigma_{r1} + \sigma_{r2} + \sigma_{r3} + \sigma_{r4} + \sigma_{r5}) = 0.8662.\qquad(7.30)$$

In a similar way one obtains:

$$\Phi' = Ex°_u{}'/Ex°_{rf} = (65.6 + 12)/100.2 = 0.7745,\qquad(7.31)$$

$$\Phi'' = Ex°_u{}''/Ex°_{rf} = (65.6 + 12 + 9.2)/100.2 = 0.8663.\qquad(7.32)$$

These values are practically coinciding with the previous ones.

7.5 ANALYSIS ON POSSIBILITIES OF INCREASING THE ENERGY PRODUCED BY YOP GAS TURBINE

7.5.1 Possibilities by Variations of Fundamental Parameters without Further Energy Contributions

The fundamental parameters of blast-furnace gas which characterize the energy production of turbine are: (i) mass flow rate of gas; (ii) its temperature at the turbine inlet; (iii) the pressure drop available for turbine.

Mass flow rate is strictly linked to the iron to be produced; only a slight increasing (1 - 2%) can be obtained by the injection of powdered coal into blast furnace.

The temperature at the turbine inlet can be increased, reducing the water flow rate and increasing the water temperature after the cooling towers. It is to be remarked that the decrease of the water flow rate, besides to increasing temperature, raises the pressure too; however, it causes an increase of dust in the gas. In addition, a temperature of water above 50°C causes precipitation of carbonates. Thus, a compromise is necessary among opposite demands.

A notable increase of the gas temperature at the turbine inlet is obtained by dry cooling and pipeline insulation; these actions are particularly useful in the case of injection of powdered coal into blast furnace.

It is sometimes possible to raise the pressure drop available for the turbine by reducing the water flow rate in the scrubber to the value strictly necessary to have the fixed value of dustiness (usually 1 mg/m^3 (nTp)). A greater advantage is obtained by using electrofilters, which have a pressure drop much lower than scrubbers. At the turbine outlet in some plants pressure has been reduced by using a Pitot tube or other low-loss flow tubes instead of a concentric orifice to measure gas flow rate.

As an example, we report the following approximate data:

(i) Reducing the differential pressure across the gas scrubber from 220 mbar to 160 mbar provides a 2% increase in the generator output.
(ii) Lowering the network gas pressure downstream from the turbine by modifying the feed system to the plant's hot blast stoves could result in a 6% increase in the generator output.
(iii) Reducing the water volume in the gas scrubber could provide for a further 2% increase in generator output while reducing pump load demand slightly.

7.5.2 Possibilities by Further Energy Contributions

Valuable increases of the energy produced by the turbine are obtained by the addition of thermal energy; initially this was done to avoid formation of condense or even of ice in the turbine.

The combustion of a small part of top gas behind the turbine is the more used system.

In Fig. 7.4, as an example, the ratio of actually recovered mechanical energy to the value with no auxiliary heat, E_m/E_{mo}, vs specific auxiliary thermal energy, Q_a, is shown. One notes that 20 kJ/kg correspond to the combustion of about 1% of top gas; the increase of recovered mechanical energy is remarkable (e.g., + 43% by the combustion of 2% of top gas).

In addition, if the top gas outgoing from the turbine is utilized by the blast-furnace regenerators, their energy consumption is reduced, since the gas is at a higher temperature. Finally, the danger of condensation or freezing is surely avoided in any operative condition.

On the basis of second law analysis, the employment of waste thermal energy to heat the top gas behind the turbine is more convenient; this waste energy is generally available in steel works. The convenience is obviously higher, when a wet cleaning plant is used.

7.6 FINAL REMARKS

The analysis of optimal interconnections among different plants of large-size works allows a more economical employment of energy resources.

On the contrary, there are sometimes management difficulties owing to reciprocal links among the various plants of the same works.

In addition to the normal energy recovery possible from using the top gas as an in-plant fuel, top gas contains a large amount of pressure and also thermal exergy and it is convenient to exploit these exergies through conversion into electrical power. Sometimes it is also more convenient to utilize physical exergy to compress air to be used in blast furnaces (this air is usually called "cold wind").

The influence of the type of gas cleaning (wet or dry) on the total exergy efficiency of the gas-cleaning system/gas-turbine combination is noteworthy.

Exergy destruction in electrostatic filters is much lower than that in scrubbers for both components of physical exergy (lower pressure drop and considerably lower drop in temperature). On the other hand, the exergy destruction in turbine is a little higher in the case a dry cleaning plant.

Let us consider the exergy component depending upon temperature; in dry cleaning plants, for the gas outgoing from the turbine, this exergy component is utilized if the gas is burnt directly in blast-furnace hot stoves, but remains wholly useless if the gas enters a gas-holder and (at the environment temperature) is subsequently distributed to the various customers. This topic must be taken into account in the research for the optimal solution in the utilization of blast-furnace gas.

In a comparison reported in the paper as an example, the dry cooling advantage appears noteworthy; by this system the recovered mechanical energy is equivalent to 65.6% of the physical exergy of the blast-furnace gas, which should be compared with the value 43.7% of a corresponding wet cooling plant. The exergy efficiency of the considered dry cooling system is included, according to the type of gas customers, within the values 77.4% and 86.6%.

Gas cleaning by means of electrostatic filters (or other dry cleaning systems) is specifically convenient when powdered coal is injected into blast furnace and thus the top gas temperature is increased. This technology is developing, particularly in Germany, as a means for reducing coke consumption in blast furnaces.

It is to be remarked that, in the considered examples, the exergy analysis allows the visualization of the relative entropy productions in the various parts of the global systems, with obvious practical applications.

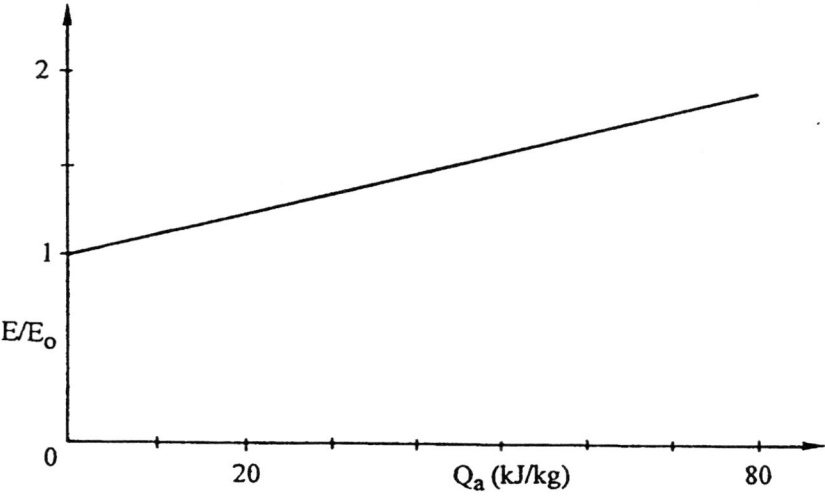

Fig. 7.4. Ratio of actually recovered mechanical energy to the value with no auxiliary heat, E_m/E_{mo}, vs specific auxiliary thermal energy, Q_a.

Chapter 8

COMBINED HELIUM AND COMBUSTION GAS TURBINE PLANT EXPLOITING LIQUID HYDROGEN (LH$_2$) PHYSICAL EXERGY

8.1 GENERAL REMARKS

In the last few years, studies have been carried out concerning the use of hydrogen as an energy vector. Particularly in Germany research is being done on the convenience of producing hydrogen in Canada by means of power from hydroelectric plants and of transporting it to Germany, either in liquid phase or chemically bound, e.g., in toluene (Grawe and Holzer, 1989; Sprengel, 1991). Further research is being carried out on the convenience of producing hydrogen by solar energy, chiefly in North Africa and Saudi Arabia (Grawe and Holzer, 1989; Hassmann et al., 1991).

As regards to the hydrogen that has been transported in liquid phase, this fluid must be vaporized before any exploitation and it seems convenient to utilize the physical exergy of hydrogen due to its liquid phase at a temperature of 20 K, instead of destroying this exergy in the vaporization with heat obtained from sea-water or, even worse, by burning a fraction of the hydrogen.

Several processes have been considered to use the physical exergy of liquids at atmospheric pressure by vaporizing, at cryogenic temperatures, e.g. nitrogen, hydrogen and natural gas (Griepentrog, and Weber, 1978; Oshima et al., 1978; Weber, 1989; Bisio and Cerullo, 1992).

Two general alternatives may be envisaged:

(a) direct utilization in cryogenic facilities (cold storage or various process uses);
(b) indirect utilization in systems which are generator of electric power.

Direct utilization poses some problems:

(i) it entails coupling two plants with asynchronous characteristics;
(ii) it is essential to ensure that the operation of the LH$_2$ (liquid hydrogen) or LNG (liquid natural gas) terminal is not hampered by malfunctions in the plant of the cryogenic customer;

(iii) the available exergy cannot be sufficiently exploited in relation to both its quantity and its temperature level.

Indirect utilization in the generation of electric power avoids the drawbacks of direct utilization and uses the available exergy in a more efficient way.

LH_2, owing to its high exergy value, is specifically suitable for this exploitation by means of a combined system employing a closed cycle helium turbine with two exergy sources. The former, at temperatures above that of the environment, is given by the waste gas of an open cycle combustion gas turbine, and the latter, at temperatures under that of the environment, is given by the vaporization and superheating of LH_2.

Despite its expense, the helium cycle has been chosen because it is the only suitable fluid due to its very low critical point (4.125 K). It does not present explosion hazards and the technology of helium plants is well developed.

In the following subsections the energy and exergy analyses of a combined plant made up of a conventional gas turbine (heavy-duty or aeroderivative) and a closed helium turbine cycle which exploits liquid hydrogen (LH_2) as a lower exergy source are carried out

8.2 SYSTEM LAYOUT

The layout of the combined system is shown in Fig. 8.1. The helium cycle, in which hydrogen vaporization is the heat sink, is represented in Fig. 8.2 by a temperature (T) vs specific entropy (s) diagram. Point 1, corresponding to the helium compressor inlet, is characterized by a temperature around 50 K. The helium is then compressed (process 1-2). In the recuperator, thermal energy of the turbine outlet (process 5-6) is transferred to the compressed helium (process 2-3). Then in the gas-helium heat exchanger, the helium is heated by the exhaust gas of the combustion turbine (process 3-4) until it reaches its peak temperature (about 770 K). Hence, in the subsequent expansion of helium (process 4-5) the useful power (in addition to that necessary for the compressor) is obtained. The thermal energy outgoing from the helium cycle (process 6-1) vaporizes the hydrogen (compressed by a pump at p_8=10 MPa) and superheats it to the temperature T_9, over 100 K in the helium-hydrogen heat exchanger (process 8-9). With the considered data (pressure p_8), liquid hydrogen is transformed into superheated vapor without the system having been separated into two phases (i.e. heating at supercritical pressure).

Moreover, if it is so desired, the hydrogen can be expanded to pressure p_{10} ($\approx$ 0.5 MPa; lower values may cause a very low turbine outlet temperature or even the inlet into the two-phase area) and then, e.g., warmed again with heat obtained from seawater.

A system without hydrogen expansion has also been considered since a hydrogen turbine working at cryogenic temperatures has not been thoroughly evaluated.

Fig. 8.3 shows a preliminary balance of the system energy. Around 39% of the thermal energy employed by the system is converted into electrical energy by the closed helium cycle, around 35% by the open gas turbine cycle, around 7% by the open hydrogen cycle, for an overall value of around 81%. Without hydrogen expansion, the overall energy efficiency is around 74%.

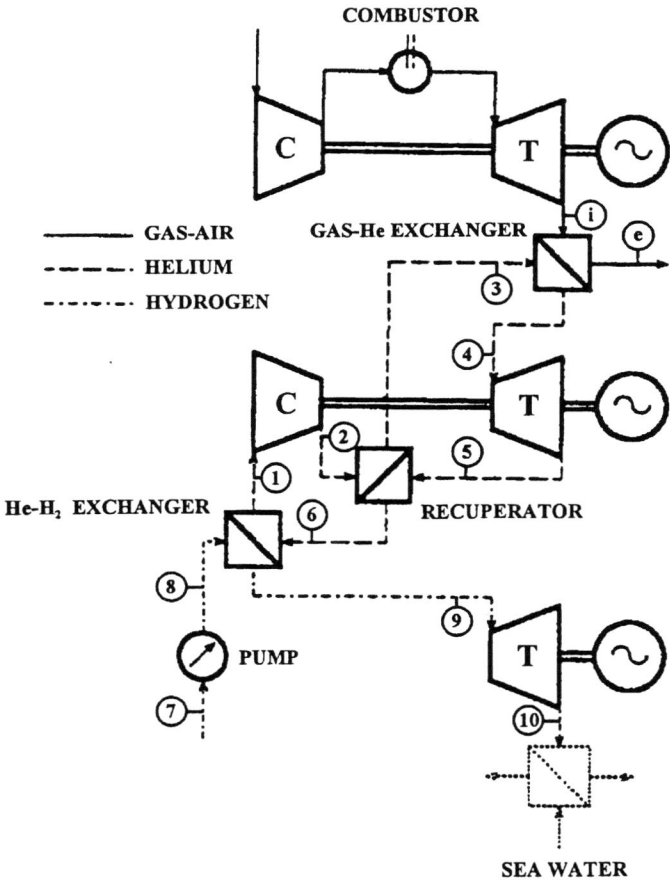

Fig. 8.1. Layout of the proposed combined plant.

8.3 THERMODYNAMIC ANALYSIS

8.3.1 General Remarks

For estimating the system performances, an extremely fast and flexible code, that allows a complete thermodynamic analysis of the plant, was developed.

The helium and hydrogen thermodynamic characteristics determine the operative conditions of the system points shown in Fig. 8.2. The values of functions p (pressure), T (temperature), i (specific enthalpy), s (specific entropy) and ex (specific physical exergy) corresponding to the states of helium and hydrogen environment and to the states of the cycles points (1-6 for helium, 7-10 for hydrogen) are estimated utilizing the data of Reynolds (1979), Raznjevic (1970) and Woolley et al. (1948).

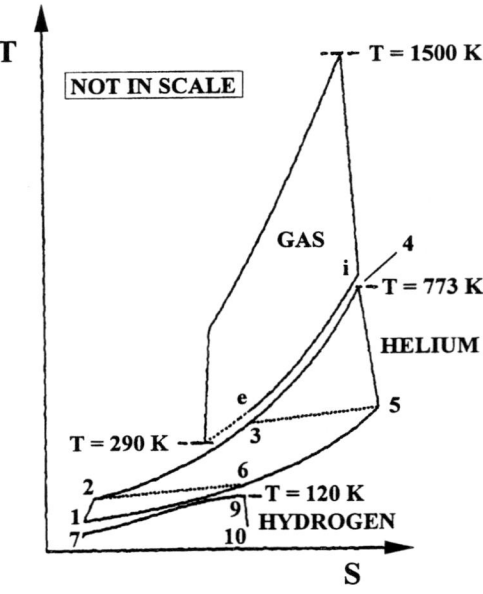

Fig. 8.2. Temperature-specific entropy diagram of the proposed combined cycle.

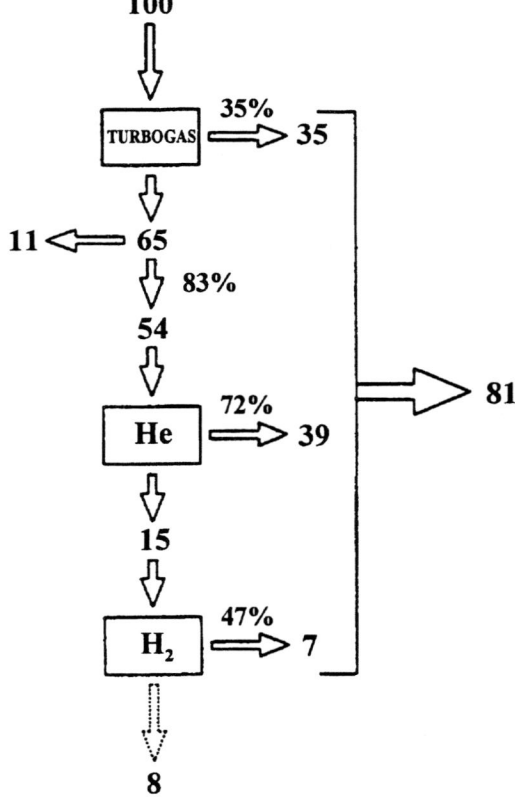

Fig. 8.3. Preliminary energy balance of a combined plant.

The performance and the characteristics of the top gas turbine cycle, fuelled with natural gas, were fixed during the system analysis: a cycle with energy efficiency 35% and net specific work 295.45 kJ/kg [kW/(kg/s)] (Farmer, 1994). Table 8.1 reports the thermodynamic functions at the inlet and at the exit of the exhaust gas heat exchanger.

Table 8.1 - Top Turbine Waste Gas Processes.

	environment (o")	inlet state (i)	exit state (e)
p – Mpa	0.1	0.125	0.115
T – K (°C)	290.15 (17)	813.15 (540)	378.15 (105)
i – kJ/kg	290.3	837.3	379.27
s – kJ/(kg K)	6.838	7.8430	7.0653
ex – kJ/kg	0	255.4	23.02

Pressure losses and component efficiencies are taken into account. The main equations utilized for the thermodynamic analysis are reported in Appendix (subsection 8.7).

8.3.2 Exergy Analysis of the Helium Cycle

The helium cycle examined in this paper (Table 8.2), even if it is formally similar to other power cycles, differs greatly from them on the basis of second-law analysis.

Indeed, one has exergy inlet both by waste energy of the top turbine and by "vaporization" and superheating of hydrogen at low temperatures.

The exergy efficiency of the helium cycle is given by:

$$\Phi_{He} = W^*_{ne}/[(ex_i - ex_e) G_g/G_{He} + (ex_8 - ex_9) G_{H_2}/G_{He}] . \tag{8.1}$$

where W^*_{ne} is the net electrical work per mass unit (see 8.7 Appendix).

Since the exergy coming from the "vaporization" and superheating of the liquid hydrogen can be judged free, it is convenient to consider the ratio r_f of the obtained electrical energy to the exergy coming from the waste gas of the combustion turbine:

$$r_f = W^*_{ne}/[(ex_i - ex_e) G_g/G_{He} . \tag{8.2}$$

This parameter, however, can not be called "efficiency".

8.3.3 Analysis of the Single Phases Separately

We consider the single phases and their relative entropy productions and efficiencies separately.

A) *Process 1-2* (helium compressor). The efficiency, Φ_1, and the relative entropy production, σ_{r1}, are given by:

$$\Phi_1 = (ex_2 - ex_1)/(- W^*_c) , \sigma_{r1} = 1 - \Phi_1 , \qquad (8.3)$$

where W^*_c is the compressor work referred to the mass unit.

B) *Processes 2-3 and 5-6* (regenerator). One of the extreme temperatures of the two streams is above and the other is below that of the environment. In our opinion, none of the formulations of exergy efficiency proposed in literature applies to this particular case (Kotas, 1985; Bisio 1989). Indeed, in both streams the exergy first decreases and subsequently increases attaining a minimum near the environment temperature (not exactly at the environment temperature, due to small mechanical irreversibilities).

We propose the following. Let us consider states α and β of minimum exergy reported in Table 8.2:

$$\Phi_2 = [(ex_3 - ex_\alpha) + (ex_6 - ex_\beta)]/[(ex_2 - ex_\alpha)(ex_5 - ex_\beta) , \sigma_{r2} = 1 - \Phi_2 . \qquad (8.4)$$

Table 8.2 - Helium Cycle.

	environment (o)	state 1	state 2	state α	state 3
p – Mpa	0.1	1.2	8	7.95	7.9
T – K (°C)	290.15 (17)	50 (- 223.15)	116.23 (-156.92)	290.15 (17)	355.05 (81.9)
i – kJ/kg	1519.0	272.12	636.76	1544.9	1882.0
s – kJ/(kg K)	29.7882	15.4471	15.9071	20.7062	21.7685
ex – kJ/kg	0	2914.2	3145.4	2661.0	2689.9
	state 4	state 5	state β	state 6	
p – Mpa	7.8	1.3	1.27	1.25	
T – K (°C)	773.15 (500)	398 (124.85)	290.15 (17)	156.73 (-116.42)	
i – kJ/kg	4051.8	2083.3	1523.1	838.07	
s – kJ/(kg K)	25.8344	26.1029	24.5100	21.3405	
ex – kJ/kg	3680.0	1633.6	1535.6	1770.2	

Table 8.3 - Hydrogen Processes.

	envir. (o')	state 7	State 8	state 9	state 10	state 11
p – Mpa	0.1	.101325 ($x_7 = 0$)	10.2	10	0.5	10
T – K (°C)	290.15 (17)	20.28 (- 252.87)	28 (- 245.15)	120 (- 163.15)	41.25(-231.9)	290.15 (17)
i – kJ/kg	4085.8	263.8	430.1	1739.1	917.65	4136
s – kJ/(kg K)	70.18	16.75	16.837	38.73	39.864	52.33
ex – kJ/kg	0	11680.7	11821.8	6778.2	5628.1	5229.4

Table 8.4. – Main Results Obtained.

W_{ne}	1557 kJ/kg	η_{He}	0.7140	R	0.2595	P_{tHel}	159190 kW
P_{tH_22}	41532 kW	P_{eH_21}	25541 kW	P_{eH_22}	5554 kW	m_{H_2}	31.73 kg/s
Φ_{He}	0.4736	r	1.407	η_t	0.806	F_t	0.767
$Ex_{rf}°$	241199 kW	$S_s°_{rf}$	831.29 kW/K				
Processes	σ_{ri}	$S_s°_{ai}$ (kW/K)	σ_{ri}'	Processes	σ_{ri}	$S_s°_{ai}$ (kW/K)	σ_{ri}'
1) 1-2	0.3799	35.76	0.0430	4) 4-5	0.0575	29.77	0.0358
2) 2-3, 5-6	0.5683	84.59	0.1018	5) 6-1	0.4681	258.17	0.3106
3) 3-4	0.1048	29.33	0.0353				

C) *Process 3-4* (exhaust gas heat exchanger).

$$\Phi_3 = G_{He}(ex_4 - ex_3)/[G_g(ex_i - ex_e)], \sigma_{r3} = 1 - \Phi_3. \tag{8.5}$$

D) *Process 4-5* (helium turbine).

$$\Phi_4 = W^*_t/(ex_4 - ex_5), \sigma_{r4} = 1 - \Phi_4 \tag{8.6}$$

E) *Process 6-1* (heat exchanger between helium and hydrogen).

$$\Phi_5 = G_{He}(ex_1 - ex_6)/[G_{H_2}(ex_8 - ex_9)], \sigma_{r5} = 1 - \Phi_5. \tag{8.7}$$

8.3.4 Analysis of the Single Phases with Reference to the Entropy Production Rate of the Whole Helium Cycle

As was already dealt with by Bisio (1994), for the single phases of a cycle, it seems more meaningful to consider as relative entropy production of the phase i, σ_{ri}', the ratio of the actual entropy production power of this phase, $S_s°_{ai}$, to the reference entropy production power of the whole cycle, $S_s°_{rf}$. In a similar way, an alternative definition of exergy efficiency, Φ_i', of a single phase with reference to the losable exergy power of the whole system is proposed:

$$\sigma_{ri}' = S_s°_{ai}/S_s°_{rf}, \Phi_i' = 1 - \sigma_{ri}'. \tag{8.8}$$

The reference exergy power of the whole cycle is:

$$Ex_{rf}° = G_{H_2}(ex_8 - ex_9) + G_g(ex_i - ex_e), \tag{8.9}$$

and then the reference entropy production power:

$$S_s°_{rf} = [G_{H_2}(ex_8 - ex_9) + G_g(ex_i - ex_e)]/T_o. \tag{8.10}$$

Thus, let us consider the actual entropy production rates.

A) *Process 1-2* (helium compressor).

$$S_{s\,a1}^{\circ} = G_{He}\,[-W_c^* - (ex_2 - ex_1)]/T_o. \tag{8.11}$$

B) *Processes 2-3 and 5-6* (regenerator).

$$S_{s\,a2}^{\circ} = G_{He}\,[(ex_2 - ex_3) - (ex_6 - ex_5)]/T_o. \tag{8.12}$$

C) *Process 3-4* (exhaust gas heat exchanger).

$$S_{s\,a3}^{\circ} = [G_g\,(ex_i - ex_e) - G_{He}\,(ex_4 - ex_3)]/T_o. \tag{8.13}$$

D) *Process 4-5* (helium turbine).

$$S_{s\,a4}^{\circ} = G_{He}\,[(ex_4 - ex_5) - W_t^*]/T_o. \tag{8.14}$$

E) *Process 6-1* (heat exchanger between helium and hydrogen).

$$S_{s\,a5}^{\circ} = [G_{H_2}\,(ex_8 - ex_9) - G_{He}\,(ex_1 - ex_6)]/T_o. \tag{8.15}$$

Obviously, the following relations are verified:

$$\sigma_r = \sigma_{r1}' + \sigma_{r2}' + \sigma_{r3}' + \sigma_{r4}' + \sigma_{r5}'\,,\quad \Phi_{He} = 1 - \sigma_r. \tag{8.16}$$

The value obtained for the exergy efficiency of the whole cycle is practically coincident with that previously calculated.

8.4 ANALYSIS RESULTS

Tables 8.2, 8.3 and 8.4 show the results concerning a calculation example of the plant whose assumptions are reported in Table 8.5. The overall energy efficiency is equal to 80.6%, the exergy efficiency 76.7% (without a hydrogen turbine 72% and 68.5% respectively). Regarding the single helium cycle, its energy efficiency is extremely high (since the cycle works between very large temperature extremes), about 72%, while the exergy value is equal to 47%.

The ratio of the electrical power to the mass flow rate of every cycle is noteworthy: obviously the helium cycle gives the higher value, 1556 kW/(kg/s), while the hydrogen cycle and the gas turbine cycle give respectively 630 kW/(kg/s) and 295 kW/(kg/s).

The following figures show the results of a parametric analysis; since the helium cycle is the one that affects the system more deeply, performances have been estimated by varying the helium maximum pressure and the helium recuperator effectiveness, while the assumptions are those reported in Table 8.5.

Table 8.5. – Main Assumptions.

Inlet chemical exergy power of gas turbine	309400 kW
Inlet thermal power of gas turbine	294300 kW
Net electrical power of gas turbine	103200 kW
Gas mass flow rate	349.3 kg/s
Helium maximum pressure	8 Mpa
Helium minimum pressure	1.2 Mpa
Helium maximum temperature	773.15 K
Helium minimum temperature	50 K
Hydrogen maximum pressure	10.2 Mpa
Outlet hydrogen turbine pressure	0.5 Mpa
Helium compressor efficiency	0.867
Helium turbine efficiency	0.958
Hydrogen turbine efficiency	0.95
Helium recuperator effectiveness	0.848

Fig. 8.4 shows the overall energy efficiency, while the efficiencies of the single helium cycle are shown in Figs. 8.5 and 8.6. It is interesting to observe that high values of the combined system efficiency are obtained equally utilizing a low helium recuperator effectiveness (0.5); the difference in comparison of the maximum values is around 2%. Moreover, this permits a relatively small regenerative exchanger. The advantage of having low recuperator effectiveness can be explained by analyzing Figs. 8.7 and 8.8. In fact, as the helium recuperator effectiveness decreases, the hydrogen maximum temperature increases (see Fig. 8.7) and therefore the hydrogen cycle efficiency increases. This is illustrated by Fig. 8.8, in which the cycle energy efficiencies are shown vs helium recuperator effectiveness (the helium maximum pressure was fixed equal to 10 MPa).

By varying the recuperator effectiveness from 0.5 to 0.95, the hydrogen cycle efficiency decreases from 56% to 45%, the helium cycle efficiency increases from 60% to 76% while the overall efficiency increases only slightly from 79% to 81.5%. It is also possible to obtain equally high system efficiencies without hydrogen expansion (Fig. 8.9): around 75% for the system energy efficiency, 71% for the system exergy efficiency.

Many of the curves shown in the previous figures have not been drawn for helium maximum pressure lower than a certain value, since a minimum limit (20 K) was fixed for the temperature difference between the outlet exhaust gas heat exchanger and the cold side outlet helium recuperator (point 3 of Fig. 8.2).

It is interesting to analyze the entropy production of the helium cycle. From the example shown in Table 8.4, one notes that the maximum values of entropy production rate takes place in the heat exchanger between helium and hydrogen; this is visualized by the parameter σ_{r5}' which is much higher than the other parameters σ_{ri}' (even if σ_{r2} is almost equal to σ_{r5}). Figs. 8.10 and 8.11 show the relative entropy production of helium phases vs maximum pressure (the recuperator effectiveness is fixed equal to 0.85) and vs recuperator effectiveness (the maximum pressure is fixed equal to 10 MPa). It should be noted that, by varying the maximum pressure, the value of phase 6-1 remains nearly constant, the value of phase 1-2 (compression) increases strongly, that of phase 2-3 and 5-6 (regeneration) decreases strongly, while the values of phases 4-5 (expansion) and 3-4 decrease slightly. Instead, by varying the recuperator effectiveness, the value of phase 2-3/5-6 has a maximum point, the values of phases 4-5 and 1-2 keep nearly constant, the value of phase 6-1 increases slightly, while that of phase 3-4 decreases strongly.

In all results presented here, the conditions of the exhaust gas at the exit of gas-helium heat exchanger have been kept the same. Particularly for the temperature, a value of 379 K was chosen: this allows a recovery of waste heat from the open-cycle gas turbine equal to 83%. Utilizing a "clean" combustible as, for example, the same hydrogen and decreasing the temperature of the gas to the environment temperature of 290 K, it is possible to recover the whole waste heat (100%) and reach a value of the overall energy efficiency near to 90% (around 85% for the exergy efficiency), while without the hydrogen turbine the obtainable values are respectively 78.7% and 74.9%.

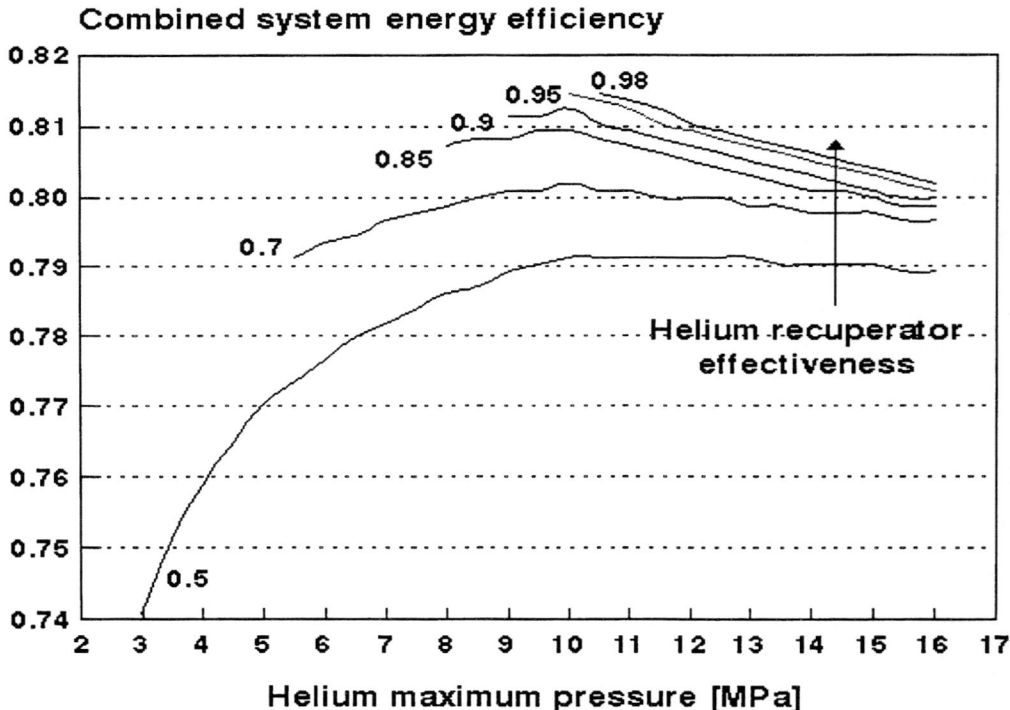

Fig. 8.4. Helium maximum pressure and recuperator effectiveness influence on combined cycle efficiency.

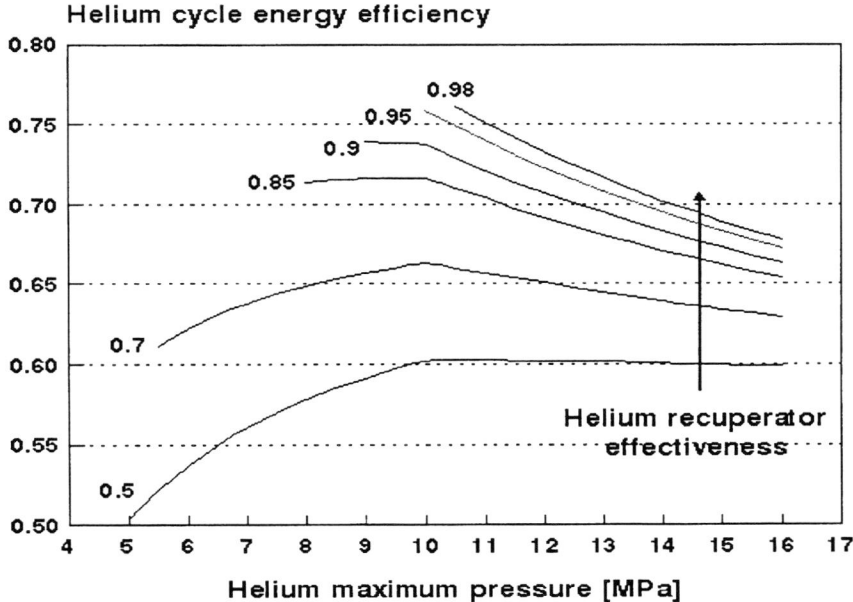

Fig. 8.5. Helium cycle energy efficiency versus maximum pressure and recuperator effectiveness.

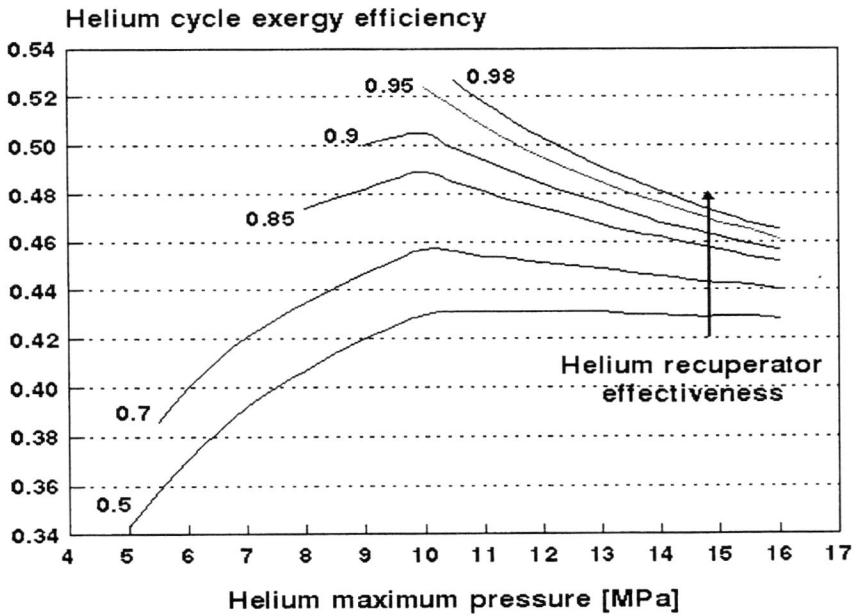

Fig. 8.6. Helium cycle exergy efficiency versus maximum pressure and recuperator effectiveness.

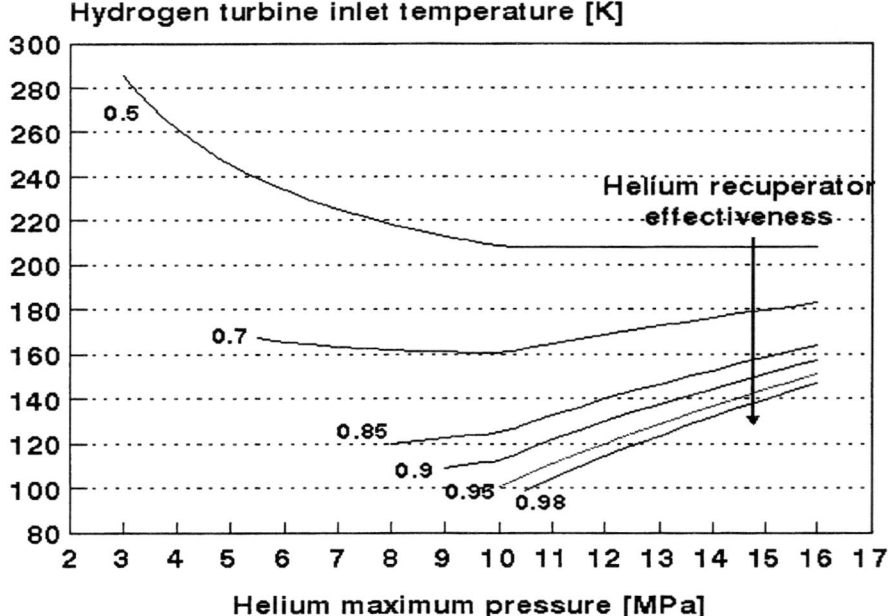

Fig. 8.7. Hydrogen turbine inlet temperature versus helium maximum pressure and recuperator effectiveness.

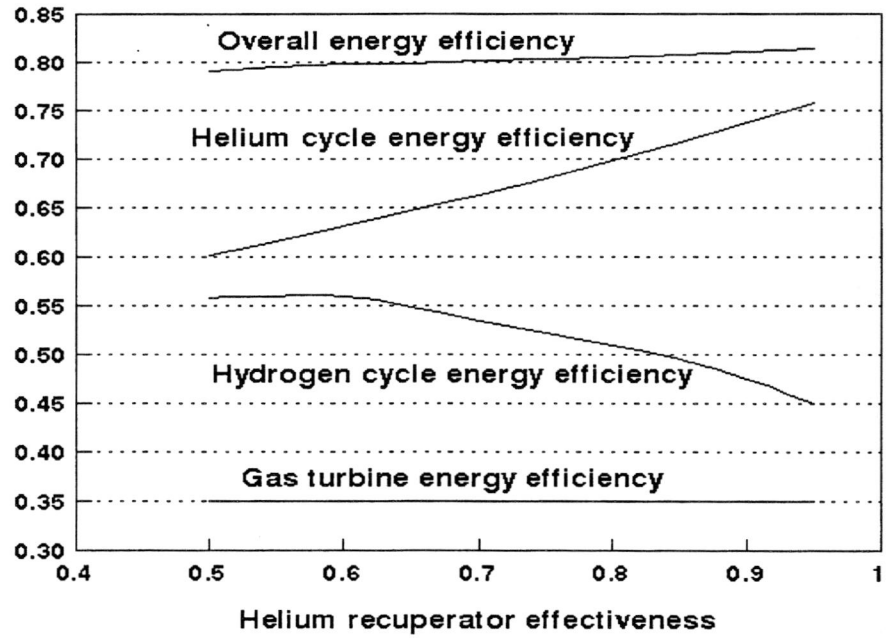

Fig 8.8. Cycle efficiency versus helium recuperator effectiveness.

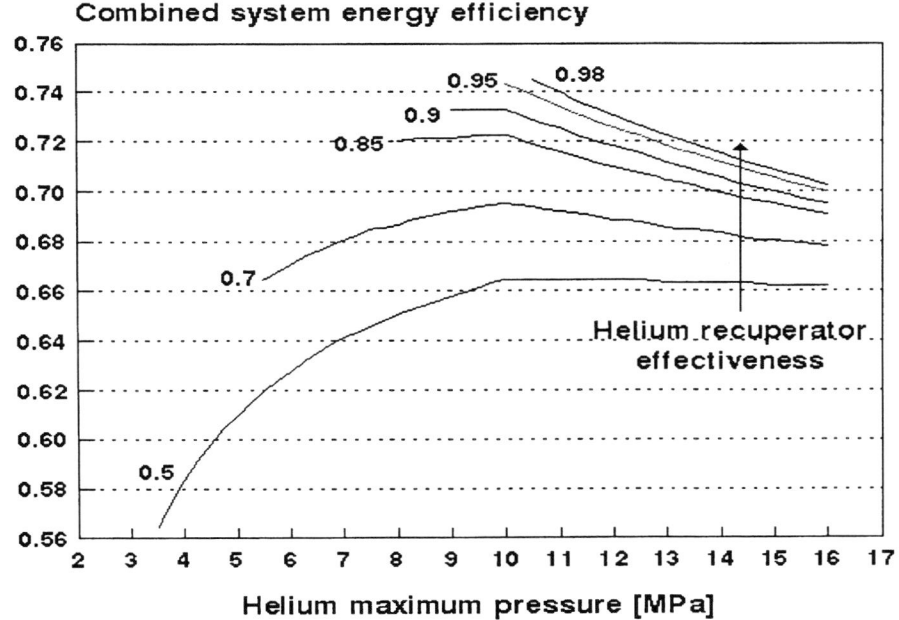

Fig. 8.9. Combined system (without hydrogen turbine) efficiency.

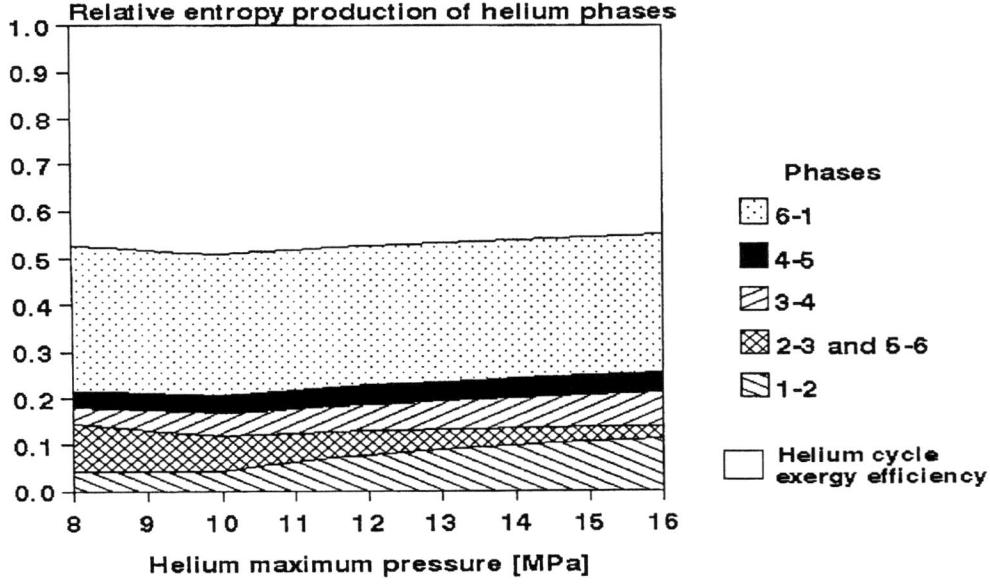

Fig. 8.10. Relative entropy production of helium phases versus maximum pressure (recuperator effectiveness = 0.85).

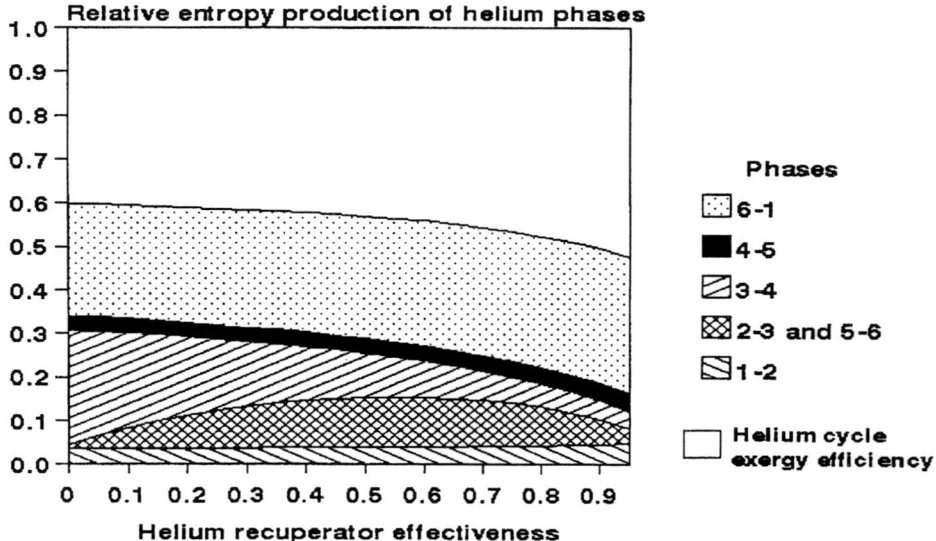

Fig. 8.11. Relative entropy production of helium phases versus recuperator effectiveness (maximum pressure = 10 MPa).

8.5 HELIUM AND COMBUSTION GAS TURBINE

As reported by Farmer (1994) the thermal efficiency of combustion gas turbines has increased steadily over the last half century. Today simple cycle machines are running at over 40% efficiency and combined cycles at 55%, with an increase to over 58% for machines soon to enter service (Korakianitis, 1994a and 1994b). Many new thermodynamic cycles will lead to efficiencies of over 60% before the year 2000. One of the major factors in efficiency advancement has been the continuously increasing level of turbine inlet temperature, made possible by material technology and turbine blade cooling techniques.

The temperature capability of closed-cycle gas turbine has been limited by the external heater. By using a nuclear heat source with the graphite (ceramic) core and a direct cycle gas turbine, this metallurgical limit in the heater is obviated (Fig. 8.9; McDonald and Etzel, 1994).

The key to the design of the high efficiency helium turbomachine is the technology from the combustion gas turbine industry, both heavy-duty and aeroderivatives. State of the art technology from these gas turbines is directly applicable to the design of the helium turbomachine, particularly in the areas of design methodology, performance materials and fabrication methods (Massardo and McDonald, 1995).

With its high specific heat working fluid the helium gas turbine can be characterized by high specific power (> 900 kW/(kg/s)); as an example with a rating of 290 MWe the turbomachine is compact by virtue of the high degree of system pressurization; it is physically smaller than the 226 MWe simple cycle heavy-duty industrial gas turbine that is in utility service today.

The difference between air and helium is manifest in several areas. Combustion machines require fewer compressor and turbine stages. Very high specific power can be realized with helium (at elevated pressure) resulting in a more compact turbocompressor. With a clean closed cycle very small hydraulic diameter passages can be utilized, which, with high thermal conductivity for helium, result in a very compact recuperator (McDonald, 1994). For systems using a low molecular mass gas like helium there are areas that will require detailed design attention, namely: seal design to minimize by-pass flow; flange design to obviate leakage and electrical insulation in the generator and magnetic bearings windings.

In the context of this paper, the helium gas turbine has two technology bases, that are being fully utilized: operating experience from helium cooled reactors and the Oberhausen II gas turbine plants and design know-how from the air-breathing machines, namely, gas turbines and heat exchangers (recuperators and compact aircraft aerospace units).

The possibility of realizing the hydrogen turbine working at cryogenic temperatures has not been thoroughly evaluated; nevertheless, it has been employed in space with satisfactory results, particularly with rockets that employ hydrogen as a propellant. In any case, it must be remarked that the system without hydrogen expansion also reaches considerable performances.

8.6 FINAL REMARKS

The main conclusions are the following:

First, it is to be remarked that the helium cycle examined in this paper, though it is formally similar to other usually considered cycles, differs greatly from them on the basis of the second-law analysis. Indeed, one has inlet exergy both by exploiting the waste energy of an open gas turbine cycle and by vaporizing and superheating hydrogen at a temperature under that of the environment. This allows very high energy and exergy efficiencies of the combined system to be obtained.

Since the helium cycle works between very large temperatures extremes, the recuperator exchanges a considerable thermal power, reaching remarkable size, but the parametric analysis of the system has shown that high plant efficiencies are obtainable even with low values of the helium recuperator effectiveness.

Positive considerations about the realization and technological aspects of helium turbine have been taken into account.

However, in general, the usefulness of these combined systems is conditioned by various parameters, which are variable in relation to the location of the system (e.g., possible exploitations of LH_2 exergy, existence and size of gas hydrogen storage systems, availability of waste thermal energy).

8.7 APPENDIX

With reference to helium mass unit, the heat transfers are given by:

$$Q^*_{34} = i_4 - i_3 \, , \, Q^*_{61} = i_1 - i_6 \, . \tag{A8.1}$$

The turbine and compressor works are given by:

$$W^*_t = i_4 - i_5 , \quad W^*_c = i_1 - i_2 . \tag{A8.2}$$

The cycle net work is given by:

$$W^*_n = W^*_t + W^*_c . \tag{A8.3}$$

Indicating by $\xi_{\beta 1}$ and $\xi_{\beta 2}$ the efficiencies of the electrical machines, the net electrical work output is:

$$W^*_{ne} = W^*_t \, \xi_{\beta 1} + W^*_c / \xi_{\beta 2} . \tag{A8.4}$$

The energy efficiency of the helium cycle can be written as:

$$\eta_{He} = W^*_{ne} / (Q^*_{34} / \xi_\alpha) , \tag{A8.5}$$

where ξ_α is the thermal efficiency (or effectiveness) of the heat exchanger of the top turbine exhaust gas.

In addition, the thermal energy Q^*_{61} is utilized to "vaporize" and superheat the hydrogen with a further recovery factor R_f:

$$R_f = |Q^*_{61}| / (Q^*_{34} / \xi_\alpha) . \tag{A8.6}$$

We use "vaporize" because, with the data utilized in this work (Tab. 8.3), liquid hydrogen is transformed into superheated vapor, without separating into two phases.

The outlet thermal power from the open-cycle turbine in the waste-gas heat exchanger is given by:

$$P_{tg} = G_g (i_i - i_e) , \tag{A8.7}$$

corresponding to inlet thermal power and mass flow rate of helium:

$$P_{tHe1} = \xi_\alpha P_{tg} , \quad G_{He} = P_{tHe1} / Q_{34} . \tag{A8.8}$$

The outlet thermal power from the helium cycle is:

$$P_{tHe2} = G_{He} |Q^*_{61}| , \tag{A8.9}$$

corresponding to mass flow rate of hydrogen:

$$G_{H_2} = P_{tHe2} / (i_9 - i_8) . \tag{A8.10}$$

The electrical power of the helium cycle is given by:

$$P_{eHe} = G_{He} W^*_{ne}. \tag{A8.11}$$

The electrical power for pumping liquid hydrogen can be written as:

$$P_{eH_22} = G_{H_2} (i_8 - i_7)/\xi_{\beta 2}. \tag{A8.12}$$

The energy efficiency of the helium cycle and of the pumping of liquid hydrogen is:

$$\eta_{He2} = (P_{eHe} - P_{eH_22})/P_{tg}. \tag{A8.13}$$

The electrical power generated by the hydrogen turbine is:

$$P_{eH_21} = G_{H_2} (i_9 - i_{10}) \xi_{\beta 3}. \tag{A8.14}$$

With reference to the whole combined system, the energy efficiency, η_t, and the exergy efficiency, Φ_t, can be defined by:

$$\eta_t = (P_{eg} + P_{eHe} + P_{eH_21} - P_{eH_22})/P_{tc}, \tag{A8.15}$$

$$\Phi_t = (P_{eg} + P_{eHe} + P_{eH_21} - P_{eH_22})/Ex_c^\circ, \tag{A8.16}$$

where:

P_{eg} net electrical power of combustion gas turbine cycle,
P_{tc} inlet thermal power of gas turbine,
Ex_c° inlet chemical exergy power of gas turbine.

Chapter 9

THE POSSIBLE UTILIZATION OF THE THERMAL ENERGY DISCHARGED FROM SINTERING PLANTS OF STEEL WORKS

9.1 THE PINCH POINT PROBLEM AND THE KALINA CYCLE

Many thermodynamic cycles have been considered for the utilization of the thermal energy in a hot gas stream for the production of mechanical work. The most often used cycle is some form of Rankine cycle, with steam as the working fluid.

In the Rankine cycle, usually more than half of the heat transfer occurs during the boiling process. Since the heat recovery steam generator operates at essentially constant pressure, temperature is also constant during boiling; the gas at the pinch point, where the water starts to boil, must be at a higher temperature than the boiling water (Fig. 9.1). The pinch point is a limitation on power output because:

(i) It can force a higher than otherwise necessary discharge gas temperature.
(ii) The gas at the point where vaporization is complete will be at a much higher temperature than the steam and the large temperature difference results in a useless destruction of exergy.

Various ways have been proposed and applied to overcome the above inconveniences also in the energy recovery systems for sintering plants of steel works and one is shown in a successive section. A promising system, already partially applied without an exhaustive thermodynamic analysis in the iron and steel industry for energy recovery, is the Kalina cycle (Kalina, 1984; Kalina, 1987; Hanliang et al., 1989; Marston, 1990) (Fig. 9.2).

The Kalina cycle utilizes a mixture of ammonia and water as the working fluid. When the liquid mixture is heated, the more volatile ammonia tends to vaporize first and at a lower temperature than does pure water. The temperature of the remaining saturated liquid rises as the ammonia concentration decreases. Thus, a better match to the temperature change of the gas is obtained and the potentiality exists for significant increases in cycle exergy efficiency. Moreover, different parts of the cycle can have different concentrations of ammonia. Thus, condensation can take place at a pressure slightly above atmospheric, using a relatively low concentration of ammonia, although a relatively high concentration is appropriate in the boiler.

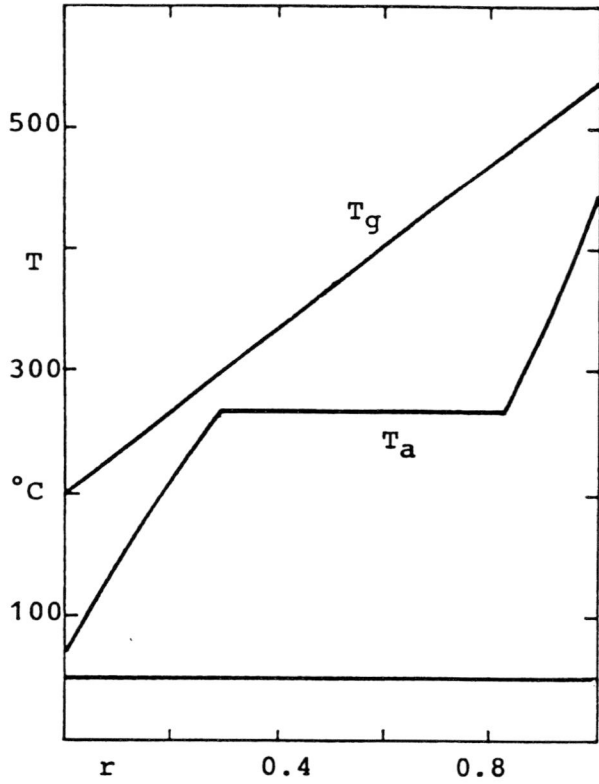

Fig. 9.1. Temperature (T) vs enthalpy fraction (r) in a heat recovery steam system.

The fluid dynamic design of the turbine is not different from that of a steam turbine since ammonia has almost the same molecular mass as water (17 vs 18). However, copper-based alloys are subject to corrosion in the presence of ammonia and, consequently, must be avoided.

Figure 9.2 shows a simplified Kalina cycle power system with one distillation step. Superheated ammonia-water vapor (10) is expanded in a turbine (E). The turbine exhaust (11) is cooled (12) in a recovery heat exchanger (F), diluted with ammonia-poor liquid (13), and (14) adduced to a low-pressure condenser (G). The saturated liquid after condensation (15), by a low-pressure pump (A) is compressed to an intermediate pressure (1); then, it is separated into two parts. The former (2) is heated (5) in the recovery heat exchanger (F) and separated in a flash tank (H) into an ammonia-poor liquid (7) and an ammonia-rich vapor stream (6); the ammonia-poor liquid is then decompressed (13) in a throttling valve (I). The latter part (3) of the original condensate is added to the ammonia-rich vapor in order to obtain the desired ammonia concentration of the working fluid (4), which is then condensed (8) in a high pressure condenser (B), compressed (9) by a pump (C) and evaporated (10) in an evaporator (D).

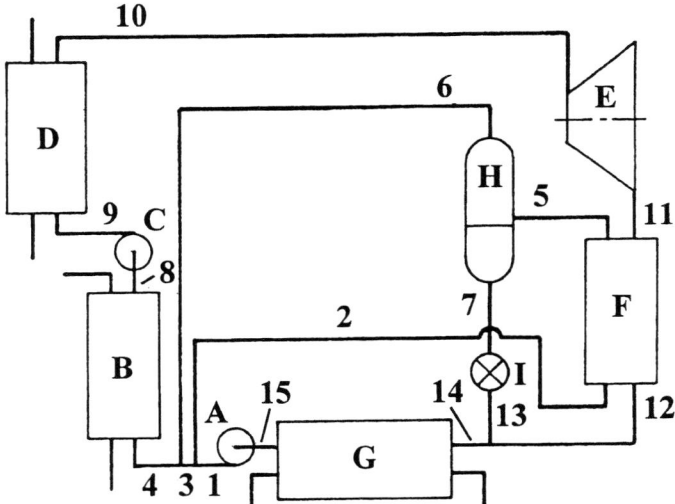

Fig. 9.2. Illustration of a Kalina cycle power system: (A) low pressure pump; (B) high pressure condenser; (C) high pressure pump; (D) evaporator; (E) turbine; (F) recovery heat exchanger; (G) low pressure condenser; (H) flash tank; (i) throttling valve.

While ammonia-water mixtures have been used for many years in cooling cycles, the Kalina cycle appears to be a genuinely new development for power generation. It can be used with high exergy efficiencies compared to other systems in these cases:

(i) as a bottoming cycle in a combined system;
(ii) in energy recovery systems, when the recovery fluid temperature is low.

In both cases discharge temperatures as low as 92°C can be achieved, if not limited by other constraints such as plume buoyancy or acid dew point.

9.2 SINTERING PLANTS AND THEIR ENERGY FLOW

In many works, sintered ore constitutes more than 70% of the blast-furnace burden. Iron ore, initially in form of dust, in the sintering plants is transformed into a material with size, porosity and specific strength the most suitable to guarantee good permeability and reactivity of the burden.

The most common sintering system is the "Dwight Lloyd" process. For a modern sintering plant of this kind, the enthalpy flow is synthetically shown in Fig. 9.3. The inlet enthalpy is given for the most part by coke breeze and, in a lower amount, by ignition combustible gas (usually coke-oven gas). More than 60% of the total enthalpy is discharged into the atmosphere by the combustion gas (as "sensible heat" or thermal enthalpy, and as "latent heat" or chemical enthalpy due to the unburned CO) and by the air which cools the sinter.

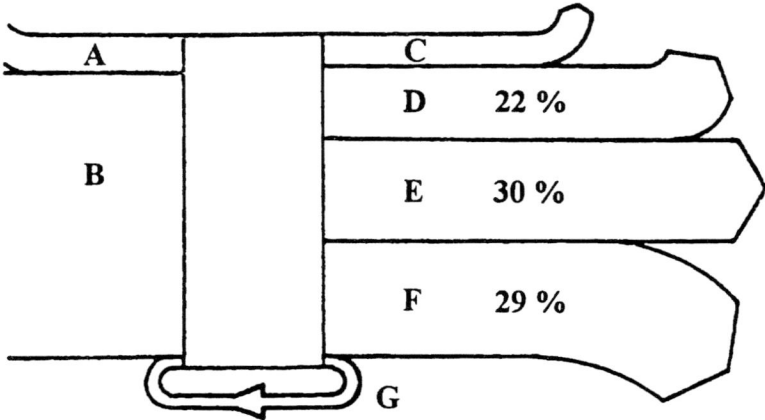

Fig. 9.3. Enthalpy flow of a sintering plant: (A) ignition combustible gas; (B) coke breeze; (C) imperfect combustion (CO) loss; (D) waste gas; (E) sintered ore; (F) reaction enthalpy variation; (G) recycle.

The utilization of the thermal energy of waste gas presents various problems (e.g., the high dustiness) and has had till now very few employments for steam production; on the contrary, it has been employed to heat the waste gas after desulfurization. The most part of the energy recovery and saving systems up to now carried out utilizes the thermal energy of the sinter at the outlet of the sintering machine (Tanaka, 1980; Shibuya et al., 1880; Tani and Shinoda, 1981; Reinitzhuber, 1981; Winzer and Reichenstein, 1981; Horio et al., 1982; Hoffmann, 1982; Nakagoshi et al., 1983; Abe et al., 1983; Kubo et al., 1983; Wakuri, 1983; Barry, 1983; Liestmann, 1984; Pöttken and. Voigt, 1985; Peters and Beer, 1986; Cappel and Hastik, 1986).

In the next subsection, the main realizations are dealt with; in particular, some judgments on the exergy values of the recovered energies are expressed.

9.3 RECOVERY AND SAVING SYSTEMS FOR THE THERMAL ENERGY OF THE SINTER

9.3.1 Fundamental System for Energy Recovery

A relatively simple flow system for energy recovery in sintering plants is shown in Fig. 9.4 (Shibuya et al., 1981). In sintering plants, the red-hot material produced by the sintering lines has to be cooled down to ambient temperature, so as to make possible transportation on belt conveyors and storage in blast furnace stock-houses. The hot sinter, at a temperature of 600-650 °C, falls down on a continuous train of grate bottom carriages, travelling on a track set on the top of a circular channel. Large quantities of air, blown by fans into the channel, cross the hot sinter bed and cool down the sinter to the suitable temperature. In this way, a large part of the thermal energy of the sinter is transferred to the cooling air. In most plants, now, this energy is lost because the air is discharged straight into the atmosphere. In the system of Fig. 9.4 the thermal energy of the highest temperature air crossing the sinter is utilized, taking that air to a boiler where steam is produced. To reach the aim of a maximum recovery value, a part of the air from the boiler outlet is recycled; in this way, air is fed at a temperature of about 150°C into the channel in the recovery zone. The recycling of a high percentage of the air and the filtration upstream the boiler allow us to solve an important ecological problem too.

When the aim of the sinter energy recovery is to produce electrical power by means of a steam turbine, it is convenient to examine the way by which the global exergy value recovered is affected by the flow rate of the cooling air and by the parameters (temperature and pressure) of the steam.

The increase of the air flow rate takes away more thermal energy from the sinter, and the outlet air has a lower temperature and, consequently, a lower specific exergy. The decrease of the temperature and pressure of the steam allows the transfer to it of a higher amount of energy of lower specific exergy. Thus, there is an optimum flow rate that allows the maximum transfer of exergy to the steam.

For a plant similar to that represented in Fig. 9.4, the optimum value of the steam pressure has been examined, by varying the superheating of the steam and the cooling air rate, and assuming a minimum difference of 20°C between the temperatures of the heat exchanging fluids. Some results are shown in Figs. 9.5, 9.6, and 9.7.

In Fig. 9.5, the specific exergy of steam vs pressure is shown for two values of superheating (30 and 80°C).

In Fig. 9.6, the steam exergy vs pressure, with an air flow rate of 280,000 m^3(nTp)/h for the above two superheating values. As already said, both curves present one maximum: at about 10 bar for a superheating of 30°C and at about 9 bar for a superheating of 80°C. Both curves are not even approximately symmetric as regards to the maximum point, but go down more on the side of lower pressures.

In Fig. 9.7, the same curves of Fig. 9.6 with an air flow rate of 320,000 m^3(nTp)/h are shown: the aspect is similar. The maximum for both curves corresponds to a pressure of about 7 bar.

The increase of the air flow rate (from 280,000 m^3(nTp)/h to 320,000 m^3(nTp)/h), certainly taking away a greater amount of energy from the sinter, allows a lower value of the steam exergy, owing to the lower temperature of the air leaving the sinter.

As a conclusion, we can say that exergy analysis allows us to determine the most convenient steam parameters and air flow rate.

Obviously, other considerations (e.g., the existence of a steam network) can suggest parameters different from the ones corresponding to the maximum exergy recovery.

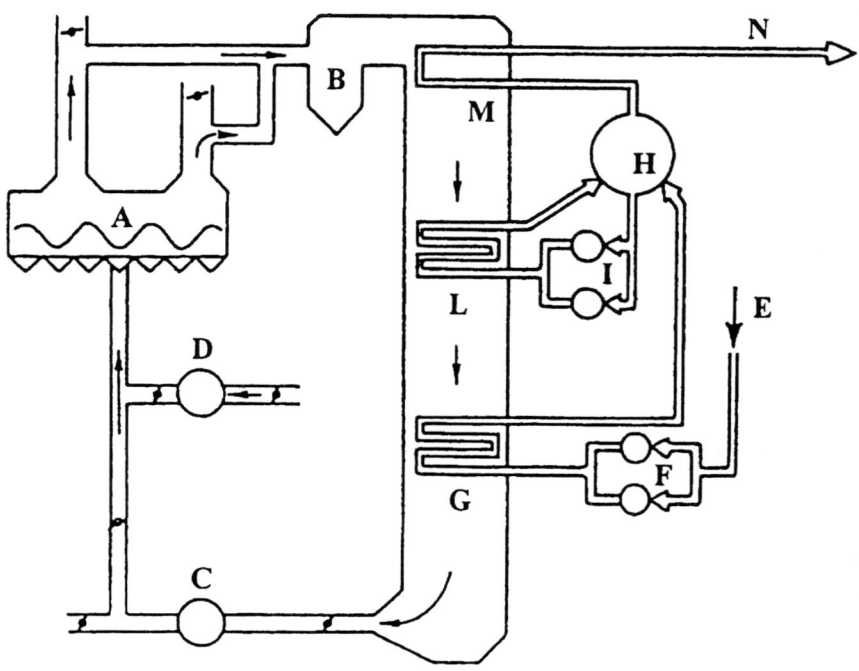

Fig. 9.4. Flow system for the recovery of the thermal energy of the sinter: (A) sinter cooler; (B) filtration system; (C) induced drive fan; (D) forced drive fan; (E) feed water; (F) feed pumps; (G) economizer; (H) drum; (I) recycling pumps; (L) evaporator; (M) superheater; (N) steam.

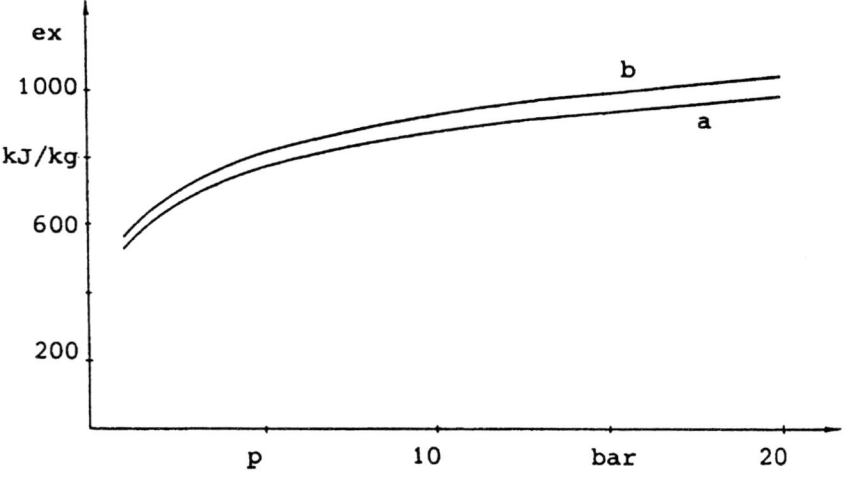

Fig. 9.5. Steam specific exergy, ex, vs pressure, p, for two superheating values: (a) $T=T_s+30$; (b) $T=T_s+80$.

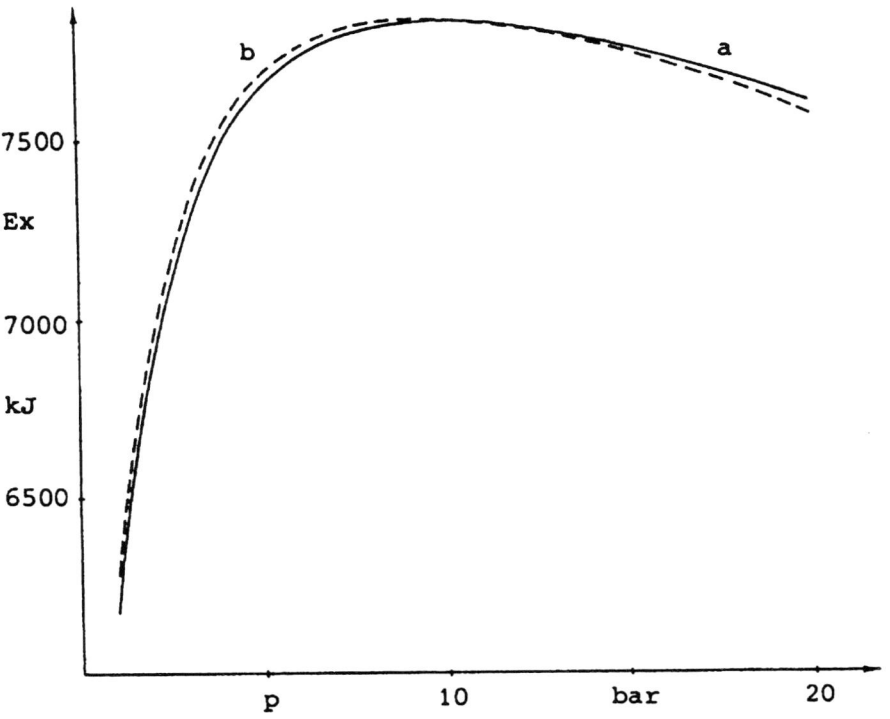

Fig. 9.6. Steam exergy, Ex, vs pressure, p, with an air flow rate of 280,000 m³(nTp)/h for two superheating values: (a) $T=T_s+30$; (b) $T=T_s+80$.

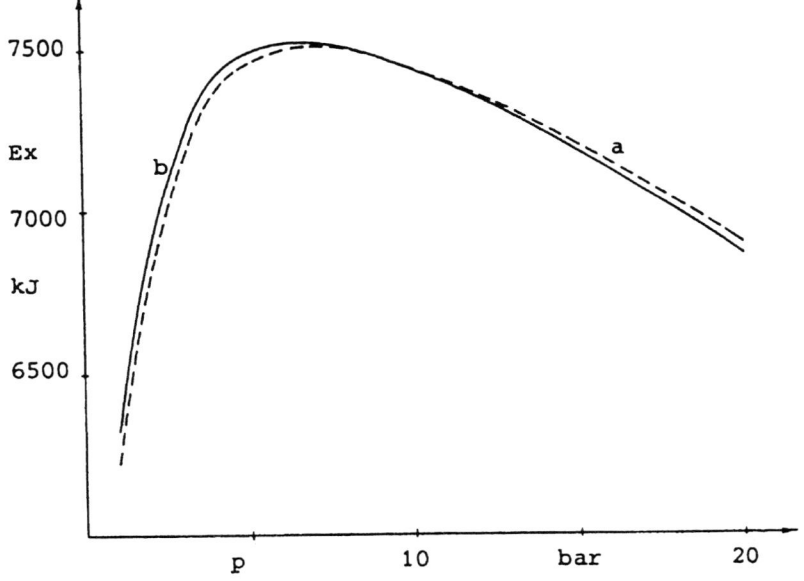

Fig. 9.7. Steam exergy, Ex, vs pressure, p, with an air flow rate of 320,000 m³(nTp)/h for two superheating values: (a) $T=T_s+30$; (b) $T=T_s+80$.

9.3.2 Recovery System with Water Turbine and Flash Steam Turbine

A more complex recovery system is schematically represented in Fig. 9.8.

The air coming from the warmer zones of the sinter cooler at a temperature of $\approx 350°C$ is adduced for a small part to the ignition furnace as combustion air (detail not represented in the figure) and for the most part to a heat exchanger, that produces water in conditions very near to saturation ($\approx 249°C$ and 51 bar).

The air outgoing from the heat exchanger is adduced to the preheating of the mixture to be sintered. Other air, drawn from the middle zone of the sinter cooler at a temperature of 150-180 °C, is used to heat to 80°C the water for the mixture. Also these details are not represented in Fig. 9.8.

The pressurized water is adduced to a tank having the functions of accumulator and regulator; in this tank, the water is in conditions of saturation at a pressure of 39 bar. From this accumulator, the water goes to a special hydraulic turbine, which is keyed on the same axis of a steam turbine and of an electric generator. The fluid outgoing from this turbine has a pressure of ≈ 6 bar and a dryness of 0.18-0.2; it goes to a separator.

From the separator, the saturated vapor is adduced to a flash turbine, where it expands to a pressure of ≈ 0.05 bar.

The saturated liquid goes to a three-stage flasher; after every flash, the produced vapor is adduced to that flash turbine stage having the same pressure.

In this way, while a part of fluid for the expansion in the turbine is recovered, a too great lowering of the vapor dryness in the last stages is avoided. The concept, that is the basis for cooling plants with two compressions and two throttlings, is here applied in an inverse way.

The liquid outgoing from the three-stage flasher is mixed with that discharged from the flash steam turbine condenser and returns to the heat exchanger.

This recovery system with two different turbines presents the following advantages:

(i) The fact that waste heat is recovered as hot water avoids the pinch point problem, described in section 1.2, and so a higher exergy recovery is possible.
(ii) A waste heat hot water generator involves simple construction since no evaporation process is involved.
(iii) Hot water piping can be made smaller than steam piping.
(iv) Fluctuations in the supply of waste heat can be absorbed by storing hot water in the accumulator.
(v) Since water is the operating medium, the hot water cycle is low in cost, high in safety and easy in operation and maintenance.

However, the whole system is more complex than the other usual ones, and an accurate project is necessary to obtain the possible advantages.

A first hot water turbine with a power of 100 kW started a test operation in October 1976 in Japan, and, always in Japan, in March 1980 an industrialization test of the whole recovery system was completed.

The thermal energy recovered by this system is $\approx 7.4\%$ of the energy entering the sintering machine, as chemical energy of the coke breeze and coke-oven gas. However, if we refer to the exergy value and consider the produced electrical energy, the recovery is ≈1% and this last value is the meaningful one in order to evaluate the "merit" of the recovery system.

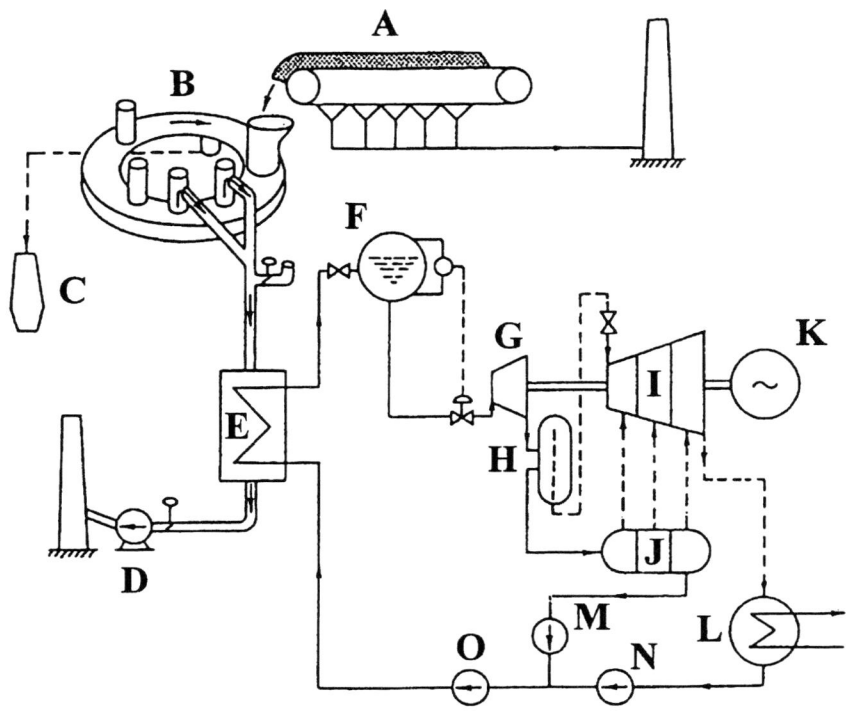

Fig. 9.8. Layout of a recovery system with water turbine and flash steam turbine: (A) sintering machine; (B) sinter cooler; (C) blast furnace; (D) induction fan; (E) hot water generator; (F) accumulator; (G) hot water turbine; (H) water separator; (I) flash-steam turbine; (J) three-stage flasher; (K) electric generator; (L) condenser; (M) booster pump; (N) condenser pump; (O) feed pump.

9.3.3 Recovery System with Organic Fluids

Another layout for the recovery of the sinter thermal energy is represented in Fig. 9.9 (Nakagoshi et al., 1983); the system utilizes a condensation turbogenerator with fluorinol as the working fluid. The fluorinol is a mixture of CF_3CH_2OH (85 mol %) and water (15 mol %).

The vapor parameters at the turbine inlet are about 40 bar and 270°C. The air arrives at the evaporator with a temperature of 345±50 °C and exits at 110°C; then, it is discharged into the atmosphere.

It is to be noted that this system operates partially according to the concepts of the Kalina cycle, in order to avoid the constant temperature vaporization and so the pinch point problem. The process is meaningful when the use of the recovered energy is for electrical energy production.

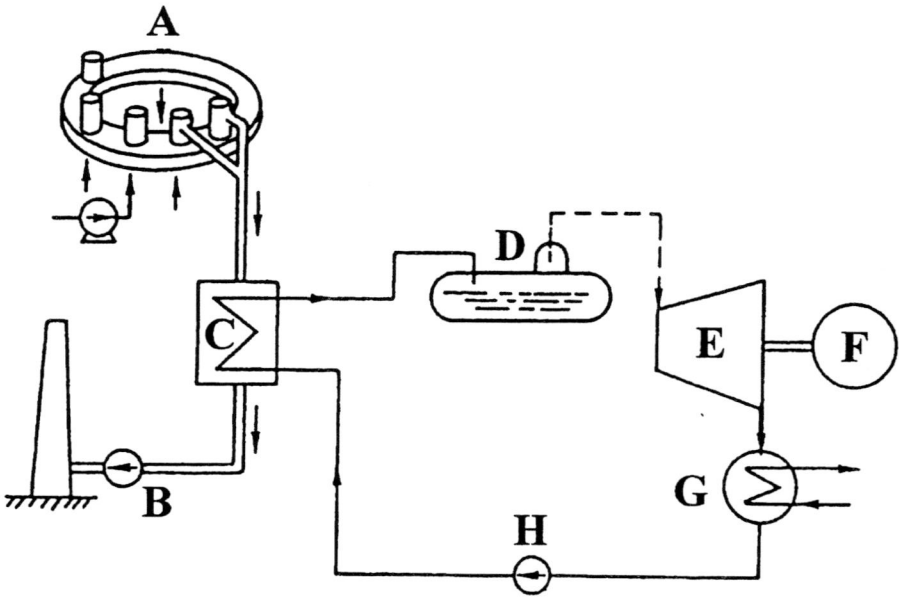

Fig. 9.9. Layout of a recovery system with fluorinol-water mixture as the working fluid: (A) sinter cooler; (B) induction fan; (C) evaporator; (D) accumulator; (E) turbine; (F) electric generator; (G) condenser; (H) feed pump.

9.3.4 Recovery System Interesting Two Different Plants

A more complex system of energy recovery, that involves another plant in addition to the sinter plant, is represented in Fig. 9.10. Pressurized water is adduced to the hood of a LD converter, where it warms up at $\approx 100°C$ and then goes to a heat exchanger, where it warms up at $\approx 115°C$ by means of sinter cooling air. This water, in successive heat exchangers, vaporizes and preheats Freon 11. The Freon drives a turbogenerator for electrical energy production; the Freon parameters are 5.4 bar ($\approx 88°C$) at turbine inlet and 0.8 bar at the turbine outlet.

Freon 11 is preferred since it is the fluid that presents the highest exergy efficiency for a maximum temperature of $\approx 100°C$, owing to the almost verticality of the vapor phase boundary in the T vs s diagram. Furthermore, it is chemically stable and has a specific volume lower than that of water vapor; thus, the turbine dimensions are lower.

This kind of recovery is specifically valid for thermal energy of low level (100-150 °C). In this way, the sinter cooling air, which is warmer, can be utilized for the combustion of ignition gas, with a partial saving of the gas itself.

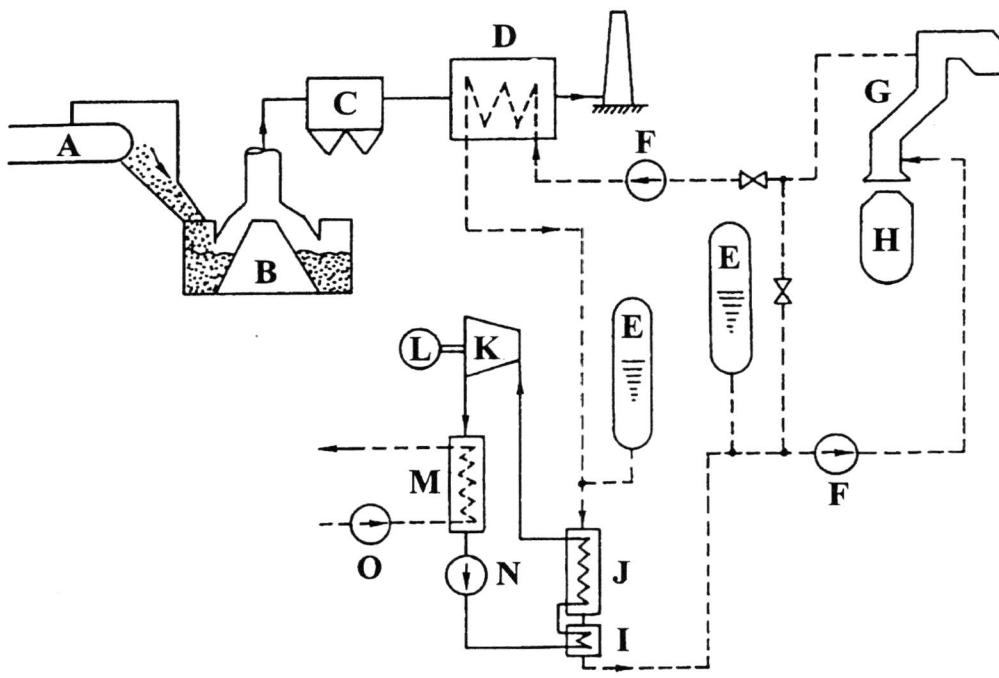

Fig. 9.10. Layout of a recovery system interesting both sinter and steelmaking plants with Freon 11 as the working fluid: (A) sintering machine; (B) sinter cooler; (C) dedusting system; (D) heat exchanger; (E) accumulators; (F) hot water pumps; (G) hood; (H) LD converter; (I) Freon preheater; (J) Freon evaporator; (K) Freon turbine; (L) electric generator; (M) Freon condenser; (N) Freon pump; (O) cooling water pump.

9.3.5 Other Systems

The cooling air of the sinter can be used with the primary aim of reducing the consumption of the ignition gas, by utilizing it as combustion air, at least in part. In the hypothesis that the air is preheated at 300°C, theoretical calculations show the possibility of reducing ignition gas by 24% (Tanaka, 1980).

The utilization of the warm air of sinter cooling seems the prevailing trend in the German iron and steel industry (Reinitzhuber, 1981; Hoffmann, 1982; Liestmann, 1984; Pöttken and Voigt, 1985; Peters and Beer, 1986; Cappel and Hastik, 1986).

The recovered steam has been exploited also in the sintering plant itself to humidify and preheat the mixture to be sintered. With a constant production, a combustible gas saving near to 10% has been attained in France (Barry, 1983).

In these last systems, the energy saving is preferred to the energy recovery, and this is more valid, when possible, on the basis of the second law of thermodynamics.

9.4 FINAL REMARKS

The utilization of the sinter thermal energy presents many interesting possibilities, even if the industrial realizations have been carried out for the most part in Japan.

From the above analysis, one can draw the following:

(i) The most convenient system, according to the second law, is the partial utilization of the warmer air of sinter cooling for the combustion of ignition gas and, consequently, for a direct saving of a precious combustible gas (usually coke-oven gas). It is indeed well known that, in every recovery system, there is always a preference, when possible, for those systems that, by using waste energy, allow the reduction of the consumption of primary energy with high exergy value in comparison with the use of the above waste energy in other plants with a notably lower exergy value.

(ii) In the recovery systems, the pinch point problem must be duly considered. Kalina cycle and similar others which empirically have approached the above cycle seem suitable to overcome such a problem when the aim is only of producing electrical energy. However, they cannot be utilized when there is also the necessity of steam for various purposes, since these cycles employ particular fluids (ammonia-water or fluorinol-water).

(iii) A promising system, always for overcoming the pinch point problem, is the use of pressurized water to recover the sinter thermal energy through cooling air. Two turbines keyed on the same axis, the former fed with hot water partially vaporizing in the expansion, and the latter fed at the inlet with steam and also at the intermediate stages with flash steam, coming from a multistage flasher, allow a good energy recovery, in comparison with other systems, when the temperature of the sinter cooling air is not high.

(iv) When the temperature of the available thermal energy is very low, the systems with Freon 11 as the working fluid are particularly convenient. This fluid, indeed, presents the highest exergy efficiency for a maximum temperature of $\approx 100°C$, owing to the almost verticality of the vapor phase boundary in T vs s diagram.

(v) In some cases, the combination of the recoveries of two plants differing between them, as regards both the type and the location, is suitable. In this paper, the combination of the systems for the cooling of the sinter and of the LD converter hood is considered as an example. However, it is to be pointed out that the coupling between plants usually disjoined may cause problems of operative stiffness and constraints to the total exploitation of the available thermal energy.

(vi) For one of most usual energy recovery plants, in this paper the pressure value that maximizes the recovered exergy is determined. This value (7 - 10 bar) is somewhat low and often in actual plants a slightly higher value is chosen to achieve the parallel with an existing steam network.

(vii) As regards the value of the energy recoveries from a sinter plant, the remarks made by Ottmar et al. (1983) present validity even greater in this case. Indeed, the recovered energy is usually 7-8% of the primary energy, but the recovered exergy is only $\approx 1\%$ of the primary exergy. This remark could seem depressing towards the realization of the above systems, also owing to the notable plant costs. This is not the purpose of the paper, especially for the large plants, in which an exergy recovery of 1% is by no means negligible. We think, however, that only exergy analysis can be well grounded for the technical choice of the optimal solution.

Chapter 10

HEAT TRANSFER, ENERGY SAVING AND POLLUTION CONTROL IN UHP ELECTRIC-ARC FURNACES

10.1 ENERGY PROBLEM IN IRON AND STEEL WORKS

The iron and steel industry is the maximum industrial energy consumer. After the employee costs, the energy costs (about 30% of the total) represent the second cost element in integrated steel works. Thus, the lowering of energy consumption is a major objective of the steel industry. Usually this objective can be associated to a general plant examination with the aim of reducing the various kinds of environment pollution. To put in evidence the weight of the topic, let us consider the scheme of enthalpy flows in Fig. 10.1A: waste enthalpy flow is 66% of inlet enthalpy flow, while about 57% of inlet enthalpy flow is recirculated. However, the scheme of exergy flows in Fig. 10.1B puts in evidence that waste enthalpy flow has a lower exergetic and economic value. From Fett et al. (1993), one draws that the German steel industry has obtained the following mean annual reductions in the specific enthalpy consumption: 2% from 1960 to 1970, 1.2% from 1970 to 1980, 1% from 1980 to 1990 and the value 0.5% has been hypothesized from 1990 to 2000. To evaluate the meaning of these reductions, one must consider that every further progress is usually possible only by means of plant modifications with higher investments.

10.2 TRENDS IN THE DEVELOPMENT IN ELECTRIC-ARC FURNACE STEELMAKING

The worldwide steadily increasing steel demand will even in future be met by running the two main production routes. The BOF route starting from the ore reduction blast furnace and the electric-arc furnace technology with its capability of recycling steel scrap complement each other most favorably. Around the world there is now a trend towards the ever more frequent use of electric-arc furnaces for steelmaking. This has also applied to Europe and, in particular, to Germany, in the past few years, also a successful way to benefit resources and environment (Borowski, 1998, Ameling, 2000a and 2000b).

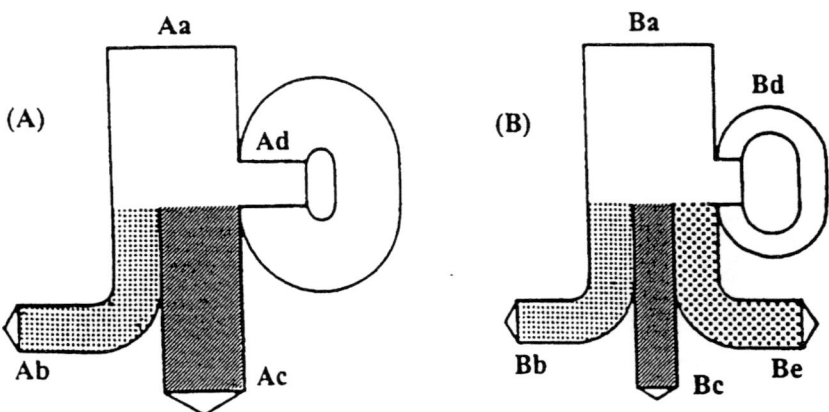

Fig. 10.1. Enthalpy (A) and exergy (B) flows of an iron and steel plant: (Aa) inlet enthalpy; (Ab) outlet enthalpy utilized; (Ac) enthalpy not utilized; (Ad) enthalpy recirculated; (Ba) inlet exergy; (Bb) outlet exergy utilized; (Bc) exergy not utilized; (Bd) exergy recirculated; (Be) exergy destroyed.

The energy potential presented by scrap as a raw material, its chiefly price, its good availability in most regions of the world, and the necessity to recycle scrap are "raw-material related reasons" for the expansion of electric steelmaking.

The production capacity and thus the productivity and cost-efficiency of electric-arc furnaces have, in addition, risen quite extraordinary over the past few years. Another advantage is that the steelmaking costs of electric-arc furnace steel plants are not so heavily dependent on the capacity utilization rate.

10.3 ENERGY AND POLLUTION PROBLEMS IN ELECTRIC-ARC FURNACES

Among the various iron and steel plants, electric-arc furnaces are the ones characterized by the highest specific energy (and particularly exergy) consumption. In addition, the productivity of electric-arc furnaces has been growing from seventies by the utilization of the modern UHP (ultra high power) which allow a high melting rate. In recent years, DC (instead of AC) electric-arc furnaces are becoming the preferred choice for new constructions and modernization of electric steel mills (Vervacke and Fehn, 1994).

The task of lowering energy consumption is particularly valid for the modern UHP electric-arc furnaces. Indeed, the utilization of water cooled elements has been applied in electric-arc furnaces for long time (e.g., electrical feeders, electrodes), but the development of UHP furnaces in these last years has made compulsory the cooling of the furnace wall at least, due to the significant wear of refractory lining. Independently of any possible recovery of the water thermal energy, there is the possibility of an energy saving in the water cooled UHP furnaces, since the saving due to more speedy melting and refining is always higher than the additional losses owing to cooling. As an example, Ameling et al. (1983) reported a case with additional losses of 10 kWh/t and an energy saving of 100 kWh/t. However, it is convenient also to recover energy from the necessary cooling of these furnaces. It should be mentioned that only those parts of the furnace can be cooled which do not come into contact with the steel.

In the absence of suitable measures, UHP furnaces can cause the following pollution kinds: (i) Thermal pollution of wastewater. (ii) Air pollution by primary and secondary waste gas. (iii) Very high noise pollution, especially during meltdown both in the works and outside the works. Indeed, A-weighted sound levels until 120 dB at 5 m from the furnace wall in AC furnaces and slightly lower in recent DC furnaces have been recorded.

In the modern electric-arc furnaces, there is a limited use of practically pure oxygen, both alone or in association with natural gas. In connection with this technology, the automatic regulation of furnace pressure has proved to be convenient (Stockmeyer et al., 1990; Köhle, 1995). In these cases the exergy of oxygen can be calculated assuming as reference species oxygen at his conventional mean partial pressure in the atmosphere (20.39 kPa), according to what is reported in subsection 2.2.

10.4 DIFFERENT KINDS OF COOLING SYSTEMS

As in various other papers (Bredehöft et al., 1986; Scholz and Reiners, 1986; Brod et al., 1989; Bisio and Farina, 1990), it is possible to distinguish three kinds of electric-arc furnace plant cooling, each one with its characteristics.

(i) *Cold cooling* ("Kaltkühlung") (Ameling, 1981; Altfeld and Schneider, 1982; Fett et al., 1982; Fett et al., 1993). The water operates at temperatures of 35-60 °C and at pressures of about 3 bar and must be partially softened. Heat transfer is obtained by convection and subcooled boiling with water velocity of about 1 m/s. The maximum heat flux amounts to 2100 kW/m^2 with steel cooling elements and to 6000 kW/m^2 with copper elements.

Cold cooling was initially applied to all kinds of electric-arc furnace cooling and it is still the unique system applied in some plants. In all the furnaces, it is always used for the following refrigerated parts: electrical feeders, supporting arms, electrodes, furnace working door and others.

The water is usually refrigerated by means of a cooling tower to avoid consumptions, almost everywhere unacceptable. Only in a few cases there is the possibility of particular applications of the recovered thermal energy: e.g., for the evaporation of liquid nitrogen, hydrogen and methane, as examined in (Bisio and Benvenuto, 1993; Bisio et al., 1996).

The exergy factor is very low: usually $\theta \approx 0.06$.

(ii) *Warm cooling* ("Warmkühlung") (Noda et al., 1981; Ottmar et al., 1983; Ameling et al., 1986a). The water operates at temperatures of 100-130 °C and at pressures of about 8 bar and must be totally softened. Heat transfer is obtained by convection and subcooled boiling with water velocity and maximum heat flux equal to those of the previous case.

The use of warm cooling is mandatory for the cooling of the furnace wall in correspondence to the electrodes (the so called "hot spots"); in addition, it is sometimes used also for the cooling of the whole furnace wall, the furnace roof and the waste gas.

The heated water can be used in a closed circuit for space heating and other low-temperature applications.

The exergy is higher than in the previous case, but it is low: usually $\theta \approx 0.15$.

(iii) *Evaporative cooling* ("Verdampfungskühlung") (Zimmermann et al., 1981; Bettzieche et al., 1984; Nagel and Gierig, 1984; Pöttken and Voigt, 1985; Ameling et al., 1986b; Unger et al., 1986; Becker and Hammer, 1986; Becker and Hammer, 1986/87; Andritzke et al., 1987). The water-steam system operates at temperatures of 192-264 °C and at pressures of 13 - 50 bar. Feed water must satisfy the regulations for boiler water. Heat transfer is obtained by nucleate boiling with water velocity of about 3 m/s. The maximum heat flux amounts to 930 kW/m^2 with steel refrigerating elements. It is impossible to use copper elements owing to their low mechanical resistance and very low chemical resistance to boiler feed water.

Evaporative cooling is generally applied for the cooling of the furnace wall, with the exclusion of the "hot spots", and sometimes for the cooling of the furnace roof and the waste gas.

The produced steam, especially at higher pressures, is usually utilized for electric power generation or it is brought into the steam network at medium pressure of the works.

The exergy factor depends upon the characteristics of the steam; for saturated steam at 30 bar, one has: $\theta \approx 0.41$.

It must be remarked that, apart from the exergy value, the recovered energy has a very different worth according to the works with which the recovery system is integrated; the existence or not in the above works of other low temperature recoveries is the discriminating element.

10.5 HEAT TRANSFER IN ELECTRIC-ARC FURNACES

10.5.1 Energy Transfer of an AC Electric Arc

Theoretical model to describe the energy transfer of an AC electric arc are only approximate (Strachan and Barrault, 1976; Ramakrishnan et al., 1978; Ushio et al., 1981; Szekely et al., 1983). Experimental data for a free-burning arc are reported in Fig. 10.2 (Jordan et al., 1970; Kruger et al., 1998). By free-burning arcs, 10 to 15% of the energy is transferred to the furnace wall and 5 to 10% to the furnace roof. About half furnace surface is arranged for hot spots.

The actual fluid flow within the molten steel bath is caused by a number of driving forces, which include the electromagnetic-force field, generated by the arc; thermal natural convection due to the temperature differences in the melt (the center core where the arc impinges is obviously hotter than the region near the wall), and the interaction between the plasma jet and the bath.

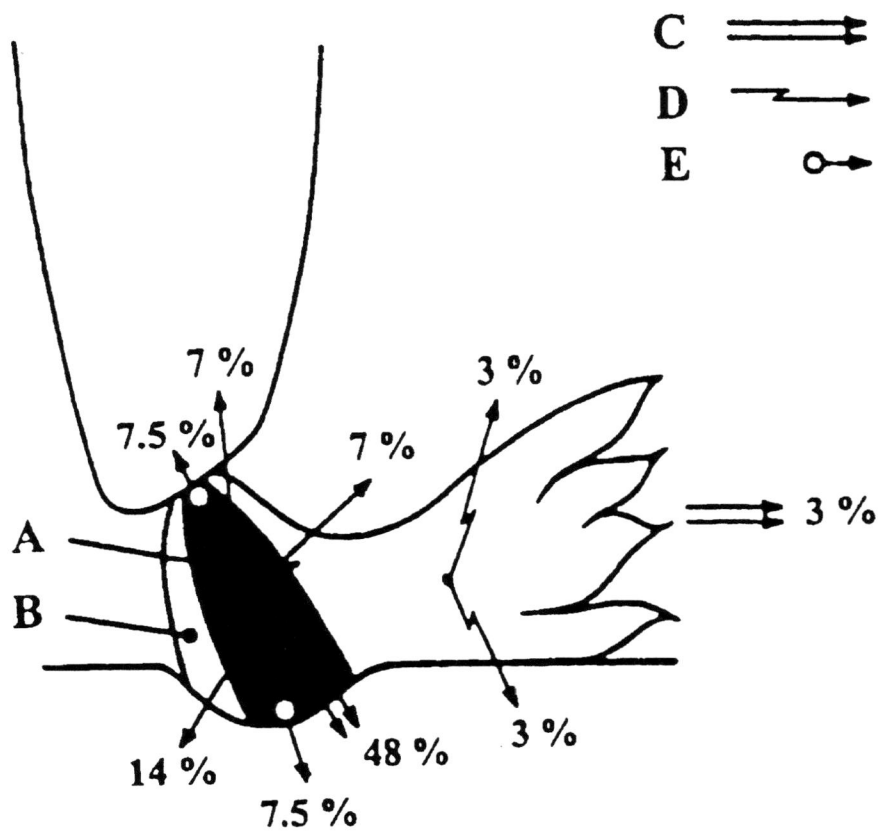

Fig. 10.2. Energy transfer of a free-burning AC electric arc: (A) electric arc; (B) flame; (C) convection; (D) radiation; (E) electrode-effects.

10.5.2 Thermal Transmission from Outer Wall of Refrigerating Elements to Water

Steel or copper are the materials of the electric arc furnace refrigerating elements. Fig. 10.3 shows the temperature gradients in the plain wall (A) and in the tube wall (B) for steel (k = 30 W m^{-1} K^{-1}) and copper (k = 320 W m^{-1} K^{-1}) with a heat flux per unit area of (Q_A = 0.2 MW/m^2). In both cases a thickness of (h_r = 10 mm) is assumed, in the second case the interior diameter is 60 mm.

It is to be remarked that the bending influence is limited in the present case (relatively small thickness) and then reference can be generally made to the plain plate case. On the contrary, the influence of the wall material on the temperature value of the external surface is considerable.

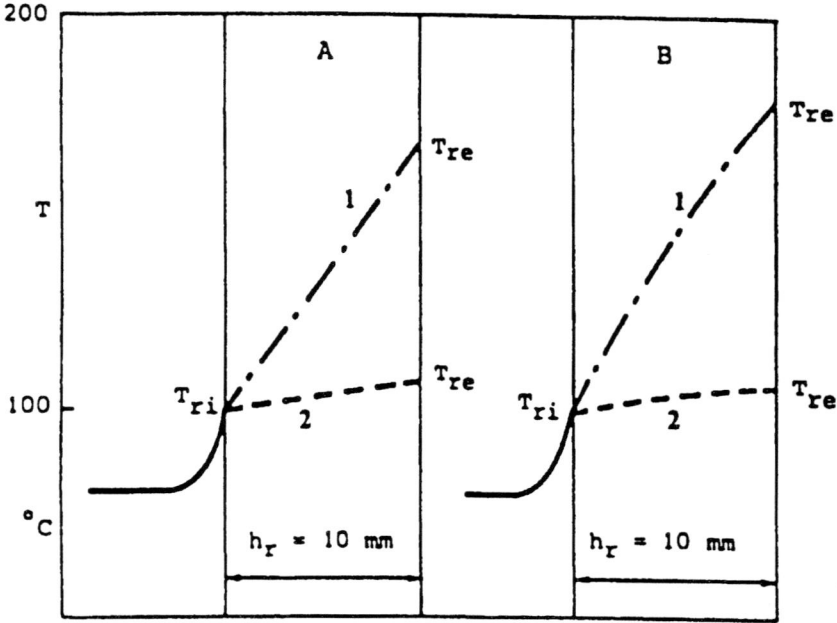

Fig. 10.3. Temperature variations in the plain wall (A) and in the tube wall (B) for steel (1) ($k = 30$ W m^{-1} K^{-1}) and copper (2) ($k = 320$ W m^{-1} K^{-1}) with heat flux per unit area $Q_A = 0.2$ MW/m^2.

10.5.3 Thermal transmission from the Furnace Inside to the External Wall of Refrigerating Elements

If one considers a furnace with the internal wall entirely covered by cooling boxes, heat is transferred to wall by radiation from three sources: (a) from the bath surface which is covered by slag at temperature of 1600°C; (b) from the bath surface which is free from slag at temperature of 1720°C; (c) from the electric arcs. In the range of technical interest, i.e. for temperature values of the external surface of the refrigerating elements $T_{re} \leq 350$°C, heat flux per unit area is practically independent of T_{re} and has the following approximated values:

(i) 0.2 MW/m^2 in zones which are limitedly influenced by electric arcs,
(ii) 2 MW/m^2 in the area face to face with the electrodes ("hot spots").

Really, the refrigerating elements cover themselves by solid slag until a thickness that has a temperature equal to that of slag melting, T_{ms}. Slag thickness can be determined by the relation:

$$Q_A = [T_{ms} - (T_i - T_o)/2]/[(1/\alpha) + (h_r/k_r) + (h_s/k_s)], \tag{10.1}$$

where:
k_r thermal conductivity of refrigerating element,
k_s thermal conductivity of solid slag,

T_i	water inlet temperature,
T_o	water outlet temperature,
α	water heat transfer coefficient with the interior pipe wall,
h_r	thickness of refrigerating pipe,
h_s	thickness of solid slag on refrigerating pipe.

Gradients of temperatures T_{ri} and T_{re} (both for steel (1) and copper (2) tube) and gradients of the slag layer solidified on a tube wall vs applied heat flux per unit area Q_A are shown in Fig. 10.4, assuming $\alpha = 10000$ W/(m² K).

In the zones where bath radiation prevails ($Q_A \approx 0.2$ MW/m²) one has $h_s \approx 10$ mm, $T_{re} \approx 100°C$ for copper tube and $T_{re} \approx 120°C$ for steel tube. In the "hot spots" zone it would follow $h_s \approx 2$ mm, $T_{re} \approx 250°C$ for copper tube and $T_{re} \approx 1000°C$ for steel tube; the last value is unacceptable and then in this zone the use of copper tubes is mandatory.

10.5.4 Subcooled Boiling

Boiling beginning can take place without the mean fluid temperature reaching the phase change temperature. When subcooled boiling takes place, it is necessary to control that critical heat flux is not approached.

Both subcooled boiling beginning and critical heat flux can be determined only experimentally in a valid way.

10.5.5 Maximum Critical Flux Per Unit Area

Maximum critical flux per unit area depends upon various elements; as a first choice, the following values can be assumed:

(i) "Cold cooling" with water velocity of ≈ 1 m/s: ≈ 2 MW/m² with steel refrigerating elements and ≈ 6 MW/m² with copper refrigerating elements.
(ii) "Warm cooling" with water velocity of ≈ 2 m/s: ≈ 2 MW/m² with steel refrigerating elements and ≈ 6 MW/m² with copper refrigerating elements.
(iii) "Evaporative cooling" with water velocity of ≈ 3 m/s: ≈ 0.9 MW/m² with steel refrigerating elements.

It is to be remarked that a great amount of information regarding the critical heat flux is given in literature. However, this information varies within wide limits. It is therefore important, before applying any empirical equation, to know exactly the marginal conditions involved, and to check its applicability to the problem under consideration. In view of this imponderability, an adequate safety margin should be ensured in any case. Examples of empirical equations for the pool and film boiling ranges are given by Scholz and Reiners (1986).

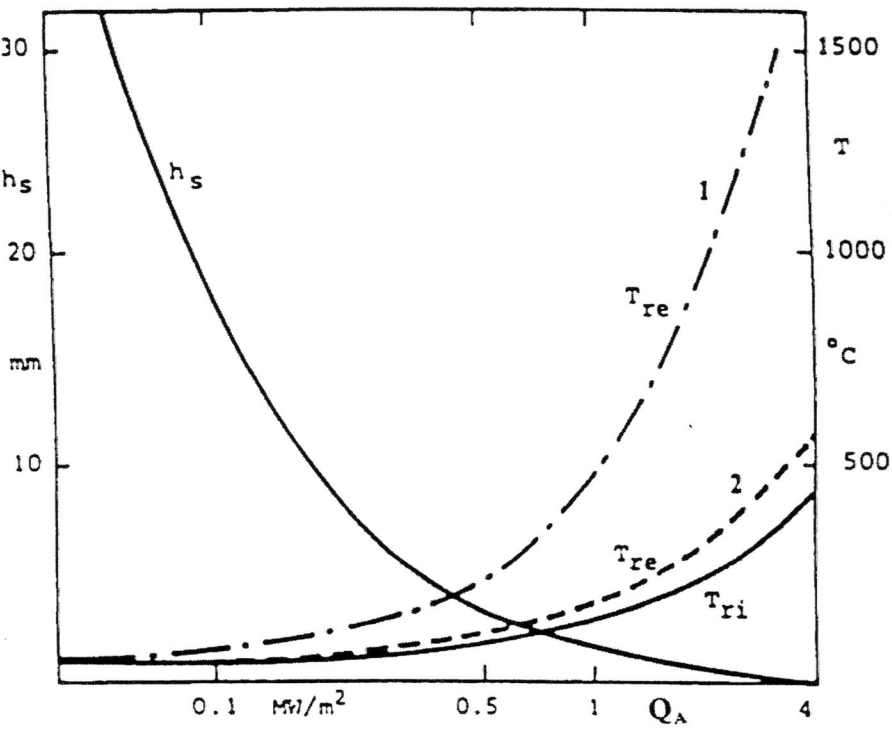

Fig. 10.4. Variations of temperatures T_{ri} and T_{re} (both for steel (1) and copper (2) tube) and variations of the slag layer solidified on a tube wall vs applied heat flux per unit area Q_A.

10.6 STEADY STATE AND TIME VARIATIONS

10.6.1 Steady State Dependence upon the Melting Temperature of Slag

The melting temperature of slag depends upon its composition; generally it is within 1300 and 1500°C. Figure 10.5 (derived from Kruger et al., 1998) shows the thermal power of a furnace refrigerating system vs the melting temperature of the slag. The variation of thermal power is very high and then it is important to obtain the highest possible melting temperature. This is particular important when there is no energy saving in the refrigerating system, but it is useful also in the case of evaporative cooling, since in any case the exergy factor of the recovered energy is much lower than one.

In a cold or warm cooling, if the volume flow rate of water increases, the water outlet temperature goes down; however, the thermal power of the refrigerating system remains practically constant.

The thickness of the accreted slag layer on the refrigerated sidewall when arcs are completely covered by slag depends upon the melting temperature and thermal conductivity of the slag (Fig. 10.6). As can be seen by Figure, the slag layer varies about from 25 to 100 mm as its melting temperature varies from 1250 to 1500°C and increases slightly as the thermal conductivity increases.

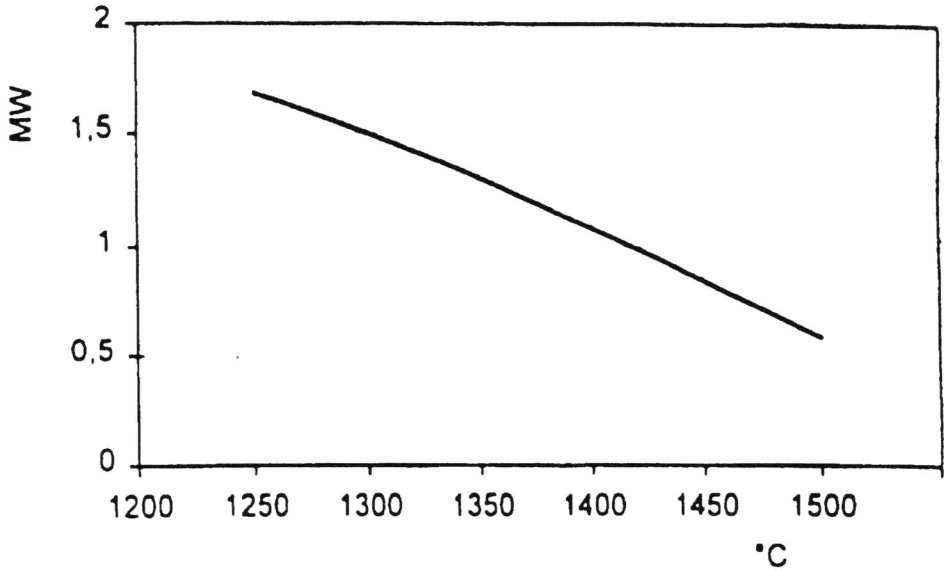

Fig. 10.5. Thermal power of a furnace refrigerating system vs the melting temperature of the slag.

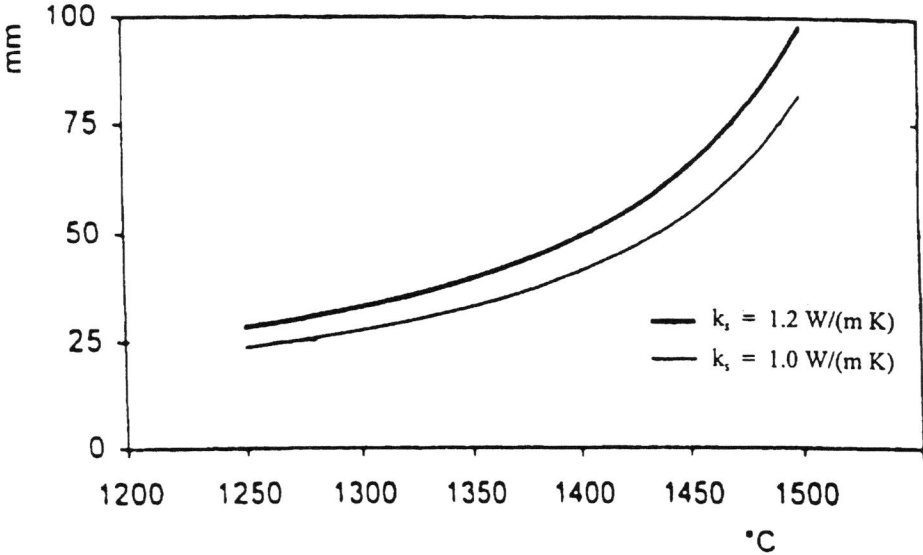

Fig. 10.6. Thickness of the accreted slag layer on the refrigerated sidewall when arcs are completely covered by slag vs the melting temperature of the slag.

The slag layer depends slightly upon the parameters of the refrigerating system. Copper pipes entail an increase of the slag layer of about 0.2 mm in comparison with steel pipes. The doubling of water heat transfer coefficient from 12500 W/(m² K) to 25000 W/(m² K) entails an increase of the slag layer only of about 0.1 mm.

10.6.2 Time Variations

What has been said in the previous subsection is applicable when the arc is totally plunged in the slag. However, sometimes free-burning takes place and the arc radiates a remarkable part of its energy directly to the furnace wall.

Figure 10.7A shows the melting of the slag layer on the refrigerated sidewall for three values (10%, 12.5%, and 15%) of that part of the electric-arc energy which is transferred to the furnace wall. The slag layer thickness on the cooling system is reduced to a value of about 2 mm in a time from 1.5 min to 2.5 min. Figure 10.7B shows that in the same time a remarkable increase in the outlet temperature of the cooling system (Kruger et al., 1998). A Figure that shows the influence of the foamy slag on the efficiency of the energy transmission from the electrode to the metal bath is reported from Borowski (1998).

Consequently, there is the necessity of a governing system that reduces electrical power when free burning takes place.

A dynamic melting control system for AC electric arc furnaces was developed by Knoop et al. (1997). The system acts as a higher control loop above the voltage tap and electrodes, monitoring the electric variables and the thermal load of the wall panels. In case of thermal overload, arc radiation onto the affected wall area is reduced by operating the furnace asymmetrically. This is achieved by decreasing the transformer voltage of the affected phase, when the voltage taps of the three phases can be chosen independently. Unsymmetrical impedance setpoints for the electrode controller also help to reduce arc radiation locally. Furthermore, in periods without thermal wall load, the system modifies the impedance set-points to control the currents and thus power input at their optimal values.

According to Knoop et al. (1997), during ten months of testing at the arc furnace in the Bochum steel plant of Krupp Thyssen Nirosta, productivity increased by 3 - 8%. Consumption of refractory gunning material was reduced by approx. 10 %.

Figure 10.8 shows the slag accretion on a water-cooled temperature after covering free-burning arcs. One can remark that the steady state value of the slag layer is reached after about 30 min. Then, free-burning arcs must be avoided as much as possible.

10.7 POSSIBILITIES OF REDUCING NOISE AND AIR POLLUTION

Current pollution control requirements in all industrialized countries for new and existing electric-arc furnace shops demand effective capture and collections of primary and secondary fume emissions during all phases of furnace operation. At the same time, substantial reductions of the noise levels caused by electric-arc furnace shops are required both in the works and outside the works. The noise source can be slightly reduced (4 dB) by the use of D.C. (instead of A.C.) electric power. To reduce fume and noise emissions, the clearance between electrodes and the corresponding holes in the furnace roof has been reduced, evidently with the respect of other technological demands. However, the devices that can resolve both noise and air pollution are various kinds of sound-absorbing encasing of the furnaces; obviously, there is the necessity in these enclosures of the presence of some movable elements for the transits of materials and equipment. The topic has been considered by some authors, e.g., Grubert et al. (1984), Neugebauer et al. (1988); Le Louer and Engler (1988), Brod et al. (1989); Haering et al. (1989), Bisio (1996b).

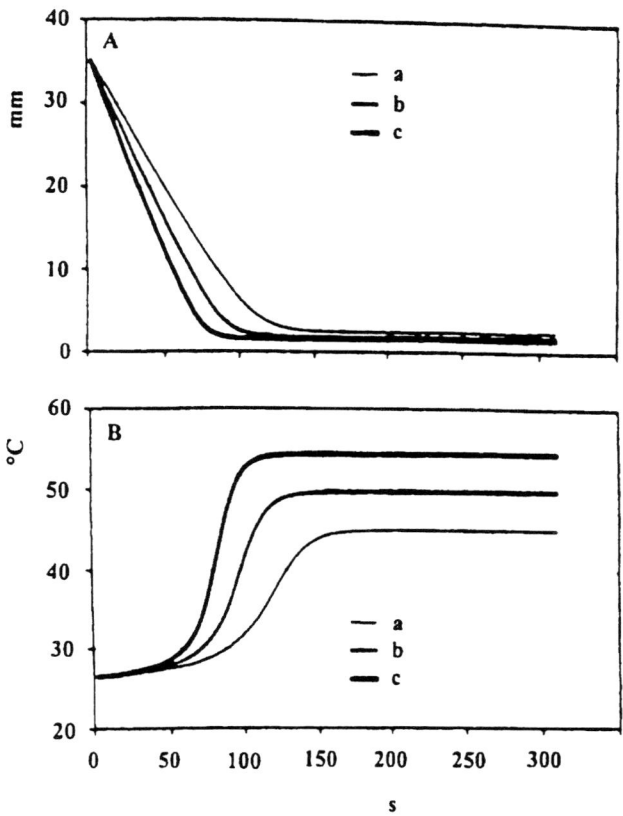

Fig. 10.7. Behavior of a water-cooled sidewall when arcs suddenly burn freely: (A) slag layer thickness on the cooling system vs time; (B) water outlet temperature vs time; a=10%, b=12.5%, c=15% of the electric-arc energy.

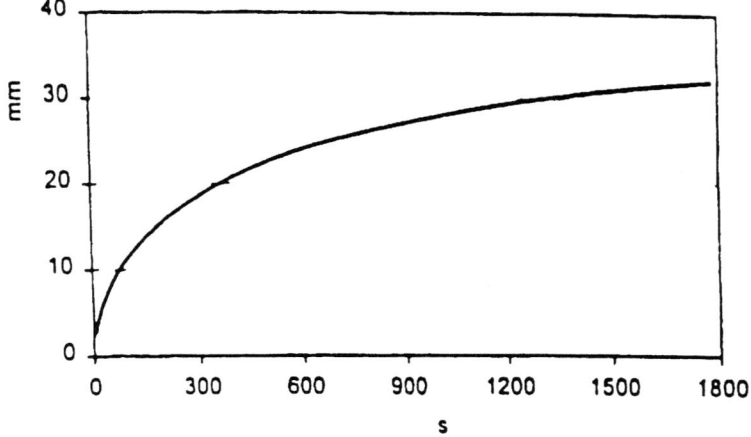

Fig. 10.8. Slag accretion on a water-cooled temperature after covering free-burning arcs: slag layer thickness accretion vs time.

The several enclosures can be grouped in three types:

(A) The first solution consists in the almost total closing of the furnace bay by sound absorbing and insulating walls and roof. In the contiguous casting bay, connected with the furnace bay through sliding doors, it is possible to obtain a reduction of the maximum A-weighted sound level of 20-30 dB. A better acoustical insulation is useless, owing to the presence of other noise sources in the casting bay. In the working floor, the noise reduction is about 10 dB and thus the single working locations in the furnace bay must be acoustically insulated in a separate way.

(B) In the second type of solution, the acoustically insulated volume is more reduced and comprises a single furnace and the overhanging volume. The charging crane can enter this volume, after the shifting of some movable parts of the enclosure. This solution, in comparison with the first, allows a remarkable noise reduction also in the furnace bay, without other local insulations.

(C) In the third type, the acoustically insulated volume is reduced to the minimum possible around the furnace; also in this case there are some suitable movable parts of the enclosure.

The types (B) and (C) are the most used; two enclosures of these types, and dealt with by Haering et al. (1989), are shown in Fig. 10.9.

In addition to the noise reduction, the enclosures of the types (B) and (C) allow the complete control of dust and fume with lower volume suction flows. Haering et al. (1989) quote a case in which the investment costs for the construction of the enclosure and of the filters for combined primary and secondary emissions suitable for a volume flow rate of 300000 m^3/h were less than 2/3rds of the costs of direct extraction with roof hoods. However, the above-mentioned advantages have to be balanced against the possible hampering of meltshop operations and reduced access around the furnace.

10.8 LAYOUT OF A MODERN UHP ELECTRIC-ARC FURNACE

A 150 t UHP electric-arc furnace is schematically shown in Fig. 10.10 (Fett et al., 1993); by a dot and dash line one indicates the system boundary for which enthalpy and exergy flows are considered in the next section.

Boiler water is delivered to the pressurized tank E, which is used as a steam-water separator-reservoir. By the pump F1 the water is delivered to the wall refrigerating elements located above the liquid steel level. The mass flow rate must reach a value such that the steam-water mixture has a dryness fraction not higher than 0.04, to avoid any danger of burn-out. By the pump F2, the water is delivered to the primary waste gas refrigerant G for steam production.

A circuit (O-P) with water having an outlet temperature of about 130°C is used for the cooling of the roof and the wall parts corresponding to the "hot spots", where there is the possibility of thermal fluxes higher than those allowable for nucleate boiling.

We remark that water-cooled elements have been recently applied also in areas below bath liquid level (Ameling, 2000c).

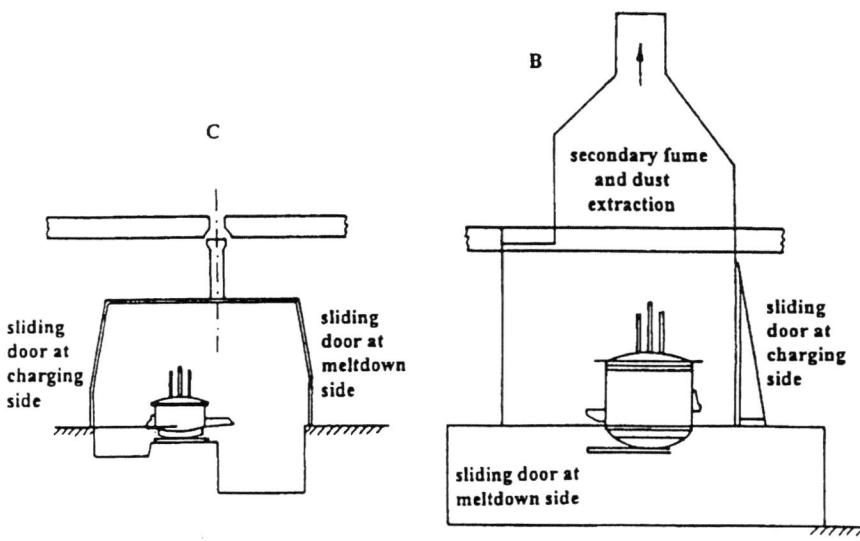

Fig. 10.9. Layout of two kinds of encasing (B and C) of UHP electric-arc furnaces.

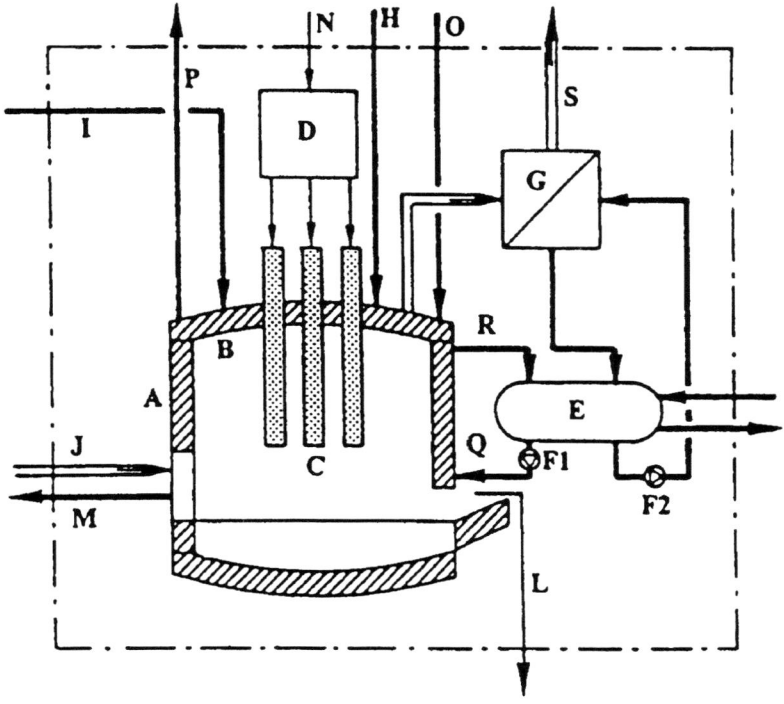

Fig. 10.10. Material and energy flows in a UHP electric-arc furnace: (A) furnace wall; (B) furnace roof; (C) electrodes; (D) transformer; (E) steam-water separator-reservoir; (F1, F2) circulation pumps; (G) primary waste gas refrigerant; (H) scrap inlet; (I) inlet of additives: lime, limestone, coal, ore; (J) oxygen inlet; (L) steel outlet; (M) slag outlet; (N) electric power feed; (O) water inlet for warm cooling; (P) hot water outlet; (Q) water inlet for evaporative cooling; (R) steam-water mixture outlet; (S) refrigerated primary waste gas outlet.

Two other circuits (not represented in the Figure for simplicity's sake) with water having an outlet temperature of about 60°C (and then with very low possibility to be used) are employed for the cooling of the electrodes C, transformer D and electrical feeders.

One notes that the whole furnace is surrounded by a sound absorbing-insulating enclosure as described in the preceding section.

10.9 ANALYSIS OF ENTHALPY AND EXERGY FLOWS

Enthalpy and exergy flows are considered for the electric-arc furnace schematically represented in Fig. 10.10. Percentage enthalpy flows are shown in Fig. 10.11. One notes that in correspondence of an inlet electric power of 100%, there is additional inlet enthalpy owing to electrode consumption, exothermic chemical reactions in the liquid bath and CO post-combustion of 40.8%. As outlet enthalpy there is -86.7% for liquid steel, -5.7% for slag, -2.1% for endothermic chemical reactions in the liquid bath, -6.0% for cooling water at low temperature, -6.1% for cooling water at medium temperature, -7.9 for steam, -26.3% for waste heat through the waste gas and the wall. One can define energy efficiency, η', as the ratio of outlet enthalpy flows, with the exclusion of waste heat, to inlet enthalpy flows. Then, one obtains:

$$\eta' = 114.5/140.8 = 0.813 \,. \tag{10.2}$$

Instead, if one considers the enthalpy flows relative to slag and cooling water at low temperature as not utilized, energy efficiency, η'', is given by:

$$\eta'' = 102.8/140.8 = 0.730 \,. \tag{10.3}$$

Percentage exergy flows are shown in Fig. 10.11. One notes that in correspondence of an inlet electric power of 100%, there is additional inlet exergy owing to electrode consumption, exothermic chemical reactions in the liquid bath, pure oxygen inlet and CO post-combustion of 35.1%. As outlet exergy, there is -63.7% for liquid steel, -4.3% for slag, -2.1% for endothermic chemical reactions in the liquid bath, -0.4% for cooling water at low temperature, -0.9% for cooling water at medium temperature, -3.3 for steam, -60.4% for exergy destruction owing to internal irreversibilities and waste heat through the waste gas and the wall.

The refrigerant fluids have the following exergy factors θ:

(i) cooling water at low temperature: $\theta = 0.063$;
(ii) cooling water at medium temperature: $\theta = 0.150$;
(iii) saturated steam at 30 bar: $\theta = 0.409$.

The following merit factors Γ can be assumed:

(i) carbon: $\Gamma = 0.72$;
(ii) oils and fats: $\Gamma = 0.7$;
(iii) CO in the waste gas: $\Gamma = 0.52$.

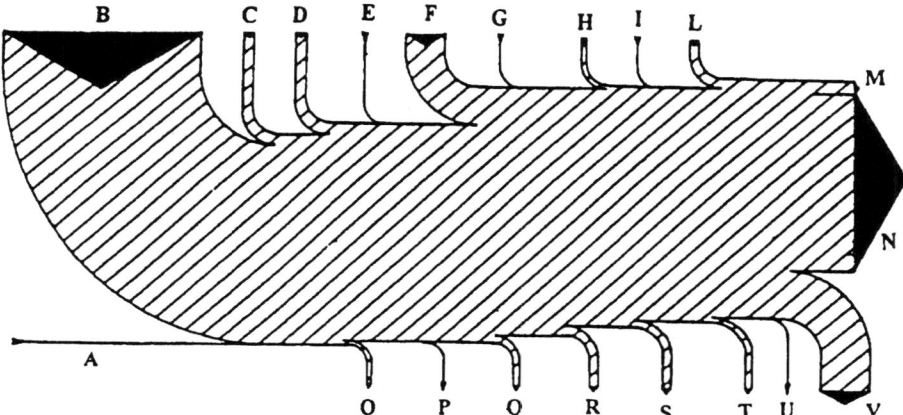

Fig. 10.11. Percentage enthalpy flows in a UHP electric-arc furnace: (A) scrap: 0%; (B) electric power: 100%; (C) electrode consumption: 5.4%; (D) oil and fat combustion: 7.6%; (E) oxygen: 0%; (F) reaction enthalpy in silicon oxidation: 19.7%; (G) reaction enthalpy in carbon oxidation: 1.2%; (H) reaction enthalpy in chrome oxidation: 2.2%; (I) "false" air: 0%; (L) reaction enthalpy in CO post-combustion: 4.7%; (M) slag: -5.7%; (N) liquid steel: -86.7 %; (O) reaction enthalpy in deacidification: -2.1%; (P) cooling water of electrodes: -1.8%; (Q) cooling water of transformer and electric feeders: -4.2%; (R) cooling water of roof and part of wall: -6.1%; (S) steam from part of wall: -4.3%; (T) steam from waste gas cooling: -3.6%; (U) waste heat to environment: -1.2%; (V) waste gas: -25.1%.

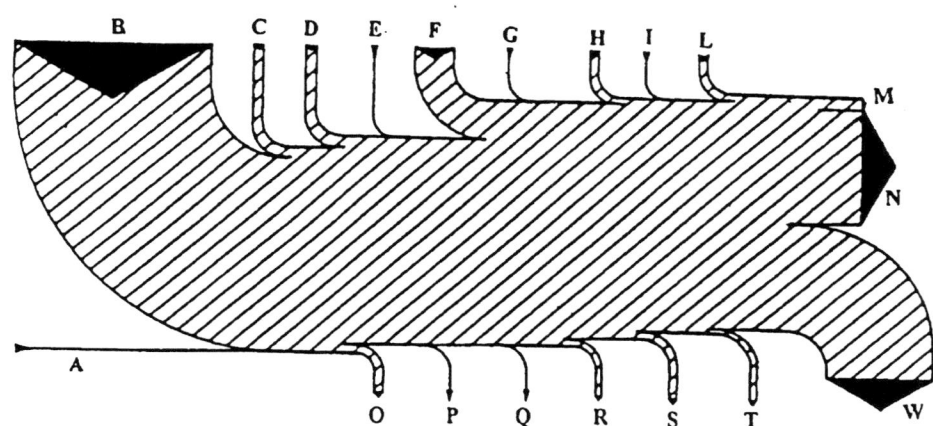

Fig. 10.12. Percentage exergy flows in a UHP electric-arc furnace: (A) scrap: 0%; (B) electric power: 100%; (C) electrode consumption: 3.9%; (D) oil and fat combustion: 5.5%; (E) oxygen: 0.5%; (F) reaction exergy in silicon oxidation: 19.7%; (G) reaction exergy in carbon oxidation: 0.9%; (H) reaction exergy in chrome oxidation: 2.2%; (I) "false" air: 0%; (L) reaction exergy in CO post-combustion: 2.4%; (M) slag: -4.3%; (N) liquid steel: -63.7%; O) reaction exergy in deacidification: -2.1%; P) cooling water of electrodes: -0.1%; (Q) cooling water of transformer and electric feeders: -0.3%; (R) cooling water of roof and part of wall: -0.9 %; (S) steam from part of wall: -1.8%; (T) steam from waste gas cooling: -1.5%; (W) exergy destroyed: -60.4%.

As reference species for the calculation of the injected oxygen exergy, the oxygen in the atmosphere is assumed with its conventional mean partial pressure (20.39 kPa), according to what is reported in subsection 2.4.

One can define exergy efficiency, Φ', as the ratio of outlet exergy flows, with the exclusion obviously of exergy loss flows, to inlet exergy flows. Then, one obtains:

$$\Phi' = 74.7/135.1 = 0.553 \ . \tag{10.4}$$

Instead, if one considers the exergy flows relative to slag and cooling water at low temperature as not utilized, exergy efficiency, Φ'', is given by:

$$\Phi'' = 70.0/135.1 = 0.518 \ . \tag{10.5}$$

This last value is the more meaningful owing to the following reasons: (i) Only exergy efficiency considers the operative value (and then also the economical one) of the various energies. (ii) The possibilities of utilizing the low exergy value of the thermal energy of cooling water at low temperature are limited as said in section 3. (iii) Notwithstanding the high exergy value of the slag thermal energy, the possibilities of energy recovery are scarce, owing to notable technological problems (Bisio, 1997b).

However, an only thermodynamic optimization is generally not sufficient to determine optimal solution. It is convenient to remember the statement of Szargut (1967 and 1971) on the thermodynamic value, and not also directly economical, of the exergy. At the same time, Bejan (1982), dealing with the optimal economical solution, notes that, even if thermodynamic and economical optima do not coincide, they tend to approach themselves as exergy costs increase.

10.10 FINAL REMARKS

The different cooling systems of electric-arc furnaces (and in analogous way of other similar plants) can be distinguished among them in the more meaningful way on the basis of the water subcooling value at the refrigerating element inlet: $\approx 100°C$ in "cold cooling" system, $\approx 50°C$ in "warm cooling", $\approx 5°C$ in "evaporative cooling".

Evaporative cooling is the system that allows the maximum exergy recovery, especially if pressure is raised up to that value that allows also the maximum critical heat flux: ≈ 70 bar. Employing this pressure value, the operative value of recovered energy is ≈ 0.48. Higher investment costs (compared with a cold water cooling system with heat transfer to atmosphere via closed cooling towers) and higher maintenance costs of the evaporative cooling system are to be compared to the significant credit for the exported steam. If need of steam is existing, pay back times of less than one year are possible.

Energy and exergy analyses have been carried out in the paper for a modern AC UHP furnace, considering the maximum possible energy recovery.

The energy efficiency value ≈ 0.81 is obtained, if one considers all the outlet flows as usable, obviously save the waste heat through the furnace walls and the gases outgoing into the atmosphere. Instead of the above value, the value ≈ 0.73 is got, if one considers also the enthalpy flows corresponding to the slag and cooling water at low temperature as not usable.

The exergy efficiency value ≈ 0.55 is obtained, if one considers the entire outlet (and not destroyed) exergy flows as usable. Instead of the above value, the value ≈ 0.52 is got, if one considers also the exergy flows corresponding to the slag and cooling water at low temperature as not usable.

Apart from the exergy value, the warm cooling recovery has a very different worth according to the works with which the recovery system is integrated; the existence or not in the above works of other low temperature recoveries is the discriminating element.

In the absence of suitable measures, UHP furnaces can cause the following pollution kinds: (i) thermal pollution of wastewater, (ii) air pollution by primary and secondary waste gas, and (iii) very high noise pollution.

The use of suitable sound-absorbing encasing of the furnace united with energy recovery in closed circuits of the cooling fluids allows the total elimination of thermal pollution of wastewater, a considerable reduction of air pollution and a very high reduction of noise pollution. From the acoustical point of view, the problem is reduced to that of other steel plants for people living near the works; only a convenient distance from the boundary of works can allow sound level values acceptable during night-time.

Chapter 11

ENERGY RECOVERY BY EVAPORATIVE COOLING IN SEVERAL PLANTS OF THE IRON AND STEEL INDUSTRY

11.1 GENERALITIES

Before the second world war, and more especially immediately after it, added momentum was given to the utilization of waste energy in German and Austrian steelworks by the ever-present shortage of inland fuels, and by the abnormal increase in fuel prices. When in 1957-58 this shortage of fuel, the chief obstacle to the expansion of steel production, had been overcome, a new factor was having an indirect bearing on energy economy of both countries, namely, the much stricter Government regulations with water and air pollution. Among other systems, this fact gave birth to a particular system of energy recovery, which was named "Heißkühlung". In this system, the open-cycle water, as a means for cooling metal parts at high temperatures of furnaces of several kinds, is substituted by closed cycle pressurized water, generally with steam production. In some cases, warm cooling plant operates by itself, even if included in the main plant, of which it allows the working, by cooling the main metal parts. More often, warm cooling operates in parallel with recovery boilers (utilizing waste gas of the main plants or other waste gas).

Three kinds of cooling are employed.

(i) *Cold cooling*. The water operates at temperatures of 35-50 °C and at pressures of 3 bar.
(ii) *Warm cooling*. The water operates at temperatures of 100-120 °C and at pressures of ≈ 8 bar.
(iii) *Evaporative cooling*. The water-steam system operates at temperatures of 192-264 °C and at pressures of 13-50 bar. The feed water must satisfy the regulation for boiling water.

In next subsections, the evaporative cooling in several plants of the iron and steel industry is synthetically analyzed. The evaporative cooling in electric-arc furnaces is examined with more details in section 12, considering at the same time the problems of energy recovery and of the pollution control.

11.2 "HEIßKÜHLUNG" IN SIEMENS-MARTIN OPEN-HEARTH FURNACES

This application is considered only for historical reasons, since Siemens-Martin furnaces are obsolete. As well known, in an open-hearth furnace several parts must be cooled: door frames, buckstays for supporting open-hearth vault, burners. In the past, it was usual to supply water with an inlet temperature of 15-21 °C and an increase of 12-20 °C before leaving the furnace. Most steelworks have to conserve water wherever possible, and then a recirculating system of some kind was generally used. A typical arrangement involves a storage tank, from which the water is gravity-fed to the furnaces and hence to a hot well. The water is then pumped to a cooling tower, from which it passes to a cold well, ready to be pumped again to the storage tank.

Since the actual furnace-operating temperature is about 1700-1800 °C, it is obvious that an increase in the working temperature of the cooling water of 200-250 °C would not affect the performance of the furnace coolers, since the relative temperature gradient is still considerable. This idea, although not new, was put into practice in Germany in 1950s, using a technique in which the heat normally lost in the furnace-cooling water was harnessed to produce steam and then generally electrical energy (Harnisch, 1953; Lardy, 1953; Poppe, 1953; Priester, 1954; Feltoe and Moreton, 1954; Wesemann, 1956; Pracht, 1956; Schemmann, 1957; Heil, 1957; Zur, 1957; Vonnemann, 1957; Bartu, 1958; Wesemann et al., 1963; Brooks and Gray, 1963; Kilby, 1963; Wesemann, 1963).

In Fig. 11.1, a layout of evaporative cooling by forced convection of an open-hearth furnace is represented. The circulating system is designed so that each door frame or buckstay cooler is, in effect, a small water-tube boiler of the forced-circulation type. Water, at the saturation temperature, corresponding to the pressure used (15-30 bar) is pumped from the boiler drum through the various furnace coolers, in which the evaporation enthalpy is absorbed. The resulting steam-water mixture (dryness fraction: $x = 0.04$) returns to the drum, where the steam separates and passes to a superheater, whilst the water, to which whatever make-up has been added, is again circulated around the coolers. The system is arranged so that in emergencies the boiler drum and circulating pumps can be automatically isolated, and straight-through cooling can be used. This would be necessary, for example, if the circulating pumps failed, or if pressure fell in the door frame owing to a fracture. This complication is regarded as one of the main disadvantages of the system, but, in fact, the high-pressure door frames are no more vulnerable to damage than the conventional type.

Figure 11.2 shows this system, when, in a more suitable way, it is operated in conjunction with a La Mont waste heat boiler, raising steam from the thermal energy of the furnace flue gases. This arrangement is particularly convenient, because the special boiler drum and circulating pumps do not have to be purchased solely for the furnace-cooling system.

With furnaces, in which only doors were cooled by open-cycle water owing to technological difficulties, the steam production has been ≈ 0.7 t/t_{steel}.

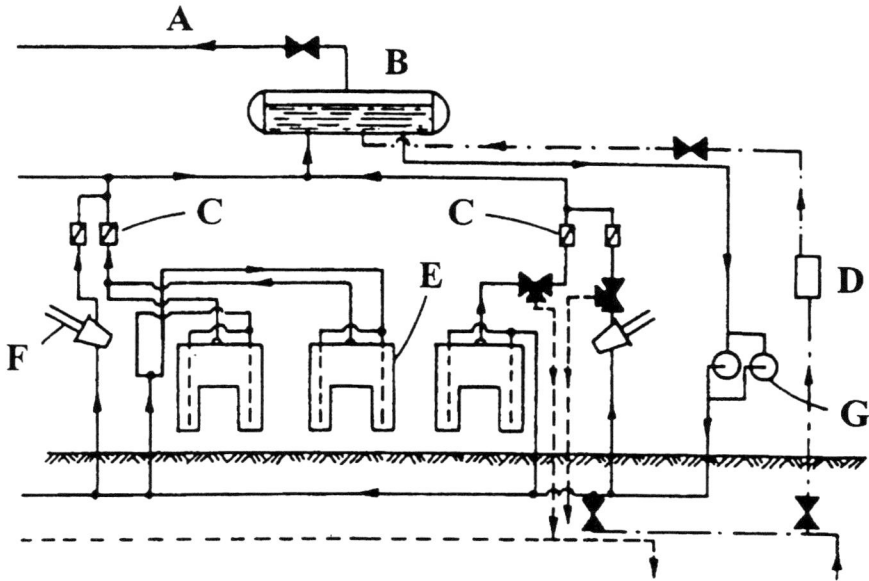

Fig. 11.1. Layout of an evaporative cooling by forced convection for a Siemens-Martin open-hearth furnace: (A) to steam power station; (B) boiler drum; (C) non-return valves; (D) feed-water plant; (E) door frames; (F) burners; (G) circulating pumps.

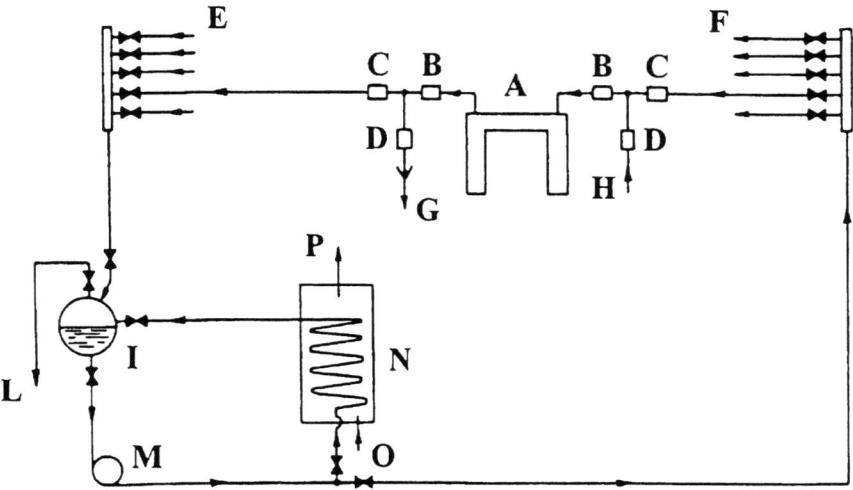

Fig. 11.2. Layout of an evaporative cooling by forced convection in conjunction with a waste heat La Mont boiler for a Siemens-Martin open-hearth: (A) furnace door frame, (B) non-return valves; (C) automatic valves that close on fall of pressure in door frame; (D) automatic valves that open on failure of circulating pump; (E) from other door frames; (F) to other door frames; (G) emergency cooling water drain; (H) emergency cooling water inlet; (I) boiler drum; (L) to superheater; (M) circulating pump; (N) La Mont boiler; (O) hot gases from furnace; (P) waste gases to chimney.

Some evaporative cooling plants have been realized also by natural circulation at low pressure (about 1.5) as that represented in Fig. 11.3. The water from the boiler drum goes through the pipes (C) and (D) into the lower parts of the cooling elements and through the pipes (B) returns to boiler drum by natural convection. The tube (F) is used as an exhaust pipe in case of an increase of the water level or pressure above the fixed values.

Owing to the low values of pressure, this steam can be utilized only for some auxiliary services, as for boiler degasers or for room heating.

These kinds of plants for open-hearth furnaces have rapidly developed in 1950s particularly in Germany and Austria; in 1960s, however, the oxygen converters caused the open-hearth to become obsolete.

11.3 "HEIßKÜHLUNG" IN BLAST FURNACES

Blast furnaces have the necessity of large flow rates of cooling for the wall fire-bricks and wind boxes. Also for blast furnaces, warm cooling plants have studied and realized especially in Germany (Wesemann, 1956; Schilcher, 1956; Vonnemann, 1957; Nolzen, 1984). A layout of a plant of this kind, operating by natural circulation is represented in Fig. 11.4. The working pressure has been usually chosen not higher than 3-4 bar, owing to the necessity of never exceeding the blast-furnace interior pressure for safety reasons.

Consequently, only few plants of this type have been constructed for blast furnaces due to the difficulties of finding pressure uses for the recovered energy. Greater possibilities of using this energy may result from raising the steam and temperature to higher levels by means of compression.

A layout of a possible application is presented in Fig. 11.5 (which reproduces Fig. 6.2).

11.4 "HEIßKÜHLUNG" IN PUSHER-TYPE REHEAT FURNACES

The cooling plants applied in pusher-type reheat furnaces are more valid than those of the previous subsection are (Wesemann, 1956; Kilby, 1963; Wesemann, 1963; Andon'ev et al., 1974; Fontana et al., 1977; Pozzi, 1981; Klammer and Porst, 1981; Perin, 1983; Nolzen, 1984).

As is known, in these furnaces slabs are supported by skids, which must be necessarily cooled by circulation of water in their inner. It is easy the substitution of the open circuit water by a closed system with steam production. Pressures up to 50 bar have been applied and then there good possibilities of utilization.

Figure 11.6 represents the layout of an evaporative cooling plant connected with a waste heat boiler situated after the regenerators that, by waste gas, heat the air for the furnace. Skids are suitably insulated but, during the furnace operation, such insulation is worn out and then the steam production increases.

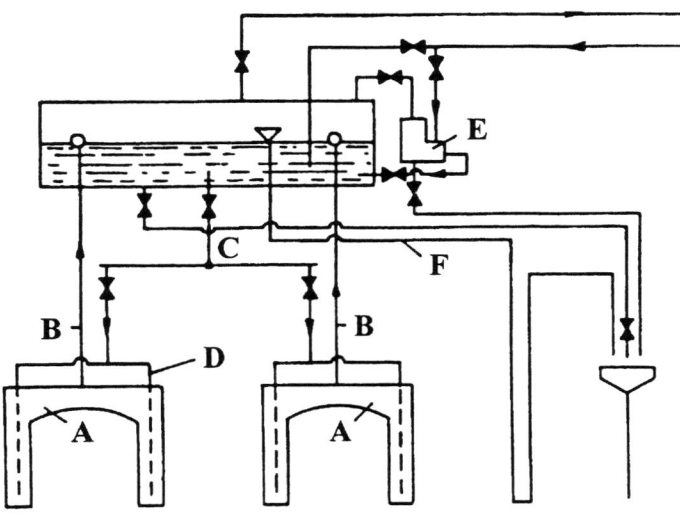

Fig. 11.3. Layout of an evaporative cooling by natural convection for a Siemens-Martin open-hearth furnace: (A) door frames; (B) ascent pipes; (C) and (D) descent pipes; (E) feed water regulator; (F) emergency discharge on water level or pressure increase above stated limits.

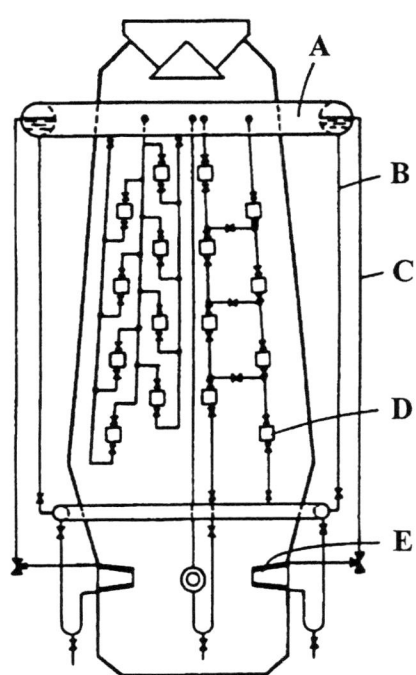

Fig. 11.4. Layout of an evaporative cooling by forced convection for a blast furnace: (A) ring boiler; (B) descent pipe; (C) ascent pipe; (D) cooling water boxes; (E) "hot wind" boxes.

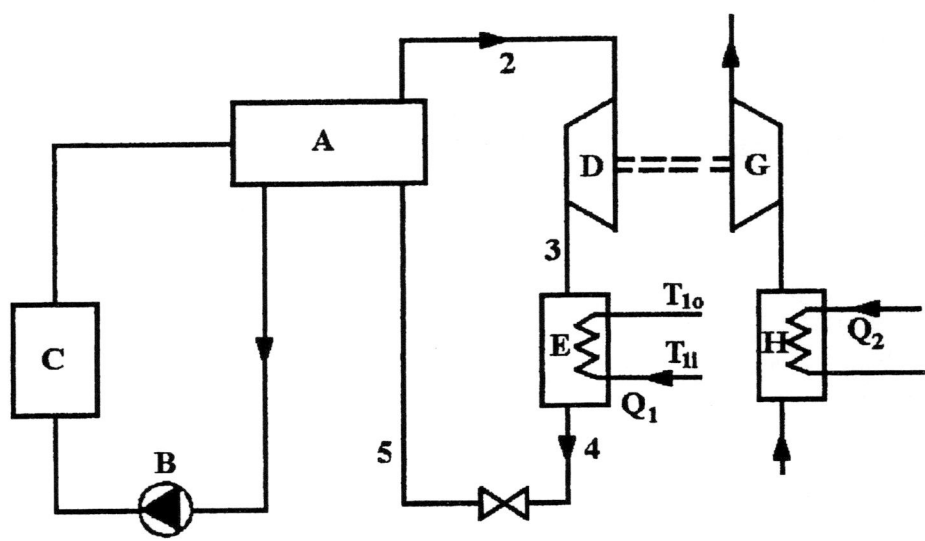

Fig. 11.5. Flowsheet for exploitation of vent steam by compression using NG expansion: (A) steam-water separator; (B) pump; (C) refrigerating elements of the blast furnace; (D) compressor; (E) heat exchanger; (F) throttling valve; (G) NG turbine; (H) NG heater.

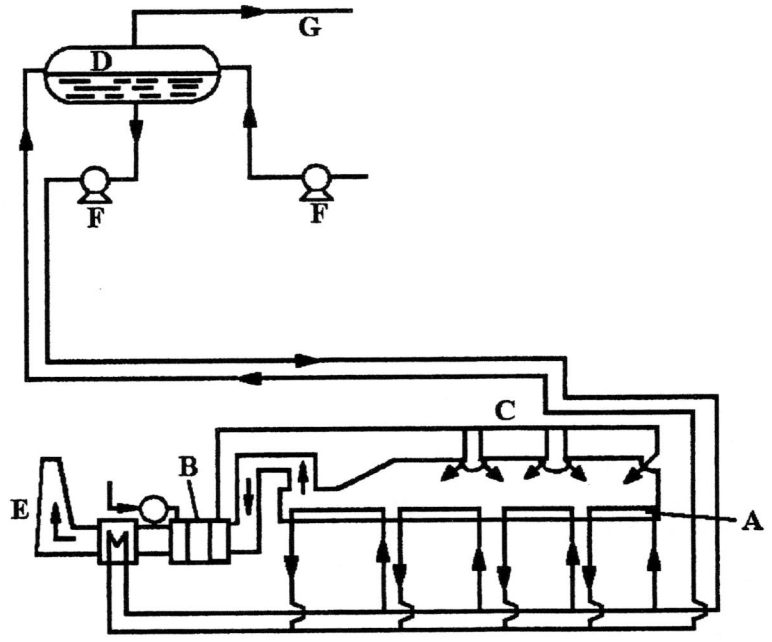

Fig. 11.6. Layout of an evaporative cooling by forced convection for a pusher-type reheat furnace. (A) skid; (B) recuperator; (C) combustion air; (D) waste-heat boiler; (E) stack; (F) pumps; (G) stack; (H) boiler drum.

11.5 "Heißkühlung" in Walking Beam Reheat Furnaces

Walking beam furnaces differ from pusher-type furnaces essentially as to the movement of the charge, which rests on fixed and of mobile skids alternatively. These, at regular intervals, lift and move forward all the pieces, which are placed in the furnace at a certain distance from each other. To obtain this cycle, the mobile skids are fixed to a frame located under the furnace chamber and supported by a set of wheels. The lower ones run, during the lifting and lowering stages, on inclined planes anchored to the foundations; the upper ones allow for the horizontal movement of the frame. Both movements are usually obtained by means of hydraulic cylinders connected to the mobile system.

The energy balance for a walking beam furnace is reported in Fig. 11.7. This furnace uses an evaporative cooling system that produces saturated steam at about 26 bar.

11.6 "Heißkühlung" in Continuous Casting Machines

The replacement of forced water cooling in a continuous casting machine by evaporative cooling enables the thermal energy of billet to be partially utilized, more uniform cooling to be obtained, the consumption of cooling water to be reduced and the service life to be increased.

One of the first evaporative secondary cooling was carried out on one strand of a continuous casting machine of Krasnoe Sormovo works (Maiorov et al., 1974) and is represented in Fig. 11.8. The system includes a drum separator, circulating pumps, tube systems and a monitoring-measuring instrument. Provision is made for operation with both natural and forced convection. The chemically purified water from the drum separator passes through the pumps (or without them) to the coolers. The water heated by cooling the billet is partially vaporized, and a steam-water mixture is fed to the drum separator, where the steam is separated from water and discharged from the recovery system. The water, together with make-up water is again supplied to coolers.

The specific steam production amounts to about 0.1 t_{steam}/t_{steel}. The steam is generated at a pressure of 4 bar and then with limited possibilities of utilization. As said in subsection 11.3 for blast furnaces, greater possibilities of using this energy may result from raising the steam and temperature to higher levels by means of compression.

11.7 Some Remarks about Waste-Energy Economics

The specific capital cost of waste-energy recovery plants is considerably higher than that of fuel-fired boilers, including ancillary equipment and buildings. As regards energy-recovery plants, the lowest specific capital cost is that of evaporative cooling with natural circulation of open-hearth furnaces; next comes evaporative cooling with forced circulation of open-hearth furnaces; and then waste heat boilers in combination with evaporative cooling in open-hearth furnaces, including, however, the cost of the super-heater. The highest specific capital cost is that of evaporative cooling with forced circulation on pusher furnaces, including cooling of the horizontal skids and a super-heater through which the waste gases are passed.

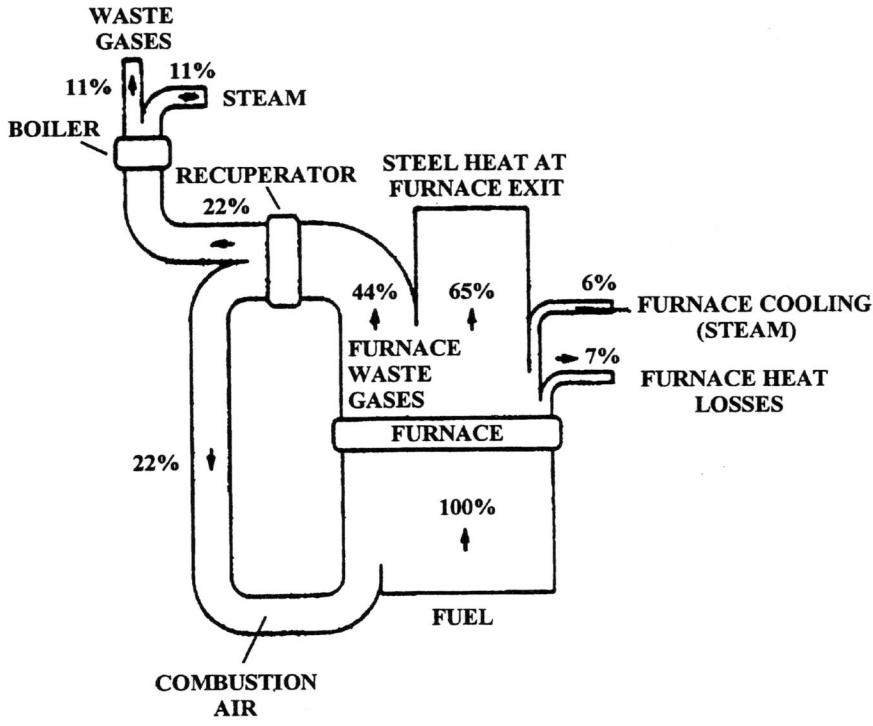

Fig. 11.7. Energy balance for a walking beam furnace (170 t/h).

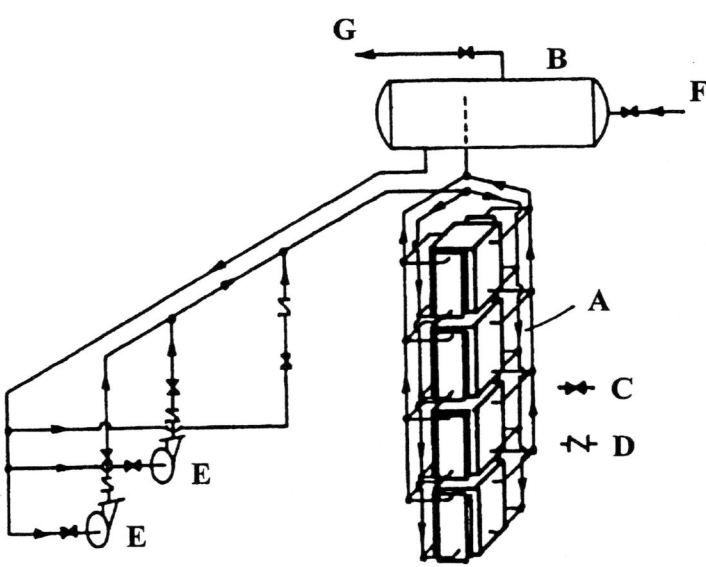

Fig. 11.8. Layout of an evaporative cooling by forced convection for a continuous casting machines: (A) cooling elements; (B) drum separator; (C) gate valves; (D) non-return valves; (E) pumps; (F) chemically purified water; (G) steam.

As regards utilization of steam or hot water produced from waste energy, it is necessary to distinguish between two alternatives:

(i) The works has no power station of its own, and must buy the required energy. This happens in several steelworks and rolling mills where there is no blast-furnace plant, and where production of energy is limited to raising of steam in coal- or oil-fired boilers. Therefore, waste-energy steam may be used for heating purposes and for the direct of power and working engines.

(ii) The works has a blast-furnace plant and a power station of its own, and so is able to generate steam and electric power from surplus blast-furnace gas; that is, from quantities which are not fed into the metallurgical plant and the coking plant. In this instance, one needs to consider if the works must buy additional energy, or if it may just cover its own energy requirements, or if it produces energy in excess of its own requirements, so that it can supply some of it to the public grid.

These factors are closely connected with the basic prerequisites for profitable waste-energy plants. A vital problem is how cost or gain will be affected when using fuel or electric energy, the production of which will be increased, or the purchase of which may be reduced, if additional quantities of waste-energy steam are raised. Important economic questions are the comparative costs of the steam raised in the power station, which in turn depends on the price paid for blast-furnace gas or the competitive electric energy when drawn from the grid, and the operating period of a waste-energy recovery plant converted to nominal capacity.

Chapter 12

OXYGEN ENRICHMENT OF COMBUSTION AIR

12.1 GENERAL REMARKS

The increases in the cost of energy after the 1970s crisis, notwithstanding subsequent decreases, spawned an intense development effort by the industrial equipment manufacturers (especially in Japan and Germany) to make more thermally efficient hardware available. This resulted in the institution of more stringent process operating practices and in the appearance of new equipment offering better exergy utilization (Bené, 1978; Pöttken et al., 1978; Fujii et al., 1980; Ikeda, 1980; Thekdy and Vereeke, 1981).

The most common and readily adaptable methods of saving fuel in industrial heat treating processes are:

(i) excess combustion air control;
(ii) waste gas heat recovery;
(iii) oxygen enrichment of combustion air to reduce the overall fuel consumption;
(iv) oxygen enrichment of combustion air to substitute a part of a valuable fuel (e.g., natural gas or coke-oven gas) by a less valuable fuel (e.g., blast-furnace gas).

In the following sections, some considerations are made about the definition of the "usable exergy" parameter and the development of permselective membranes for oxygen enrichment. On the basis of these remarks, the possibilities and convenience of oxygen enrichment for combustion air are outlined with the use of a proposed general criterion.

12.2 MERIT FACTOR

It is to be noted that the lower calorific value of a fuel, even if with a totally different definition, differs only slightly from the exergy of the same fuel; the reasons have been dealt with by Houberechts (1976) and Baehr (1981). The differences among heating values, chemical energy and chemical exergy have recently been dealt with by Stepanov (1995). In addition, as is known, two amounts of different fuels having the same products of volume flow rate by lower calorific value can have very different technical and economic values. Thus, neither net calorific value nor exergy are suitable for evaluating a given fuel.

Consequently, Bisio (1988) defined the "usable exergy" parameter of fuels in combustion processes, with particular applications to the iron and steel industry. Indeed, the chemical exergy is not suitable to quantify a fuel's technical value for two reasons: (a) prior to considering the "useful effect" - the heat transfer - it is necessary to account for an "essentially" irreversible process - combustion - which decreases the various fuels' exergy in a different way; (b) the work corresponding to the reversible expansion of the various components (in particular carbon dioxide) down to their atmospheric pressures cannot be obtained from the combustion gases, as is implicit in the exergy definition. In addition, the work differs according to the fuel. Thus, in the interpretation proposed herein, "usable exergy", Ex_u, was defined as the exergetic value following adiabatic combustion with a given air excess (e.g., 1.1), minus the exergy destruction resulting from the irreversible mixing of the combustion gases with the atmosphere, after it had reached its pressure, p_o, and temperature, T_o. Of the irreversible phenomena stated above, the first is that of greater importance; thus, Ex_u is an increasing function of the adiabatic combustion temperature.

As an example, let us consider two fuels used in iron and steel industry: blast-furnace gas with a low calorific value, LCV = 2720 kJ/(m^3 (nTp)) and natural gas with LCV = 31650 kJ/(m^3 (nTp)). Thus, in this case, the ratio of the two values of low calorific value is about 11.6 (Bisio, 1998). There is approximately the same ratio between the chemical exergies of the two fuels. On the contrary, the ratio of the usable exergies is approximately 15.

It is to be remarked that the definition of usable exergy is partially based on the same concepts used by various authors for the definition of a reference environment for chemical exergy (e.g., Szargut, 1989).

Besides the exergy losses already considered, which depend only upon the kind of fuel, one may consider, as a fixed datum of the problem, the exergy losses strictly connected to the chosen operative conditions, i.e., in the range of this examination, to the temperature and pressure of the waste gas, which are variable according to plants. Under this hypothesis, let us introduce a different value of usable exergy, indicated by Ex_{uo}. The parameter Ex_{uo} is then defined as the exergetic value following adiabatic combustion with a given air excess (e.g., 1.1), minus the exergy value corresponding to the minimum temperature and pressure chosen for the waste gas.

The parameter Ex_{uo} allows one to reach better precision. However, the parameter Ex_u allows one to reach sufficiently valid results with higher simplicity in many cases with low waste-gas temperatures.

In the second formulation of usable exergy, the authors operated in a way similar to that used in fixing the turbine efficiency "total to static" (Reynolds, 1971; Dixon, 1978).

Let us define as the "merit factor" of a fuel the ratio of its usable exergy to its lower calorific value. This factor is always lower than one and is as higher as the adiabatic combustion temperature of the fuel is higher. Thus, the merit factor characterizes the technical value and, usually, also the economic value. Let us indicate by M the merit factor corresponding to Ex_u (referred only to fuel) and by M_o the merit factor corresponding to Ex_{uo} (referred to fuel and to the chosen thermodynamic state of waste gas).

As an example, Table 12.1 shows the values of M and M_o of a natural gas and a blast-furnace gas having [LCV = 31000 kJ/(m^3 (nTp))] and [LCV = 2650 kJ/(m^3 (nTp))], respectively, for three values of the waste gas temperature (100°C, 210°C, 400°C), whereas the waste gas pressure practically coincides with that of the atmosphere (Bisio and Bosio, 2000).

Table 12.1. Merit Factors of Natural Gas and Blast Furnace Gas.

	M	M_{o100}	M_{o210}	M_{o400}
natural gas	0.700	0.697	0.681	0.637
blast-furnace gas	0.530	0.524	0.498	0.425

12.3 PERMSELECTIVE MEMBRANES FOR OXYGEN ENRICHMENT

Membrane gas separations are attractive because they are fundamentally simple with low energy requirements (Browall and Kimura, 1976; Schell and Houston, 1982; Coker et al., 1999). In the past, however, because of low membrane permeation rates, and, consequently, excessive membrane area requirements, they have not been applied to commercial gas separations. Techniques have been developed for the fabrication of membrane assemblies incorporating membranes of the order of 500 Angström units of thickness. For the first time, it is now feasible to produce oxygen-enriched air using membranes on a commercial scale.

In 1967, Robb reported the permeation properties of silicone rubber for a wide variety of gases and vapors. He also identified the possibility of using silicone rubber, which is 2.2 times more permeable for oxygen than for nitrogen, to produce oxygen-enriched air from normal ambient air. Using silicone rubber membranes which Robb was able to make as thin as $2.5 \cdot 10^{-3}$ mm, it is possible to enrich air up to as high as 37% O_2. However, in order to do so on a practical scale, either the feed air would have to be pressurized to an excessively high pressure, or an excessively large area of membrane would be required, despite the extremely high permeability of silicone rubber. A way to minimize the area is to use ultrathin membranes. For most processes, membranes less than one micron thick are required.

Ideally, for oxygen enrichment of air, the feed air is delivered at atmospheric pressure and a vacuum pump on the product side of the membrane is used to apply the transmembrane pressure difference. With a vacuum system, one works only on the product gas, whereas with a pressure feed system, one works making high-pressure gas, 80% or more of which is discarded.

A technique has been developed to make extremely thin membranes laminated to microporous support materials. The process involves the spreading of a dilute solution of polymer on a clean water surface. Using this procedure, membranes ranging in thickness from 50 Å to 500 Å can be prepared. With ultrathin membranes, an oxygen permeation rate, $\mu°$, as high as [$2.5 \cdot 10^{-3}$ m/(s bar)] has been achieved. This can be compared to [$\mu° = 0.018 \cdot 10^{-3}$ m/(s bar)] obtained with 25 mμ silicone rubber, or nearly a 150-fold increase in oxygen permeation rate.

For common polymers with reasonably high oxygen permeability, the highest oxygen/nitrogen separation factor, [$\nu = \mu(O_2)/\mu(N_2)$] is about 4.8. One can produce oxygen concentrations as high as 55% at very low-pressure ratio p_l/p_h. In actual operation, the minimum pressure ratio one achieves is of the order of 0.1. For silicone rubber, the most permeable common polymer, ν is 2.2, which gives a maximum oxygen concentration of 37%. Multistage membrane devices can be used to increase the degree of enrichment. However, these devices necessarily require the expenditure of a great amount of energy in pressurizing the product from the first stage as feed to the second, and so on.

In choosing the polymer one would use for a particular application, one must optimize the system for oxygen concentration requirement, membrane area, and power consumption. For instance, for a low oxygen concentration application, it may be less expensive to use a membrane with high selectivity and low permeability rather than one with low selectivity and high permeability. Despite increased membrane requirements and costs, power costs are decreased, since one must process less total oxygen-enriched air at higher concentrations to meet the demand.

12.4 POSSIBILITIES OF REDUCING FUEL CONSUMPTION

By enriching the combustion air with additional oxygen, the amount of inert nitrogen contained in the flue gases is lowered, thereby reducing the amount of heat loss through the furnace exhaust. Typical fuel savings are shown in Fig. 12.1 (derived from Thekdy and Vereeke, 1981), where, for example, it can be seen that 45% total oxygen in the combustion air with 1200°C flue gases provides about 34% fuel reduction. Along with fuel conservation, there is a productivity gain due to use of oxygen enriched air. The latter stems from the increase in heat transfer that results from higher flame temperature (Dupont and Bolle, 1989). The installation of a heat exchanger, which preheats air by waste gas, allows an increase in the combustion temperature and the recovery of thermal energy from the same waste gas. Figure 12.2 (derived from Foust, 1979) shows the percent available thermal energy with various flue gas exit temperatures, various amounts of excess air and for preheated air at various temperatures; all curves for preheated air are based on 10% excess air and for an environment temperature of 21°C. The graph is applicable only to cases in which there is no unburned fuel in the combustion products. It is based on natural gas, but is close quite accurate for most fossil fuels.

The average temperature just beyond the end of the hot flame may be read at the point where the appropriate percent excess air curve intersects the zero available thermal energy line.

The use of oxygen-enriched combustion air may be directly compared with preheating in the case where the power required to operate the oxygen plant is regarded as obtained by waste heat from the heating system. In general, the waste thermal energy is reduced by the use of oxygen so that there is a limit to the application. However, even where the oxygen is made with electricity from the grid, the analysis in terms of thermodynamics (e.g., reported by Thring, 1962) is valid. Indeed, the waste thermal energy can be converted into steam that is equivalent to the steam used in the power station to produce electricity from which the oxygen is made. The oxygen enrichment of combustion air increases the percentage of nitrogen oxides in the waste gas (Braud, 1981) and then there is the risk of exceeding legal limits.

In addition, the reduction of the oxygen content in the combustion gas atmosphere of a reheating furnace directly results in a decrease of energy consumption (Calon et al., 2000). One possibility to reach this goal is the zone dependent control of the air/fuel ratio based on the local analysis of the burning gas composition. Such an air/fuel ratio controller was installed on a walking beam reheating furnace. The analysis of the combustion gas provides the current oxygen content in the furnace which is used for the determination of an improved target air/fuel ratio for each control zone.

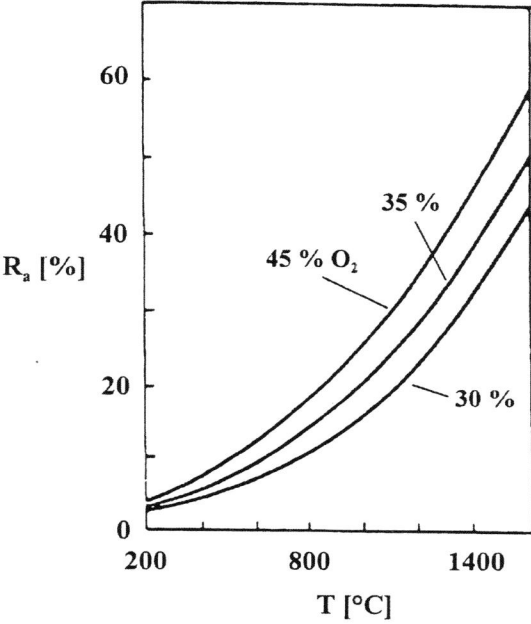

Fig. 12.1. Percent fuel reduction (R_a) vs flue gas temperature (T) with percent oxygen as parameter.

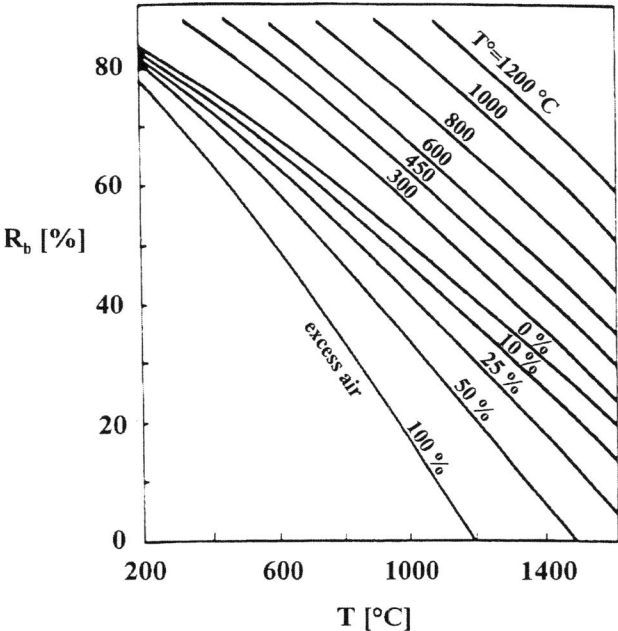

Fig. 12.2. Combustion of natural gas with no unburned fuel in the flue gas. Percent available thermal energy (R_b) with various flue gas exit temperatures (T°), various amounts of excess air and for preheated air at various temperatures (T). All curves for hot air are based on 10% excess air and an environment temperature of 21°C.

12.5 POSSIBILITIES OF PARTIAL (OR TOTAL) SUBSTITUTION OF A MORE VALUABLE FUEL: PROPOSAL OF GENERAL CRITERION

In the iron and steel industry in particular, the enrichment of combustion air with oxygen offers, in addition to the preheating of fuel and combustion air, the alternative of utilizing largely blast-furnace gas instead of natural gas. In some countries, such as Germany, that entails the substitution of an imported fuel with a locally produced fuel (Bonnekamp et al., 1978).

It is to be noted, however, that, by operating in this way, the generally lower total fuel consumption (explained as thermal energy derived from combustion) does not compensate for the higher consumption in producing the oxygen necessary for air enrichment, if one ascribes the same "value" to the thermal energy derived from the combustion of different fuels. Really, this value is different as was shown in subsection 2.

In actual applications, economic analysis by using the prices of several fuels and oxygen is suitable to highlight the convenience of oxygen enrichment of combustion air. It seems, however, suitable to define a technical parameter that clarifies the different values of several fuels and is also a guide to utilizing fuels in the more expedient applications. Naturally, that entails a good energetic integration in the factory and, better, also with other workshops. The parameters M and M_o, defined in section 2, with their pros and cons, are suitable for the purpose.

Let us make a comparison between the equivalent consumption for the combustion only of only natural gas with atmospheric air and the corresponding value for the combustion of a mixture of natural and blast-furnace gas with oxygen-enriched air at equal combustion temperatures.

The following values are obtained:

$$C_{eq}' = G_{Vng} \, LCV_{ng} \, M_{ong} \, , \tag{12.1}$$

$$C_{eq}'' = (G_{Vng}' + G_{Vng}'') \, LCV_{ng} \, M_{ong} + G_{Vbfg} \, LCV_{bfg} \, M_{obfg} \, , \tag{12.2}$$

where:

- G_{Vng} = natural gas volume flow rate at normal temperature and pressure in normal combustion,
- G_{Vng}' = natural gas volume flow rate at normal temperature and pressure in combustion with oxygen-enriched air,
- G_{Vng}'' = natural gas volume flow rate at normal temperature and pressure to produce the oxygen necessary to enrich combustion air,
- G_{Vbfg} = blast-furnace gas volume flow rate at normal temperature and pressure,
- LCV_{ng} = lower calorific value of natural gas,
- LCV_{bfg} = lower calorific value of blast-furnace gas,
- C_{eq}' = equivalent consumption in normal combustion,
- C_{eq}'' = equivalent consumption in combustion with oxygen-enriched air.

If in the waste gas outlet there is a heat exchanger which produces steam for the general network of the works, the value of $G_{Vng}"$ should take into account that a part of the electrical energy necessary to produce the oxygen can be considered as derived from this steam.

Generally, $C_{eq}"$ should be notably lower than C_{eq}' in order that oxygen enrichment can be convenient, owing to fact that one must consider also the higher installation costs.

Always assuming the combustion temperature as constant, one can examine the $C_{eq}"$ variation as a function of the variation of oxygen percentage and then choose the most suitable enrichment value.

When the waste gas temperature is low, the oxygen-enrichment of combustion air is not convenient, not even if the purpose is to substitute natural gas with blast-furnace gas, as is the case of the blast-furnace stoves, whose waste gas has temperatures of about 200°C (Bisio [9], Hoffmann and Meyer, 1981).

In iron and steel works, there is usually oxygen at concentration >99% which can be used in O.B.M. and L.D. converters. This oxygen is obtained by cryogenic separation. The addition of oxygen to the Cowper stove combustion air allows the progressive (and finally the total) replacement of natural gas with blast-furnace gas. The subsequent results are obtained:

(i) The total gas consumption, with reference to the lower calorific value, is reduced, but by a practically negligible amount and is overwhelmed by the energy consumption for producing the necessary oxygen.
(ii) The reduction of usable exergy losses, attained by the (partial or total) substitution of natural gas by blast-furnace gas is exceeded by the exergy consumption for producing the necessary oxygen.

The last statement is well based for combustion with oxygen enriched air, using >99% O_2, produced by cryogenic plants, but the results may be totally different using oxygen obtained by permselective membranes.

A key element in evaluating a process for oxygen-enriched air combustion is, of course, the cost of the oxygen. The cost of the oxygen with a membrane oxygen enricher can be significantly lower than with other techniques, particularly at low oxygen requirements of less than about 20 tons per day equivalent pure oxygen. The equivalent pure oxygen is that amount of 100% oxygen mixed with air to achieve a given flow rate at a given oxygen concentration.

An increasingly important consideration is the energy consumption of the oxygen production process. Table 12.2 compares the energy requirement for production of oxygen-enriched air with that required by conventional processes. As the selectivity of the membrane increases, the energy requirement decreases until a thermodynamic minimum is reached with a perfectly selective membrane.

It is important to note that different factors other than cost are involved in the decision to use oxygen-enriched air. Productivity could be increased with higher heat transfer rates from hotter flames. Oxygen-enrichment of combustion air can be economic in cases where temporary surpluses of blast-furnace gas or oxygen are largely available, as may be the case for cyclical or structural reasons and also during week-ends, although the overall energy consumption is higher than for use of fuel of high calorific value. After all, the time variable oxygen enrichment of combustion air may be used to regulate the energy distribution for large factories in the presence of some production and consumption data that allow only limited variations, as noted also by Risse et al. (1977).

Table 12.2. Energy Requirements for Oxygen Production.

	kWh per ton equivalent pure O_2
Cryogenic separation (50% O_2)	400
Cryogenic separation (>99% O_2)	1100
Pressure swing adsorption (90% O_2)	550
Permselective membrane (37.5% O_2)	210
Permselective membrane (44% O_2)	300

12.6 Final Remarks

In works which are integrated in themselves and possibly also with others, there is the possibility of achieving the optimal utilization of several fuels.

In these cases, the concepts of usable exergy and merit factor, which take into account totally irreversible phenomena that are unavoidable with present-day technology (combustion and immission of waste gas into the atmosphere) or irreversible phenomena that are bound to a chosen operative condition (minimum values of temperature and pressure of waste gas) appear suitable to visualize the value of different fuels with a number in the light of the first and second laws of thermodynamics.

Theoretical adiabatic combustion temperature, already used and on which merit factor mainly depends, is fit only to give a qualitative judgment on the value of different fuels.

Consequently, it is possible to formulate, in actual applications, at least a first judgment on the substitution of natural gas with blast-furnace gas, on the convenience of utilizing oxygen-enriched air and on the most convenient percentage of oxygen from a technical point of view.

The higher the temperature of waste gas in the plant under consideration, the more convenient is air enrichment. Then, usually such enrichment is an alternative to preheating air by waste gas.

In recent years, it has become possible to use membranes to produce oxygen-enriched air. This is due to the development of an ultrathin film fabrication process allowing the use of relatively small amounts of membrane area at low transmembrane pressure differences to perform a given separation. This technology, that allows one to obtain air enriched with 30-45% oxygen by means of energy consumption much lower than with the best cryogenic plants, will allow higher use of oxygen-enriched combustion air in industrial furnaces in the near future.

In our opinion, the possibility of introducing a regulatory element in an integrated energy system, which has many production and consumption data, that can be varied only in a limited way, suggests the possibility of air enrichment in some furnaces as an alternative, in time, to greater use of more valuable fuels in the same furnaces, at least in large iron and steel works, in relation to necessity.

Chapter 13

EXERGY EFFICIENCY AND ECONOMIC CONVENIENCE

13.1 THERMODYNAMICS AND ECONOMICS

Whereas physical sciences deal with interactions between matter and energy, one can say that economy deals with the production and exchanges of goods and services. Since goods and services include matter and energy, physical sciences are interesting for economy. In particular, one can expect that the laws of thermodynamics fix constraints to economic processes, as they make with physical processes. The laws of matter and energy conservation have implications in the use of resources and in the production and handling of the several wastes. The law of entropy production in every macroscopically defined volume (second law) exhibits the fact that all economic processes reduce the operative value of energy, increasing the entropy of the Universe (Ayres and Nair, 1984).

The fact that these remarks between physics and economy are not trivial has been taken into account in 1960s. We will give a particular attention to the second law.

13.2 ECONOMIC PROCESSES

Economy deals with the production, exchange and consumption of goods and services, as already said. Generally, economists state that only resources, which are qualifiable as «scarce», can be included in the field of their science. Conventional economy has nothing to say as regard "non-scarce" resources.

A resource is scarce if it can not be used or bought without exchanging another scarce resource. Practically, money is the usual exchange means: the money amount per resource unit, i.e. its price, in a free market, is considered an economic measure of its value. In addition, a resource can be considered scarce if, to obtain and use it, one must necessarily take away it from other possible users, even if one must not pay anything to have it. The water can be included in this definition of "scarce" in some regions. Such situations are difficult to be dealt with by economists, owing to the absence of a market price for some resources.

Usually, however, every resource has its price, its value in exchange, and then economists are able to express, by monetary terms both the inputs (scarce resources) and outputs (socially useful products). That allows the aggregation of basically different things as work and capital. Thus, land, work, energies, materials and capital can be referred as "factors of production", and aggregated and disaggregated in many ways to match the requirements of the economic model.

The notion of the exchange of goods and services is central to economics. Indeed, most of economic theory is built on a very simple but powerful model of behavior: that rational "agents" (individual or firms) seek to maximize their own utility by exchanging (buying or selling) goods or services in a free competitive market. This model is so persuasive that most economists today fail to recognize either its origin in 19th century political philosophy or the fact that this simplistic form of utilitarianism conspicuously fails to explain social phenomena such as the existence of etiquette, fashion or government regulation. Aggregating all the factors of productions, economists represent the production-consumption system by a simple abstract model (Fig. 13.1a) in which consumers receives payments for their labor or the resources they control and, in turn, pay for goods and services they require. This abstract model clearly reflects the fact that payments by consumers for goods and services must be balanced by payments to consumers (as workers) in the form of wages, and to consumers (as owners of land or capital) in the form of interests and rents. Under "reasonable assumptions", it can be shown that there exists a prize that simultaneously maximizes utility for both buyers and sellers.

One of the major achievements of 19th century economic theory was the mathematical proof that a stable equilibrium exists for the sort of closed production-consumption system shown in (Fig. 13.1a). Leon Walras, a French economist, originally proved it in the 1860s; his work was extended by Gustav Cassel in Sweden in the early part of twentieth century. The model of (Fig. 13.1a) is highly simplified and restrictive: resources are fixed (and given), individual preferences are invariable (and determined), technology is unchanging, and all relationships between economic variables are linear.

The model represented in (Fig. 13.1a) also does not allow for economic growth; however a closely related model developed by John von Neumann in 1945 and by Piero Sraffa in 1960, illustrated in (Fig. 13.1b), allows for investment and technological change within the general equilibrium framework.

The closed Walras-Cassel allocation model, however, departs from physical reality in another fundamental way, which can be seen as soon as the underlying physical mass-energy flows are added to the picture. The model of (Fig. 13.1c) adds the flow of matter and energy involved in the static model of (Fig. 13.1a). Any goods (capital goods and consumption goods) embody both materials and energy; similarly, most services in an economy require some inputs of materials and energy.

The economic model of (Fig. 13.1a) has a source (production) and a sink (consumption) of economic goods. Bur real materials are not really consumed, of course; they are merely returned to the environment as waste.

The economic system can not be a closed system even if one includes the extraction and disposal of materials, unless one includes within the system the global environment and the Sun itself. If one considers such a large system, it can not be in thermodynamic equilibrium. A closed system in thermodynamic equilibrium is necessarily passive and inert, without flows of matter and energy. The flow of matter and energy through the system, in turn, precludes the existence of an economic equilibrium except in the special case of zero growth.

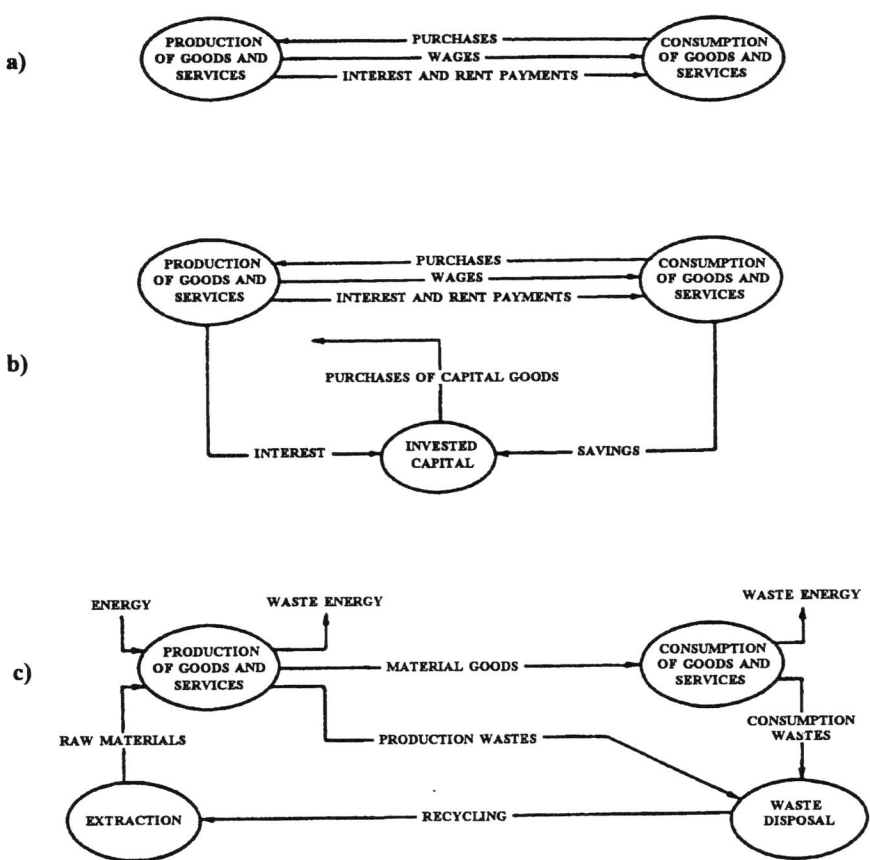

Fig. 13.1 Economic models.

It is clearly more realistic to regard the economy, like the Earth itself, as an open system through which materials and energy continuously flow. One immediate consequence of the conservation laws is that the mass and energy flow in the waste flow must equal the mass and energy flow extracted from the environment. Moreover, the waste flows are obviously proportional to the amount of mass and energy processed into material goods and, hence, to the size of the economic system (at least approximately). In other words, the bigger the GNP, the greater the aggregate quantity of waste residuals that will be generated. However, it does not follow that the amount of damage to the environment, and specifically to the human health, caused by the waste residuals is proportional to the size of the economic system. Many kinds of waste residuals, especially the bulkier ones, are either inherently harmless or can be rendered harmless. The most toxic residuals, such as pesticides, heavy metals, radioactive wastes and some chemical wastes, involve insignificant amounts of mass.

A consequence of the second law, instead, is that the exergy (i.e. the operative value of energy) in the total output in any sector of the economy must be less than the exergy in the input. This is a direct consequence of the increase in global entropy associated with any irreversible process. Materials produce entropy at every stage from extraction to final consumption, even if they may have an increase in exergy in a phase of the economic process. The wastes, from both the production and the consumption sectors have low exergy level (this level is generally zero, if reference is made to "usable exergy" concept defined by Bisio (1988) and considered with some details in subsection 12.2.

The wastes that result from an economic process can be recycled in many cases. However, owing to the second law, the degraded materials can not be returned to productive use without expenditures of additional exergy, which must, in turn, be extracted from the environment. The recycling itself thus necessarily results in additional waste, even if in the form of waste heat to be radiated into outer space.

We should emphasize that the increase in global entropy required by the second law does not prevent the decrease in the entropy of a part of the environment (Prigogine, 1967; Glansdorff and Prigogine, 1971; Prigogine, 1980; Bisio, 1997c). Thus, for example, extracting metal from an ore decreases the entropy of the metal, but the extraction process also increases, by an even larger amount, the entropy of all the material that remains and of any fuel that has been used. Likewise, living organisms maintain their states of low entropy with respect to their surroundings, in spite of dissipative processes, by consuming "materials" (as food or photons) that contain far more exergy than the organisms actually convert into mechanical work or "biomass"

13.3 EFFICIENCIES

In thermodynamics various kinds of efficiency have been defined; now, we will consider energy efficiency (or first-law efficiency) and exergy efficiency (or second law efficiency). Between the two efficiencies, there is a great conceptual difference and often a remarkable difference between the numbers that characterize them. E.g., we report some values of energy and exergy efficiency in Table 13.1 (Ayres, 1978).

In economics, efficiency is normally defined in quite a different way. It is a qualitative, not a quantitative term. An "ideal" economic system (analogous, say, to the Carnot cycle heat engine) is a competitive, free market consisting of rational, well-informed consumers and producers, and involving none of what economists call indivisibilities or externalities. The 19th century Italian economist Vilfredo Pareto suggested that the equilibrium state, or in a more precise way "the non-equilibrium steady state" (Bisio, 1997c), achieved by this system is an optimal one in the following sense: "Resources are allocated in such a way that no person can be made better off without making at least one other person worse off". The existence of such a Pareto optimum depends on each person having a well-defined set of preferences that depends only on his income.

However (and this, at least partially, is far from being negative), real people do not simply maximize a well-defined individual utility function: for example, they subordinate personal interests to the interests of larger groups, they submit to customs and laws, and they engage in altruistic behavior. Thus, the Pareto optimum is a very remote abstraction (as the Carnot cycle). Nonetheless, economists find it useful to define the efficiency of an economic system by how closely it approaches the Pareto optimum.

Table 13.1. Thermodynamic Efficiencies.

	First law	Second law
Processes of energy conversion		
From fuel to electric energy (by means of a power station)	0.4	0.4
From fuel to thermal energy at 540°C	0.8	0.65
From fuel to steam at 120°C	0.8	0.225
Electric heater for water at 49°C	0.75	0.045
Gas heater for water at 49°C	0.5	0.029
Gas heater for air at 21°C	0.6	0.028
Gas heater for air at 43°C	0.6	0.074
Otto cycle engine	0.32	0.32
Heat pump (driven by thermal motor) for steam at 120°C	1.18**	0.30
Electric motor	0.9 – 0.98	0.9 – 0.98
Car motor till the driving wheels	0.14	0.14
Processes of material transformation		
Coke-oven furnaces	-	0.88
Blast furnace	-	0.77
Siemens-Martin open hearth	-	0.66
Oxygen LD converter	-	0.93
Electric arc furnace	-	0.80
Bayer Hall process for Al	-	0.45
ALCOA process for Al	-	0.59
Chlorine production	-	0.40
Ammonia production	-	0.50
Cement production	-	0.25
Glass production	-	0.22

** "performance"

Economic efficiency, as thus conceived, involves an array of variables including incomes and prices of all goods and services: capital, labor, land and resources of materials and energy. Because of this complexity, most economists have rejected the notion that there might be any particular relationship between economic and thermodynamic efficiency.

On the other hand, some physical scientists have argued that a link should exist, at least via the prices charged for goods and services. Frederick Soddy suggested that the price of a commodity should reflect the energy used directly or indirectly to produce it. As is obvious, on the basis of what said in previous sections, exergy, instead of energy, would be the more appropriate measure.

In the 1930s, the idea of energy pricing was exposed by a technocratic political movement, under the leadership of Howard Scott, as a notional panacea for the economic ills of the Great Depression.

The idea popped up again in the 1960s, with the impetus derived mainly from environmental and resources concerns, prompted, for example, by the suspicion that some large-scale energy projects (such as solar satellites) might require more energy (or better exergy) to implement that they could hope to produce. For a few years (and partially also now) a number a physical scientists and engineers were involved in various forms of "net energy" analysis.

However, there was and is no consensus on the appropriate use of "net-energy" (or better "net-exergy") analysis in practical decision-making. What is unambiguously clear, however, is that economic optima and thermodynamic optima do not coincide except under extraordinary and unrealistic conditions. It is to be remarked that the two optima coincide in a free market if, and only if, exergy is the only scarce factor of production, that is the prices of labor, capital and so forth tend to zero.

We remark that, as said in section 10, an only thermodynamic optimization is generally not sufficient to determine optimal solution and that Bejan (1982), dealing with the optimal economical solution, noted that, even if thermodynamic and economical optima do not coincide, they tend to approach themselves as exergy costs increase.

REFERENCES

Abe Y. et al., 1983, Operation of the waste heat recovery system of Kimitsu No. 3 sintering plant, NSC, *Trans. of the Iron and Steel Institute of Japan*, **23**, B-117.

Ahern J.E., 1980, *The Exergy Method of Energy Systems Analysis*, J. Wiley & Sons, New York.

Ahrendts J., 1980, Reference states, *Energy*, **5**, 667-677.

Aichinger H.M., Hoffmann G.W., Pöttken H.G., Reinitzhuber F., Seeger M., Trappe K., 1986, Nutzung von Restenergie integrierter Hüttenwerke - Technische und wirtschaftliche Grenzen, *Stahl u. Eisen*, **106**, 1043-1052.

Altfeld K., Schneider A., 1982, Energiebilanzen von Elektrolichtbogenöfen - Auswirkungen wassergekühlter Ofenelemente, *Stahl u. Eisen*, **102**, 979-984.

Aluigi A., Bonzani, G., Colmano, R., 1988, Opzioni per il ripotenziamento di centrali termoelettriche convenzionati da 320 MW e 160 MW basato sull'adozione di cicli combinati gas-vapore, *Atti del II Convegno Nazionale Gruppi Combinati, Prospettive Tecniche ed Economiche*, Firenze, 27 Maggio, 33-51, Pitagora Editrice, Bologna.

Ameling D. et al., 1981, Entwicklungsrichtungen bei der Stahlerzeugung in Lichtbogenöfen, *Stahl u. Eisen*, **101**, 197-207.

Ameling D., Strunck F.J., Pöttchen H.-S., Strohschein H., 1983, Energy recovery from UHP electric-arc furnaces using hot cooling, in: *Steel and Energy, Proceedings of Seminar*, February 14-15, 353-374, Int. Iron and Steel Inst., Brussels.

Ameling D. et al., 1986a, Metallurgie und Verfahrenstechnik der Elektrostahlerzeugung – Entwicklung und heutige Bedeutung, *Stahl u. Eisen*, **106**, 13-21.

Ameling D. et al., 1986b, Betriebergebnisse eines Hochleistungslichtbogenofens nach Umbau auf exzentrischen Bodenabstich und Einführung einer rechnergestützen Prozeßbeobachtung, *Proceedings of 2nd European Electric Steel Congress*, Florence, September 29 - October 1, **I** (R3.4), 1-25.

Ameling D., Baer H., Bertling H., Lüngen H.B., 1998, Kokereitechnik im Jahr 2000 - Stand der Technik und neue Strukturen, *Stahl u. Eisen*, **118**, 11, 55-61.

Ameling D., 2000a, Stand und zukünftige Entwicklungen in der Elektrostahlerzeugung, *Stahl u. Eisen*, **120**, Nr. 6, 27-32.

Ameling D., 2000b, Stahlrecycling – Resourcenproduktivität und Umweltschutz, *Stahl u. Eisen*, **120**, Nr. 7, 27-32.

Ameling D., 2000c, Advanced steelmaking and rolling technology for sustainable steel, *Stahl u. Eisen*, **120**, Nr. 9, 53-57.

Andon'ev et al., 1974, Evaporative cooling plant for continuous reheating furnaces, Transl. from *Stal'*, N° 4, 376-377.

Anonymous note, 1981, Air dry cooling of coke: USS is coming along nicely, thank you, *Metal Producing*, October, 67-68.

Andritzke W., Gerling R., Pörsch K., Siegert H., Stahl R., 1987, Überwachung der Kühlsysteme bei Elektrolichtbogenofen, *Stahl u. Eisen*, **107**, 667-672.

Arendt P., Baer H., Hammermann H.-J., Huhn F., Kühl H., Opdenwinkel H., Stoppa H., Weinberg W., 2000, Neuere Untersuchungen zum Koksausbringen, *Stahl u. Eisen*, **120**, Nr. 5, 63-68.

Attig D., 1988, Betriebserfahrungen mit Gasturbinen zur gemeinsamen Erzeugung von Strom und Wärme, *Gas Wärme Int.*, **37**, 313-315.

Ayres R.U., 1978, *Resource, Environment and Economics*, J. Wiley & Sons, New York.

Ayres R.U., Nair I., 1984, Thermodynamics and economics, *Phys. Today*, **62**, 62-71.

Baehr H.D., Schmidt E.F., 1963, Definition und Berechnung von Brennstoffexergien, *B.W.K.*, **15**, 375-381.

Baehr H.D., 1968, Zur Definition exergetischer Wirkungsgrade - Eine systematische Untersuchung, *B.W.K.*, **20**, 197-200.

Baehr H.D., 1979, Die Exergie der Brennstoffe, *B.W.K.*, **31**, 292-297.

Baehr H.D., 1981, *Thermodynamik - Eine Einführung in die Grundlagen und ihre technischen Anwendungen*, 5. Aufl., Springer-Verlag, Berlin.

Baer H., Bertling H., 1984, Nutzung zurückgewonnener Energie aus der Kokstrockenkühlung zur Kohlevorerhitzung, *Stahl u. Eisen*, **104**, 595-598.

Barclay F.J., 1988, Cogeneration in arid and cool climates: a new unified perspective using exergy analysis, *Proc. Instn. Mech. Engrs*, **202**, 129-139.

Barry C., 1983, Diminution des pertes thermiques à l'agglomération, *Revue de Métallurgie-CIT*, décembre, 911-922.

Bartu F., 1858, Hundert Jahre Regenerativfeuerung. Der Werdegang des Siemens-Martin-Ofens, *Stahl u. Eisen*, **78**, 713-733.

Beck K.G., 1984, Über einige neue kokereitechnische Entwicklungen, *Stahl u. Eisen*, **104**, 339-342.

Becker L., Hammer E.E., 1986, Verdampfungskühlsystem mit Wand- und Deckelelementen an einem 70 t Hochleistunglichtbogenofen, *Proceedings of 2nd European Electric Steel Congress*, Florence, September 29 - October 1, **II**, (P1.7), 1-15.

Becker L., Hammer E.E., 1986/87, Sidewall and roof panels of a 70 t electric arc furnace with evaporative cooling system, *World Steel & Metalworking*, **8**, 26-32.

Beckmann G., Gilli P.V., 1984, *Thermal Energy Storage*, Springer-Verlag, Wien.

Beier W., Gehrmann G., Möhring H.-G., Westerdorff H., 1989, Ersatz hochwertiger Brennstoffe bei Winderhitzern durch Abwärmenutzung und Hochofengas, *Stahl u. Eisen*, **109**, 221-228.

Bejan A., 1982, Second-law analysis in heat transfer and thermal design, in: *Advances in Heat Transfer*; **15**, 1-58, Academic Press, New York.

Bené T.L., 1978, Higher operating temperature combined with recuperators increases production and saves energy, *Industrial Heating*, December, 6-9.

Bertling, H., 1979, Coke dry quenching - A process for recovering the energy, *Iron and Steel Engineer*, September, 33-38.

Bertling H., Rohde W., 1995, Neue Entwicklungender Kokereitechnik in der Welt, *Stahl u. Eisen*, **115**, Nr. 6, 37-43.

Bertling H., Stoppa H., 1998, Stand der rationellen Energienutzung und Energieverbund der Kokerei Kaiserstuhl, *Stahl u. Eisen*, **118**, 11, 65-69.

Bettzieche W. et al., 1984, Anlagentecnische Erfahrungen am UHP-Ofen der Krupp Stahl AG im Werk Bochum, *Stahl u. Eisen*, **104**, 115-121.

Bisio G., 1987, On a general statement for exergy efficiency, The Winter Annual Meeting of ASME, Boston, 13-18 December, in: *"Analysis and Design of Advanced Energy Systems: Fundamentals"*, 45-50, M.J. Moran, R.A. Gaggioli, Eds.

Bisio G., 1988, Energy savings in blast furnace regenerators, *Proceedings of the 23rd IECEC*, Denver, Colorado, July 31 - August 5, D.Y. Goswami, Ed., **4**, 75-80, ASME, New York.

Bisio G., Rubatto G., 1988, On ice banks in relation to the exergy dependence upon environment temperature, *Proceedings of the Second European Symposium on Air Conditioning and Refrigeration*, Brussels, 23-24 November, 81-88.

Bisio G., 1989a, A second-law analysis on the expediency of intermediate cooling for combustion air compressors, *Proceedings of International Symposium on Thermodynamic Analysis and Improvement of Energy Systems*, Beijing, June 5-8, 317-322, International Academic Publisher, Pergamon Press, New York.

Bisio G., 1989b, On a general statement for efficiency, *Chemical Engineering Communications*, **81**, 177-195.

Bisio G., 1989c, Energy savings in coke oven plants, *Proceedings of 24th IECEC*, Washington D.C., August 6-11, W.D. Jackson, D.A. Hull, Eds., **4**, 1719-1724, IEEE, New York.

Bisio G., 1990a, The exergy efficiency of the devices for thermal energy upgrading - Vent steam recompression as a particular case, *Proceedings of FLOWERS '90*, Florence, May 28 - June 1, S.S. Stecco, M.J. Moran, Eds., 517-528.

Bisio G., 1990b, A second-law analysis of the hot blast stove/gas turbine combine - Comparisons with other gas turbine combines, *Proceedings of FLOWERS '90*, Florence, May 28 - June 1, S.S. Stecco, M.J. Moran, Eds., 733-744, Pergamon Press, Oxford.

Bisio G., Farina F., 1990, Second-law analysis of energy recovery in UHP electric-arc furnaces, *Proceedings of 25th IECEC*, Reno, NE, August 12-17, **4**, 14-19, A.I.Ch.E, New York.

Bisio G., Pisoni C., 1991, On the exergy efficiency of solar air collectors combined with the exploitation of the LNG physical exergy, *Proceedings of 26th IECEC*, Boston, August 4-9, **5**, 123-129, ANS, La Grange Park, IL.

Bisio G., 1992, The exergy efficiency of the devices for upgrading thermal energy with thermal sources and sinks of finite capacity, *Proceedings of ECOS '92*, Zaragoza, June 15-18, 73-80, ASME, New York.

Bisio G., 1993, Exergy method for efficient energy resource use in the steel industry, *Energy - The International Journal*, **18**, 971-985.

Bisio G, Guglielmini G., 1993, Remarks on heat and work transfers in systems with uniform intensive properties, *Chemical Engineering Communications*; **120**, 1-14.

Bisio G., Benvenuto G., 1993, Possible utilizations of the pressure exergy of natural gas, *Proceedings of 28th IECEC*, Atlanta, GE, August 8-13, 2, 167-173, American Chemical Society, Washington D.C.

Bisio G., Magrini U., Rubatto G., 1993, The expediency of ice-banks - Thermodynamic remarks and applications to modern food plants, Paper written for the *Joint Meeting of Commissions C2, D1, D2 & D3*, International Institute of Refrigeration, Fez/Morocco, May 3-7, N° 31, 1-10.

Bisio G., 1994, Thermodynamic analysis of non-equilibrium fluid streams, *Proceedings of FLOWERS '94*, Florence, July 6-8, E. Carnevale, G. Manfrida, F. Martelli, Eds., 405-415, SGE, Padova.

Bisio G., Simonetti S., 1995, Thermodynamic analysis of blast-furnace top gas pressure recovery turbines, *Proceedings of 30th IECEC*, Orlando, July 31 - August 4, D. Y. Goswami, L. D. Kannberg, T.R. Mancini, S. Somasundaram, Eds., **2**, 169-174, ASME, New York.

Bisio G., 1996a, First and second law analyses on energy recoveries in blast-furnace regenerators, *Energy - The International Journal*, **21**, 147-155.

Bisio G., 1996b, Energy recovery and pollution control in UHP electric arc furnaces, *Proceedings of 3rd International Conference "Energy and Environment towards the Year 2000"*, Capri, June 6-8, **I**, 219-230. Napoli: De Costanzo Editori.

Bisio G., 1997a, Energy and exergy analysis of coke dry quenching, *Proceedings of International Conference TAIES'97*, Beijing, June, 10-13, Cai Ruixian, Michael J. Moran, Zhang Shizeng, Xiao Yunhan, Eds., 49-56, World Publ. Co., Beijing.

Bisio G., 1997b, Energy recovery from molten slag and exploitation of the recovered energy, *Energy - The International Journal*, **22**, 501-509.

Bisio G., 1997c, Exergy degradation and system evolution in the light of non-equilibrium thermodynamics with particular reference to Rayleigh-Bénard phenomena, *Proceedings of 4th World Conference on Experimental Heat Transfer, Fluid Mechanics and Thermodynamics*, Brussels, June 2-6, (invited lecture), **1**, 443-450, Edizioni ETS, Pisa.

Bisio G., 1998, A second-law analysis of the "Hot blast stove / Gas turbine" combine - By applying the parameter "Usable exergy", *Energy Conversion and Management*, **39**, 217-227.

Bisio G., Rubatto G., 1998, Thermodynamic analysis of a possible CO_2-laser plant included in a heat engine cycle, *Proceedings of 33rd IECEC*, Colorado Springs, August 2-6, No. I001, 1-7.

Bisio G., Bosio A., 2000, Oxygen enrichment of combustion air, *Proceedings of ECOS 2000*, Enschede, The Netherlands, July 5-7, G.G. Hirs, Editor, **1**, 379-390, Febodruck BV, Enschede.

Bisio G., Goffi M., Martini R., 2000, *Exergy, essergy and efficiency*, Publications of Energy and Conditioning Dept., University of Genoa, DITEC-13, January, 1-78. (ftp://ditec.unige.it/report/ditec13.doc).

Bonnekamp H., Hoffmann G.W., Seeger M., 1978, Erweiterung der Nutzungsmöglichkeiten von Brennstoffen durch Einsatz von Sauerstoff, *Stahl u. Eisen*, **98**, 141-149.

Borowski A., 1998, Entwicklungstrends bei der Stahlerzeugung im Lichtbogenofen, *Stahl u. Eisen*, **118**(2), 51-60.

Bosnjakovic F., 1963, Bezugzustand der Exergie eines reagierenden Systems, *Forsch. Ing.-Wes.*, **33**, 151-152.

Bosnjakovic F., 1967, *Technische Thermodynamik*, I. Teil, 5. Auflage, Steinkopff, Dresden.

Braud Y., 1981, Combustibles pauvres dans les fours continus de sidérurgie, *Rev. Gén. Therm. Fr.*, n. 232 (Avril), 269-284.

Bredehöft R., Hammer E.E., Unger K.-D., 1986, Umbau eines 80-t-Lichtbogenofens der Thyssen Edelstahlwerke A.G. - Kühlkreisläufe unter besonderer Berücksichtigung der Verdampfungskühlung für Wand- und Deckelelemente, *Stahl u. Eisen*, **106**, 1011-1015.

Breidenbach D., 1984, Erste Betriebserfahrungen mit einem neuartigen System zur trockenen Kokskühlung, *Stahl u. Eisen*, **104**, 1295-1298.

Breidenbach D., 1990, Das Konzept der neuen Kokerei Kaiserstuhl, *Stahl u. Eisen*, **110**, 75-80.

Brod H., Kempkens F., Strohschein H., 1989, Energierückgewinnung aus einem UHP-Elektrolichtbogenofen, *Stahl u. Eisen*, **109**, 229-238.

Brooks S.H., Gray F.A., 1963, Availability and economic recovery of waste heat in iron and steel works, *Waste-Heat Recovery*, 224-248, Chapmann & Hall LTD, London.

Browall W., Kimura S., 1976, Permselective membranes for oxygen enrichment, *Techn. Inf. General Electric*, May, 1300, Schenectady, NY.

Bussmann B. et al., 1985, Die Kokstrockenkühlanlage der Kokerei August Thyssen - Umweltschutz, Energierückgewinnung, Produktverbesserung, *Stahl u. Eisen*, **105**, 121-130.

Calon M., Dahm B., Klima R., Stroo D., 2001, Energieeinsparung und Qualitätsverbesserung durch Regelung der Verbrennungsgas-atmosphäre in Wärmöfen, *Stahl u. Eisen*, **121**, 75-80.

Cappel F., Hastik W., 1986, Möglichkeiten zur Verringerung der Abgasmenge beim Sintern von Eisenerzen, *Stahl u. Eisen*, **106**, 768-774.

Catina J.L., Fortune, H.J. Jr., Soroka G.E., 1988, Repowering Chesterfield 1 and 2 with combined cycle, *J. Eng. Gas Turbines and Power*, **110**, 214-219.

Caussade B., 1982, Récupération de l'énergie pneumatique des gaz de gueulard, *Revue de Métallurgie*, Janvier, 1-11.

Cerbe G., 1984, Theoretische Untersuchung eines Winderhitzer-Gasturbinen-Prozesses als Möglichkeit zur Energieeinsparung, *Stahl u. Eisen*, **104**, 1103-1107.

Childs L., Bridges E.E., 1963, Recovering waste heat from coke by dry-quenching, in: *Waste Heat Recovery*, The Institute of Fuel, London, 283-293, Chapmann & Hall LTD, London.

Coker D.T., Allen T., Freeman B.D., Fleming G.R., 1999, Nonisothermal model for gas separation - Hollow-fiber membranes, *AIChE Journal*, **45**, 1451-1468.

Dixon S.L., 1978, *Fluid Mechanics. Thermodynamics of Turbomachinery*, 3rd ed., Pergamon Press, Oxford.

Dupont M., Bolle L., 1981, Energy conservation in industrial furnaces, in: *New Energy Conservation Technologies*, Proceedings of an International Conference, Berlin 6-10 April, **II**, 1869-1888, Springer Verlag, Berlin.

Ehl O., Bordemann F., Korte P., 1987, Bau und Betrieb eines neuen Großhochofens, *Stahl u. Eisen*, **107**, 525-531.

Evans R.B., von Spakovsky M.R., 1987a, Essergy vs exergy - Some advantages and disadvantages of each, IVth International Symposium on Second-Law Analysis,

University of Rome, May, in: *"Second Law Analysis of Thermal Systems"*, 141-153, M.J. Moran, E. Sciubba, Eds.

Evans R.B., von Spakovsky M.R., 1987b, Essergy vs exergy: four critical postulates which separate these concepts, The Winter Annual Meeting of ASME, Boston, 13-18 December, in: *"Analysis and Design of Advanced Energy Systems: Fundamentals"*, 51-62, M.J. Moran, R.A. Gaggioli, Eds.

Faggiani D., 1968, *Fondamenti di Termodinamica Tecnica*, Di Stefano, Genova.

Farmer B., 1994, *Gas Turbine World*, **15**.

Feltoe F.J., Moreton P.M., 1954, High-temperature water cooling of OH furnaces by steam-producing elements, *J. of the Iron and Steel Inst.*, December, 391-395.

Fett F., Pfeifer H., Siegert H., 1982, Energetische Untersuchung eines Hochleistungslichtbogenofens, *Stahl u. Eisen*, **102**, 461-465.

Fett F., Reh M., Strohschein H., 1993, Energiemanagement und Energiebedarfprognose eines Hüttenwerkes, *Stahl u. Eisen*, **113**(5), 109-119.

Fiala W., 1981, Zur Exergie in einer Umgebung mit veränderlicher Temperatur, *B.W.K.*, **33**, 287-289.

Flächsenhaar E., Griebenow H., Krafft W., Reinitzhuber F., 1981, Erfahrungen mit einer Gichtgasentspannungsturbine, *Stahl u. Eisen*, **101**, 127-131.

Fontana P.G., Carrara G., Bruno T., 1977, Energy cost savings as applied to the design of reheat furnaces, *Iron and Steel Eng.*, July.

Foust T., 1979, Graphical analysis for determination of fuel savings, *Industrial Heating*, **XLVI** (July), 10-12.

Fratzscher W., Michalek K., 1989, Comparison between different reference systems for the calculation of chemical exergy, *Proceedings of the "International Symposium on Thermodynamic Analysis and Improvement of Energy Systems"*, Beijing, June 5-8, Cai Ruixian, M.J. Moran, Eds., 532-535, International Academic Publisher, Pergamon Press, New York.

Fratzscher W., Tetzlaff, F., 1993, Exergy calculation of chemically reacting systems, *Proceedings of ENSEC '93*, Cracow, July 5-9, J. Szargut, Z. Kolenda, G. Tsatsaronis, A. Ziebik, Eds., **1**, 237-244.

Fujii T., Nozaki H., Yamagishi Y., 1980, Energy saving in steelmaking processes. *Transactions ISIJ*, **20**: 40-53 (originally published in Tetsu-to Hagane).

Gallo W.L.R., Milanez L.F., 1990, Choice of a reference state for exergetic analysis, *Energy - The International Journal*, **15**, 113-121.

Gautschi E., 1981, Low-temperature heat recovery, in: *New Energy Conservation Technologies*, **2**, 1981-1991, Springer-Verlag, Berlin.

Geist J.M., 1983, The role of LNG in energy supply, *International Journal of Refrigeration*, **6**, 283-297.

Gierig H., Reinitzhuber F., Scholz H.D., 1983, Fernwärme aus der Abhitze von Winderhitzern und Stoßöfen der Thyssen AG, Duisburg, *Stahl u. Eisen*, **103**, 325-330.

Glansdorff P., Prigogine I., 1971, *Thermodynamic Theory of Structure, Stability, and Fluctuations*, J. Wiley & Sons, London.

Glasstone S., 1983, *Energy Deskbook*, Van Nostrand Reinhold Co., New York.

Gneuss G., 1983, Nutzung von Druckenergie durch Gasexpansionmotoren, *B.W.K.*, **35**, 428-432.

Gokcen N.A., Reddy R.G., 1996, *Thermodynamics*, 47-53, Plenum Press, New York.

Goto K.S., Gudenau H.W., Nagata K., Lindner K.-H., 1985, Wärmeleitfähigkeit von Hochofenschlacken und Stranggiesspulvern in Temperaturbereich von 100-1550 °C, *Stahl u. Eisen*, **105**, 1387-1394.

Grubert K. et al., 1984, Einsatz enger Elektroofen-Einhausungen zur Abgaserfassung und Lärmminderung; Betrieberfahrungen an zwei 50-t-Lichtbogen- und zwei 15-t Induktionöfen, *Stahl u. Eisen*, **104**, 235-239.

Gudenau H.W., Lindner K.-H., Maas H., Peters K.-H., 1986, Schalackenabwärmenutzung, *Stahl u. Eisen*, **106**, 1281-1286.

Gurney J.D. et al., 1988, Industrial combined heat and power: investment and decision-making, *Proc. Instn. Mech. Engrs*, **202**, 23-37.

Haering H.-U. et al., 1989, Lärmminderung durch Einhausung von Lichtbogenöfen, *Stahl u. Eisen*, **109**, 343-349.

Haltfeld K., Schneider A., 1982, Energiebilanzen von Elektrolichtbogenofen - Auswirkungen wassergekühlter Ofenelemente, *Stahl u. Eisen*, **102**, 979-984.

Hanliang B., Guiyu L., Xianding L., 1989, Optimum thermodynamic parameters for the Kalina cycle, *Proceedings of TAIES'89*, Beijing, June 5-8, 415-420, Pergamon Press, Oxford, 1989.

Harder E.L., 1982, *Fundamentals of Energy Production*, J. Wiley & Sons, New York.

Harnisch A., 1953, Heißkühlung für Siemens-Martin-Öfen, *Stahl u. Eisen*, **73**, 1026-1028.

Heil W., 1957, Betriebserfabrungen und Schadensfälle an Abhitzekesseln und Heißkühlungsanlagen für Siemens-Martin-Öfen, *Stahl u. Eisen*, **77**, 84-91.

Heilig H., 1969, Gichtgasturbinen in Hüttenwerken. Einsatz und Betriebserfahrungen, *Stahl u. Eisen*, **89**, 355-364.

Held B., Nyland H., Reinitzhuber F., 1985, Betriebliche Erfahrungen mit der Abgaswärmenutzung in Eisenhüttenwerken für Fernheizzwecke, *Stahl u. Eisen*, **105**, 1261-1267.

Held B., Reinitzhuber F., 1986, Prozessinterne und Prozessexterne Abwärmenutzung mittels Thermoöl, *Stahl u. Eisen*, **106**, 1238-1242.

Hoffmann G.W., Meyer O., 1981, Verstärker Einsatz von Hochofengas und Sauerstoff in Hüttenbetrieben - ein Beitrag zur Energieeinsparung und Strukturverbesserung der Energieträger, *Stahl u. Eisen*, **101**, 23-30.

Hoffmann G.W., 1982, Zur Wettbewerbsfähigkeit der deutschen Stahlerzeugung Entwicklung, Stand und Vergleich des Energieverbrauchs", *Stahl u. Eisen*, **102**, 997- 1002.

Hoffmann J., Held B., Reinitzhuber F., 1987, Optimierung der Betriebweise von Gichtgasentspannungsturbine, *Stahl u. Eisen*, **107**, 841-847.

Horio K. et al., 1982, Waste energy recovery at Kashima steel works, *Iron and Steel Engineer*, July, 30-36.

Houberechts A., 1976, *La Thermodynamique Technique*, **II**, éd. IV, Ceuterick, Bruxelles.

Hu S.D., 1983, *Handbook of Industrial Energy Conservation*, Van Nostrand Reinhold Co., New York.

Huang F.H., 1988, *Engineering Thermodynamics*, 2nd ed., Macmillan Publ. Co., New York.

Ikeda T., 1980, Economie d'énergie dans la sidérurgie, *Revue de Métallurgie*; n. 1, janvier, 83-84 (l'article original a paru dans le n. 63 d'octobre 1977 de la Revue Tetsu to Hagane).

Ikoku C.U., 1984, *Natural Gas Production Engineering*, J. Wiley & Sons, New York.

Jablin R., 1982, Coke quenching steam generator, *Iron and Steel Engineer*, July, 42-45.

Jacobi C., 1988, Gasturbinen, *B.W.K.*, **40**, 146-151.

Jäschke A., 1988, Der Einsatz von Gasturbinen im Kraft-Wärme-Kopplungs-Bereich, *Gas Wärme Int.*, **37**, 308-312.

Jordan G.R., Bowman B., Wakelam D., 1970, Electric and photographic measurements of high-power arcs, *J. Phys. D: Appl. Phys.*, **3**, 1089-1099.

Jung R., 1984, Studie zur Kokstrockenkühlung, *BWK*, **36**, 389-390.

Kalina A.I., 1984, Combined-cycle system with novel bottoming cycle, *J. Engng. Gas Turbines and Power*, **106**, 737-742.

Kalina A.I., 1984, An optimal efficiency and ratio of mechanical and thermal output of gas turbines in combined-cycle power plants, *Proceedings of 4th International Symposium on Second Law Analysis of Thermal Systems*, Rome, May 25-29, 105-108, ASME, New York, 1987.

Kameyama H., Yoshida K., Yamauchi S., Fueki K., 1982, Evaluation of reference exergies for the elements, *Applied Energy*, **11**, 69-83.

Kilby J.A., 1963, Waste-heat recovery at the Ravenscraig works, in: *Waste-Heat Recovery*, 249-269, Chapmann & Hall LTD, London.

Kirova-Yordanova Z., Barakov Y., Koleva, D., 1994, Exergy analysis of nitric acid plants: a case study, *Proceedings of FLOWERS '94*, Florence, July 6-8, E. Carnevale, G. Manfrida, F. Martelli, Eds., 931-939, SGE, Padova.

Klammer H., Prost G., 1981, Möglichkeiten und Grenzen der Abwärmenutzung an Wärmöfen in Walzwerken, *Stahl u. Eisen*, **101**, 33-42.

Klenke J.W., 1978, Wärme und Arbeit in der Thermodynamik, *Brennst.-Wärme-Kraft*, **30**, 45-52.

Knoop M., Lichterbeck R., Köhle S., Slig J., 1997, Steuerung des Einschmelzens im Drehstrom Lichtbogenofen zum Schutz der Wandkühlelemente, *Stahl u. Eisen*, **117** (2), 91-96.

Köhle S., 1995, Prozeßsteurung bei der Elektrostahlerzeugung, *Stahl u. Eisen*, **113** (3), 85-89.

Kotas T.J., 1980a, Exergy concepts for thermal plant, *Int. J. Heat and Fluid Flow*, **2**, 105-114.

Kotas T.J., 1980b, Exergy criteria of performance for thermal plant, *Int. J. Heat and Fluid Flow*, **2**, 147-163.

Kotas T.J., 1985, *The Exergy Method of Thermal Plant Analysis*, Butterworths, London.

Kotas T.J, Raichura R.C., Mayhew Y.R., 1987, Nomenclature for exergy analysis, IVth International Symposium on Second-Law Analysis, University of Rome, May, in: *"Second Law Analysis of Thermal Systems"*, 141-153, M.J. Moran, E. Sciubba, Eds.

Kouremenos D.A., 1989, Second law analysis of non-equilibrium fluid streams, *Forsch. Ing.-Wes.*, **55**, 10-15.

Kowalski W., Peters K.-H., Cronert W., Kuhn P, Sucker D., 1990, Optimierung der Brenner von Winderhitzern im Hinblick auf einen hohen CO-Ausbrand, *Stahl u. Eisen*, **110**, 41-50.

Kruger K., Ehrbar A., Timm K., 1998, Schlackenanbackungen und thermische Verluste eines Drehstromofens, *Stahl u. Eisen*, **118** (6), 63-67.

Kubo S. et al., 1983, Operation of the waste heat recovery system of Tobata No. 3 sintering plant, NSC, *Trans. of the Iron and Steel Institute of Japan*, **23**, B-364.

Lardy H., 1953, Wassereinsparung an Kühlvorrichtungen für Siemens-Martin-Öfen, *Stahl u. Eisen*, **73**, 1028-1032.

Le Goff P. (Coordonnateur), Tome 1, 1979; Tome 2, 1980; Tome 3, 1982, *Energétique Industrielle*, Technique & Documentation, Paris.

Le Louer P., Engler G., 1988, Noise control in new electric steelworks, *Proceedings of INTER-NOISE 88*, Avignon, 30 August - 1 September, 2, 883-886.

Liestmann W.D., 1984, Entwicklungen in der Vorstufen der Stahlerzeugung unter den Aspekten von Rohstoffen und Energie, *Stahl u. Eisen*, 104, 1129-1136.

Löffel H., Thinius D., 1985, Gasturbineneinsatz im Rahmen der Kraft-Wärme-Kopplung, *B.W.K.*, 37, 482-487.

Lozza G., Macchi E., Consonni S., 1989, Problematiche tecnico-economiche legate all'adozione di cicli combinati gas-vapore per centrali di teleriscaldamento, *Atti del III Convegno Gruppi Combinati – Prospettive Tecniche ed Economiche*, 101-125, Pitagora Editrice, Bologna.

Lütge R., 1988, Überlegungen zur Drucklufterzeugung mit einem Gasexpansionmotor, *Gaswärme International*, 37, 269-272.

Maiorov N.P. et al., 1974, Thermal schedule in the evaporative secondary cooling of a continuous-casting machine, Transl. from *Stal'*, N° 10, 963-964.

Marin J.M., Turégano J.A., 1986, Contribution to the calculation of chemical exergy in industrial processes (electrolyte solutions), *Energy*, 11, 231-236.

Marston C.H, 1990, Parametric analysis of the Kalina cycle, *J. Engng. Gas Turbines and Power*, 112, 107-116, 1990.

McGown L.B., Bockris J.O'M., 1980, *How to Obtain Abundant Clean Energy*, Plenum Press, New York.

Meckel J.F., Joseph H.G., 1978, Precarbon - Verfahren zur Vorerhitzung von Kokskohlen, großtechnische Erfahrungen, Wirtschaftlichkeit und Entwicklungstendenzen, *B.W.K.*, 30, 285-291.

Meyer O., 1984, Auswirkungen einer Abgaswärmerückgewinnungsanlage zur Brennmedienvorwärmung für Winderhitzer auf die Energieverbundwirtschaft, *Stahl u. Eisen*, 104, 1042-1048.

Molenaar R., Otterbach G., 1986, Regenerativ-Wärmetauscher zur Vorwärmung der Verbrennungsluft für Winderhitzer, *Stahl u. Eisen*, 106, 51-54.

Mori T., Fujimura T., Sato S., 1980, The coke dry quenching process as energy-saving technology", *Transactions ISIJ*, 20, 108-114.

Mori T., Matsuo M., 1983, COG sensible heat recovery using ascension-pipe heat exchanger, *Proceedings of IISI Seminar on Steel and Energy*, February 14- 15, 127-142, Committee on Technology, Brussels.

Morris D.R., Szargut J., 1986, Standard chemical exergy of some elements and compounds on the planet Earth, *Energy*, 11, 733-755.

Munsch M., Mohr T., Futterer E., 1990, Analysis of exergy and evaluation of process plants with a flowsheeting system, *Chemie-Ingenieur-Technik*, 62, 995-1002.

Nagel F.-J., Gierig H., 1984, Erfahrungen mit dem Kühlsystem der Elektrolichtbogenöfen der Thyssen Niederrhein AG in Oberhausen, *Stahl u. Eisen*, 104, 123-125.

Nakagoshi T. et al., 1983, Development of waste heat recovery system of Kimitsu No. 3 sintering plant, NSC, *Trans. of the Iron and Steel Institute of Japan*, 23, B-116.

Nashan G., 1980, Koks für die deutsche Stahlindustrie, *Stahl u. Eisen*, 100, 982-997.

Negri Di Montenegro G. et al., 1988, A comparative study on the ways of converting steam power plants to steam-gas combined cycle power plants, *Proceedings of 23rd IECEC*, Denver, July 31 - August 4, **1**, 301-306.

Neugebauer G., Haering H.-U., Möllers K.-H., 1988, Reduction of electric-arc furnace noise in the steel industry, *Proceedings of INTER-NOISE 88*, Avignon, 30 August - 1 September, **2**, 879-882.

Noda T. et al., 1981, Present and future of water cooling techniques for electric-arc furnaces, *Taikabutsu Overseas*, **1**, 10-19.

Nolzen H.-M., 1984, Möglichkeiten der Energie-Rückgewinnung in der Hüttenindustrie, insbesondere bei der Walzstahlerzeugung, *Stahl u. Eisen*, 104, 671-678.

Ottmar H. et al., 1983, Energierückgewinnung an einem Lichtbogenofen mit Warmwasserkühlsystemen, *Proceedings of 1st European Electric Steel Congress*, Aachen, September 12-14, H5, 1-10.

Palz H., 1984, Wärmerückgewinnung an Winderhitzern, *Stahl u. Eisen*, **104**, 963-968.

Pellò P.M., Vitale G., 1984, Centrali di spinta per sistemi di trasporto di gas naturale, *L'Elettrotecnica*, **LXX**, n° 2, 115-140 (1984).

Perin M. et al., 1983, Caractéristiques et premiers résultats d'exploitation du troisième four à brames de Solmer. Le dispositif de refroidissement des longerons, *Revue de Métallurgie*, octobre, 772-773.

Peters K.-H., 1985, Maßnahmen zur Senkung des Energieverbrauches bei der Roheisenerzeugung in der Bundesrepublik Deutschland, *Stahl u. Eisen*, **105**, 1135-1141.

Peters K.-H., Beer H., 1986, Verfahrenstechnische Maßnahmen zur Erhöhung der Sinterleistung im Werk Schwelgern der Thyssen Stahl AG, *Stahl u. Eisen*, **106**, 763-767.

Pfenniger H., 1960, Abhitzeverwertung und Kombination der Gasturbinen mit Dampfkraftwerken in der Hüttenindustrie, *Stahl u. Eisen,* **80**, 1540-1549.

Pickering S.J., Hay N., Roylance T.F., Thomas G.H., 1985, New process for dry granulation and heat recovery from molten blast-furnace slag, *Ironmaking and Steelmaking*, **12**, 14-21.

Poettmann F.H., 1984, Here's butane hydrates equilibria, *Hydrocarbon Processing*, June, 111-112.

Poppe K.E., 1953, Hochdruckdampf aus Abgas- und Kühlwasserwärme von Siemens-Martin-Öfen, *Stahl u. Eisen*, **73**, 1030-1032.

Pöttken H. -G., Ussar M., Strohschein H., 1978, Energienutzung bei der Stahlerzeugung - gegenwärtige Stand und Zukünftige Möglichkeiten, *Stahl u. Eisen*, **98**: 129-134.

Pöttken H.-G., Voigt H., 1985, Energiebilanzen der Verfahren für die Eiesenmetallurgie - Möglichkeiten ihrer Beeinflussung und Optimierung, *Stahl u. Eisen*, **105**, 1023-1030.

Pozzi A., 1981, Cost cutting/energy saving revamp for steel mill reheat furnaces, *Iron and Steel Eng.*, October.

Pracht E., 1956, Werkserfahrungen beim Umstellen der Dampfversorgung auf Abhitze- und Heißkühlanlagen in einem Hüttenwerk, *Stahl u. Eisen*, **76**, 1224-1229.

Priester H., 1954, Die Wasserwirtschaft der Stahlwerke Bochum AG, *Stahl u. Eisen*, **74**, 34-35.

Prigogine I., 1967, *Thermodynamics of Irreversible Processes*, 3rd ed.., J. Wiley & Sons, New York.

Prigogine I., 1980, *From Being to Becoming*, W.H. Freeman and Co., San Francisco.

Ramakrishnan S., Stokes A.D., Lowke J.J., 1978, An approximate model for high-current free-burning arcs, *J. Phys. D: Appl. Phys.*, **11**, 2267-2280.

Rant Z., 1956, Exergie, ein neues Wort für "technische Arbeitsfähigkeit", *Forsch. Ing. Wes.*, **22**, 36-37.

Reinitzhuber F., 1981, Energy conservation in blast furnaces and steel works at Thyssen A.G., in: *New Energy Conservation Technologies*, **II**, 1843-1868, Springer Verlag, Berlin.

Reynolds A.J., 1971, *Thermofluid Dynamics*, Wiley-Interscience, London.

Rice I.G., 1987a, Thermodynamic evaluation of gas turbine cogeneration cycles: Part I - Heat balance method analysis, *J. Eng. Gas Turbines and Power*, **109**, 1-7.

Rice I.G., 1987b, Thermodynamic evaluation of gas turbine cogeneration cycles: Part II - Complex cycle analysis. *J. Eng. Gas Turbines and Power*, **109**, 8-15.

Risse W., Hoffmann G.W., Pöttken H.G., Seeger M., 1977, Einfluß größer werdender Erzeugungeinheiten der Stahlindustrie auf die Energieversorgung - zeitliche Schwankungen im Energiebezug und –verbrauch, *Stahl u. Eisen*, **97**, 504-514.

Ritter K., Jank R., 1981, Use of low-grade surplus heat for district heating, in: *New Energy Conservation Technologies*, **2**, 2512-2519, Springer-Verlag, Berlin.

Rogan B., 1978, Russia's Giprokoks system - vanguard of dry coke cooling technology", *Iron and Steel International*, April, 101-104.

Salamon P., Andresen B., Berry R.S., 1977, Thermodynamics in finite time, II, Potentials for finite-time processes, *Phys. Rev. A.*, **15**, 2094-2102.

Schell W.J., Houston C.D., 1982, Process gas with selective membranes, *Hydrocarbon Processing*, September, 249-252.

Schemmann W., 1957, Stand der baulichen Entwicklung von Abhitzekessel- und Heißkühlungsanlagen an Siemens-Martin-Öfen, *Stahl u. Eisen*, **77**, 78-84.

Schilcher K., 1956, Die Heißkühlung von Hochofenblasformen, *Stahl u. Eisen*, **76**, 1229-1231.

Scholz R., Reiners U., 1986, Probleme der Wärmeübertragung bei der Wasserkühlung von Wandelementen in Elektrolichtbogenöfen, *Stahl u. Eisen*, **106**, 1017-1026.

Shibuya T. et al., 1981, A system for the recovery of waste heat from the sinter plant, *Trans. of Iron and Steel Institute of Japan*, **21**, 664-672, 1981.

Spalding D.B., Cole E.H., 1973, *Engineering Thermodynamics*, 3rd ed., E. Arnold, London.

Stecco S.S., Manfrida G., 1986, Exergy analysis of compression and expansion processes, *Energy - The International Journal*, **11**, 573-577.

Stepanov V.S., 1995, Chemical energies and exergies of fuels, *Energy - The International Journal*, **20**, 235-242.

Stockmeyer R., Heinen K-H., Veuhoff H., Siegert H., 1990, Einsparung von elektrischer Energie am Lichtbogenofen durch eine neue Ausqualmregelung, *Stahl u. Eisen*, **110**, 113-116.

Strachan D.C., Barrault M.R., 1976, Axial velocity in high-current free-burning arcs, *J. Phys. D: Appl. Phys.*, **9**, 435-446.

Szargut J., Styrylska T., 1964, Angenäherte Bestimmung der Exergie von Brennstoffen, *B.W.K.*, **16**, 589-596.

Szargut J., 1967, Grenzen für die Anwendungsmöglichkeiten des Exergiebegriffs, *B.W.K.*, **19**, 309-313.

Szargut J., 1971, Anwendung der Exergie zur angenäherten wirtschaftlichen Optimierung, *B.W.K.*, **23**, 516-519.

Szargut J., 1980, International progress in second law analysis, *Energy*, **5**, 709-718.

Szargut J., 1989, Chemical exergies of the elements, *Applied Energy*, **32**, 269-286.

Szekely J., McKelliget, Choudhary M., 1983, Heat transfer fluid flow and bath circulation in electric-arc furnaces and dc plasma furnaces, *Ironmaking and Steelmaking*, **10** (4), 169-179.

Szilas A.P, 1975, *Production and Transport of Oil and Gas*, transl. by B. Balkay, Elsevier Scientific Publishing Co., Amsterdam.

Tanaka N., 1980, Waste heat recovery from sintering plants, *Trans. of the Iron and Steel Institute of Japan*, **20**, 200-203.

Tani Y, Shinoda S., 1981, Performance of energy-saving activities and the future outlook in the Japanese steel industry, in: *New Energy Conservation Technologies*, **II**, 1811-1836, J.P. Millhone and E.H. Willis, Eds., Springer Verlag, Berlin.

Teichert E., 1984, Betrieb und Versuchergebnisse einer Pilotanlage für den Verbund von Kokstrockenkühlung und Kohlevorerhitzung der Stahlwerke Peine-Salzgitter AG, *Stahl u. Eisen*, **104**, 1123-1127.

Thekdy A.C., Vereeke F.J., Fuel efficiency improvement by oxygen enrichment of combustion air, *Industrial Heating*, June, 22-23.

Thring M.W., 1962, *The Science of Flames and Furnaces*, Chapman & Hall, London.

Thring M.W., 1963, Further possible means of recovering heat, in: *Waste Heat Recovery*, 214-223, Chapmann & Hall LTD, London.

Tiberg, N., 1981, Heat recovery from molten slag, a new Swedish granulation technique, in: *New Energy Conservation Technologies*, J.P. Millhone and E.H. Willis, Eds., **II**, 1837-1842, Springer Verlag, Berlin.

Unger K.-D., Köhler E., Hilpert L., 1986, Modernisierung und Erhöhung der Produktivität eines 80 t-Elektrolichtbogenofens für die Versorgung der AOD-Anlage bei den Thyssen Edelstahlwerken in Krefeld, *Proceedings of 2nd European Electric Steel Congress*, Florence, September 29 - October 1, **I**, (R1.1), 1-13.

Ushio M., Szekely J., Chang C.W., 1981, Mathematical modelling of flow field and heat transfer in high-current arc discharge, *Ironmaking and Steelmaking*, **8** (6), 279-286.

Utsu T., IHI's large coke dry quenching plant (CDQ), *IHI Eng. Rev.*, 1982, **15**, 1-6.

Van Gool W., 1986, The value of energy carriers, *Energy - The International Journal*, **12**, 509-518.

Van Gool W., 1992, Exergy analysis of industrial processes, *Energy - The International Journal*, **17**, 791-803.

Van Gool W., 1997, Thermodynamics and chemical references for exergy analysis, *Proceedings of FLOWERS '97*, Florence, July 30 - August 1, 949-957.

Vervacke J., Fehn U., 1994, Entwicklung von Gleichstrom-Lichtbogenöfen mit Steuerung des Lichtbogens, *Stahl u. Eisen* 1994, **114** (8), 81-85.

Voges B., 1983, Auslegung, Bau und Betrieb einer Hochtemperatur-Winderhitzeranlage für ausschließliche Beheizung mit Hochofengas, *Stahl u. Eisen*, **103**, 951-956.

Vonnemann R., 1957, Neue Verfahren der Heißkühlung, *Stahl u. Eisen*, **77**, 1126-1135.

Wakefield D., 1984, Recycling vent steam: new energy from old, *Process Engineering*, April, 53.

Wakuri S., 1983, Sensible heat recovery equipment of Oita No. 2 sintering machine, *Trans. of the Iron and Steel Institute of Japan*, **23**, B-395, 1983.

Wesemann F., 1956, Bedeutung der Verwertung von Abhitze- und Kühlwärme für die Wärme-Kraft- und Wasserwirtschaft der Hüttenwerke, *Stahl u. Eisen*, **76**, 1221-1223.

Wesemann F., 1963, Waste-heat recovery in West German and Austrian steelworks, in: *Waste-Heat Recovery*, 270-282, Chapmann & Hall LTD, London.

Wesemann F., Thring M.W., Spalding D.B., Critchley G.N., 1963, Evaporative cooling, in: *Waste-Heat Recovery*, 167-177, Chapmann & Hall LTD, London.

Westin, B., 1983, Slag heat recovery, *Proceedings of Seminar "Steel and Energy"*, International Iron and Steel Institute, Brussels, 245-256.

Winzer G., Reichenstein E., 1981, Entwicklung der Hochofentechnik, *Stahl u. Eisen*, **101**, 835-840.

Zaichenko E.M., Brodovich A.I., Melikentsova V.I., Kupryakhina K.Z., 1980, Industrial emissions at coking plants and their prevention, transl. from *Koks i Khimija*, 1980 (2), 47-51.

Zimmermann K.-A. et al., 1981, Das Elektrostahlwerk mit Knüppelstranggiessanlage der Thyssen AG in Oberhausen, *Stahl u. Eisen*, **101**, 671-678.

Zur M., 1957, Wirtschaftliche und technische Betriebsergebnisse an Abhitze- und Heißkühlungsanlagen hinter Siemens-Martin-Öfen, *Stahl u. Eisen*, **77**, 95-100.

INDEX

A

AC electric arc, 120, 126
AC furnaces, 119
actual entropy production, xi, 6, 7, 66, 71, 76, 78-80, 91
adiabatic combustion temperature, xi, 23, 24, 44, 146, 152
adiabatic expansion, 6, 70
aeroderivatives, 98
air compression, 61, 64, 65, 71
air inlet temperature, 70
air-breathing machines, 99
ammonia, 39, 103, 104
ammonia-rich vapor, 104
ammonia-water mixtures, 105
ascension pipe, 39, 40
ascension-pipe heat exchanger, 40, 45, 167
ascent pipes, 139
atmospheric pollution, 30
Aufwandsziffer, 23
auxiliary heat, 63-65, 67-70, 82, 83
auxiliary heaters, 65
auxiliary regenerators, 12
auxiliary thermal energy, 67, 68, 70, 72, 82, 83
axial turbines, 74

B

bagfilters, 74
BFG consumption, 13
biomass, 156
blast compression, 73
blast furnace regenerators, 26, 161
blast furnaces, 44, 61, 62, 65, 72-74, 82, 83, 138, 141, 169
blast stoves, 11, 53, 54
blast-furnace gas (BFG), xi, 9-15, 17-20, 23, 26, 28, 44, 45, 53-56, 73, 81, 83, 143, 145-147, 150-152
blast-furnace hot stoves, 83
blast-furnace inlet, 9, 54, 76
blast-furnace regenerators, 15, 61, 74, 77, 78, 81, 82, 162
blast-furnace slag(s), 47, 48, 51, 52, 57, 168
blast-furnace stoves, 15, 57, 151
blast-furnace top gas, 9, 162
blower isentropic efficiency, 33
boiler drum, 136-138, 140
boiler outlet, 107
BSC granulation plant, 51
buckstay cooler, 136
burners, 136, 137

C

capacity utilization rate, 118
carbon dioxide (CO_2), 146
carbon monoxide (CO), 10, 31, 105, 106, 130, 131
Carnot cycle, 156
Carnot cycle heat engine, 156
Carnot factor, 66
Cassel, Gustav, 154
ceramic counterflow heat regenerator, 9
chemical energy, 23, 24, 29, 44, 110, 145
chemical exergy, ix, 4, 6, 28, 73, 93, 101, 145, 146, 164, 167
chemical power, ix-xi, 17, 22, 23, 25, 28
circulating pumps, 59, 129, 136, 137, 141
cleaning plant/turbine system, 73, 78
closed systems, 1
closed-cycle gas turbine, 98
coal preheating, 31, 41, 45, 46
coarse deduster, 31-33
COG thermal energy, 39
coke dry cooling, 30-33, 40, 46

coke dry cooling plant, 30, 33
coke dry quenching, 31, 33, 50, 52, 162, 167, 170
coke enthalpy flow, 54-56
coke ovens, 30, 39, 44
coke-oven energy recoveries, 30, 45
coke-oven gas (COG), 9, 10, 17, 20, 23, 28-30, 39, 40, 44-46, 53, 54, 105, 110, 114, 145, 167
coke-oven operating rate, 39
coke-oven plants, 45
cold blast, 9, 10, 53
cold cooling, 132
cold storage, 85
cold wind, 82
combustion, 9-15, 18-20, 23, 24, 30, 34, 40, 42-46, 53, 54, 57, 60, 65, 82, 86, 89, 98, 101, 105, 106, 110, 112-114, 131, 140, 145, 146, 148, 150-152, 161, 162
combustion air, 10-12, 14, 15, 18, 23, 24, 30, 40, 42-46, 53, 54, 110, 113, 140, 145, 148, 150-152, 161, 162
combustion chamber, 10, 18, 20, 45
combustion gas(es), 14, 18, 20, 24, 44, 53, 54, 57, 86, 98, 101, 105, 146, 148
combustion processes, 146
combustion temperatures, 150
combustion-air channels, 12
commercial gas separations, 147
compact recuperator, 99
compact turbocompressor, 99
compressed air, 9, 54, 60, 61, 63-65, 72
compressed air utilizer, 63, 72
compression process, 60, 67
compression system(s), 59, 71
compressor isentropic efficiency, 69
computer analysis, 33, 68
condensation turbogenerator, 111
continuous casting machine, 62, 141, 142
control volume, 4
cooling chamber, 31-33, 52
cooling plants, 110, 138
coupled process, ix, x, 17, 22-28
coupling plants, 71
Cowper regenerators, 9
Cowper stove(s), 9-10, 12, 13, 18, 20, 22-24, 27, 151
Cowper subsystem, 22, 23, 28
cryogenic facilities, 85
cryogenic temperatures, 85, 86, 99
cycle net work, 100
cycles, 8, 18, 87, 89, 98, 99, 105, 114, 169

D

DC furnaces, 119

dead state, 5
descent pipes, 139
desulfurization, 106
devitrification temperature, 51
direct cycle gas turbine, 98
direct utilization, 61, 63, 65, 71, 72, 85, 86
discharge temperatures, 105
dissipative processes, 156
door frames, 136, 137, 139
drum separator, 141, 142
dry cleaning plants, 74, 83
dry cleaning system with turbine, 80
dry coke cooling, 40, 169
dry cooling plants, 29, 30
dry quenched coke, 45
dry quenching plants, 30

E

economic optima, 158
economic processes, 153
economic theory, 154
electric arc furnace refrigerating elements, 121
electric(al) energy, 3, 27, 31, 45, 50, 51, 59, 73, 86, 89, 111, 112, 114, 136, 143, 151, 157
electric(al) power, x, 22-24, 26, 28, 50, 52, 55, 61, 71, 82, 85, 86, 92, 93, 100, 101, 107, 120, 126, 129-131, 143
electric-arc energy, 126, 127
electric-arc furnace(s), 117-119, 126, 130, 132, 135, 168, 170
electric-arc furnace plant cooling, 119
electric-arc furnace shops, 126
electric-furnace (EF) slags, 47, 57
electrofilters, 74, 82
electromechanical conversion, 33
electrostatic filters, 83
energy analysis, 13, 46
energy conservation, 1, 153
energy consumption, 12, 13, 61, 82, 117, 118, 148, 151, 152
energy conversion, 23, 157
energy distribution, 151
energy efficiency, xi, 53, 86, 89, 92-95, 100, 101, 130, 132, 156
energy flow, 41, 44, 129, 155
energy flow diagrams, 41, 44
energy potential, 118
energy prices, 9, 45
energy recovery, xiii, 30, 31, 40, 44-47, 50, 65, 73, 82, 103, 105, 106, 112-114, 132, 133, 135, 161, 165
energy recovery systems, 103, 105

energy recovery turbine, 73
energy resources, 72, 82
energy saving, 10, 11, 13, 15, 26, 28, 30, 31, 39, 40, 46, 113, 118, 124, 168
energy savings, 10, 11, 13, 15, 26
energy transfers, 3
energy transmission, 126
energy vector, 85
enthalpy, x, xii, 5, 29, 34, 35, 42, 44, 52-56, 73, 104, 105, 106, 117, 118, 128, 130-133, 136
enthalpy flow(s), x, xii, 52-56, 105, 117, 130, 131, 133
entropy production, xi, 7, 68, 71, 93, 97, 98, 153
environment temperature, xi, 6, 68, 70, 71, 83, 90, 94, 148, 149, 161
environmental models, 4
environmental protection, 30, 45, 46
equilibrium environment, 3
evaporative cooling, 62, 72, 124, 129, 132, 135-142, 160
evaporative secondary cooling, 141, 167
excess combustion air control, 145
exergy analysis, 4, 46, 54, 83, 107, 115, 160, 162, 166, 170
exergy and energy multipliers, 55
exergy components, xiii, 6
exergy consumption, 13, 15, 151
exergy costs, 132, 158
exergy destruction(s), 61, 66, 74, 83, 130, 146
exergy efficiency, xii, xiii, 3, 4, 6, 22, 33, 36, 53, 61, 62, 65-68, 71, 77, 78, 80, 81, 83, 89-95, 101, 103, 112, 114, 132, 133, 156, 161
exergy factor, xi, 66-68, 119, 120, 124, 130
exergy flow(s), xii, 22, 33, 41, 44, 52, 54-56, 117, 128, 130-133
exergy flow diagrams, 33, 41, 44
exergy flow rates, 41
exergy inlet, 89
exergy loss flows, 132
exergy losses, 4, 12, 34, 43, 146
exergy methods, 44, 52
exergy parameters, 68-72
exergy power flows, 76, 77, 79
exergy pressure recovery, 73
exergy recovery, 49, 50, 107, 110, 115, 132
exergy savings, 15
exergy utilization, 145
exergy value zero, 4
exergy-flow diagram, 60
exhaust gas heat exchanger, 89, 91, 92
expansion-compression system, 64
expenditure factor, 23
external thermal energy, 18, 20

F

factors of production, 154
feed water regulator, 139
feed-water plant, 137
fine deduster, 31, 32
first law of thermodynamics, 5, 6, 28
first-law analysis, 27
first-law effect, 11-14
flash steam, 62, 110, 111, 114
flash steam turbine condenser, 110
flue gas temperature, 149
flue gases, 136, 148
fluid circuits, 12
fluorinol, 111
forced convection, 136, 137, 139-142
forced water cooling, 62, 141
fossil fuels, 148
free-burning, 120, 121, 126, 127, 169
free-burning AC electric arc, 121
free-burning arcs, 120, 126, 127, 169
Freon, 112-114
Freon parameters, 112
fuel consumption, 9, 11, 26, 44-46, 54, 145, 150
fuel reduction, x, 148, 149
fume emissions, 126
furnace bay, 128
furnace coolers, 136
furnace refrigerating system, 124, 125
furnace-cooling water, 136

G

gas cleaning, 83
gas flow rate, 33, 82
gas hydrogen storage systems, 99
gas scrubber, 73, 82
gas-helium heat exchanger, 86, 94
Giprokoks method, 32
global entropy, 155, 156
global exergy efficiency, 8
global fuel consumption, 13
goods and services, 153, 154, 157
gross national product (GNP), 155

H

heat conductivity, 48
heat exchanger(s), xi, 18, 39, 40, 49, 50, 62-65, 68, 86, 91-93, 99, 100, 104, 105, 110, 112, 113, 140, 148, 151
heat pipe exchanger, 64

heat recovery steam generator, 103
heat recovery steam system, 104
heat transfer, x, xi, 1, 31, 39, 60, 75, 76, 78-80, 99, 103, 123, 125, 132, 146, 148, 151, 160, 170
heat-storing mass, 9
heat-transfer agent, 15
Heißkühlung, 135, 136, 138, 141, 165, 169, 170
helium, 86, 87, 89, 91-93, 96-101
helium cycle, 86, 89, 92, 93, 99-101
helium gas turbine, 98, 99
helium mass unit, 99
helium recuperator effectiveness, 92, 93, 96, 99
helium turbomachine, 98
high exergy efficiencies, 105
high(ly) caloric gases, 9, 17, 54
hot air, 49, 51, 52, 53, 55, 149
hot blast, xi, 9, 10, 14, 17, 18, 20, 26, 28, 53, 54, 82, 161
hot blast stove(s), 10, 17, 18, 20, 26, 28, 82, 161
hot spots, 120, 122, 123, 128
hydrate temperature, 61
hydraulic cylinders, 141
hydrogen expansion, 86, 93, 99
hydrogen turbine, 86, 92-94, 97, 99, 101
hydrogen vaporization, 86

I

ice-banks, 3, 162
ignition combustible gas, 105, 106
ignition gas, 112-114
incandescent coke, 29, 30, 33, 36
indigenous energy resources, 29
indirect utilization, 61, 72, 85
industrial heat treating processes, 145
industrial waste energy, 62
inlet enthalpy flow(s), 53, 117, 130
inlet exergy, 78, 99, 118, 130, 132
inlet exergy flows, 132
inlet thermal power, 100, 101
inlet usable exergy flow, ix, 23, 28
insulation(s), 30, 48, 61, 81, 99, 128, 138
integrated energy system, 152
intermediate cooling, 61, 68, 71, 161
internal equilibrium, 2
internal non-equilibrium, 2
internal thermodynamic equilibrium, 2
isenthalpic expansion, x, 67
isothermal efficiency, 61
isothermal process, 60

K

Kalina cycle, 103-105, 111, 114, 165, 167

L

La Mont waste heat boiler, 136
laws of thermodynamics, 152, 153
LD converter, 50, 112-114, 157
liquid bath, 130
liquid hydrogen, 85, 86, 89, 100, 101
liquid natural gas (LNG), 59, 85, 161, 164
liquid nitrogen, 119
liquid slags, 48
living organisms, 156
losable exergy, 7, 8, 66-68, 71, 76-78, 80, 91
low calorific values, 28
low-loss flow tubes, 82
low-pressure vent steam, 62
low-sulphur fuels, 59
lower heating value (LCV), x, 14, 20, 22, 23, 146

M

mass flow rate, x, 33, 67, 81, 92, 93, 100, 128
mechanical irreversibilities, 5, 6, 12, 90
melting temperature of slag, 124
membrane permeation rates, 147
merit factor, x, xi, xii, 13, 14, 17, 44, 130, 146, 152
Merotec Pilot Plant, 48
metallurgical slags, 51
methane, 63, 68, 69-71, 119
methane exergy, 70
methane turbine, 70
mixed combustion gas, 54
molten slag(s), 47, 51, 162, 170
molten steel bath, 120
multistage flasher, 114

N

natural convection, 120, 138, 139
natural gas (NG), ix-xi, 9-15, 23, 24, 26, 28, 44, 46, 53, 54, 56, 57, 59, 61-68, 71, 72, 85, 89, 119, 140, 145-152, 162
natural gas consumption (NG) consumption, 13, 15, 26, 44, 46
net-energy, 158
NG exergy, 59, 67
NG expansion, 63, 64, 72, 140
NG hydrates, 61

NG pressure exergy, 63, 65, 71, 72
NKK air granulation plant, 50
NKK cooling drum process, 50
noise and air pollution, 126
non-equilibrium environment, 4
non-equilibrium states, xiii
non-equilibrium steady state(s), 2, 156
non-flow exergy, ix, 5
non-return valves, 137, 142

O

Oberhausen II gas turbine plants, 99
open cycle gas turbine, 17, 20
open cycle turbine, 18
open hydrogen cycle, 86
open systems, 4
open-cycle turbine, 100
open-cycle water, 135, 136
open-hearth furnace(s), 136, 138, 141
outer space, 156
outlet enthalpy flows, 130
outlet exhaust gas heat exchanger, 93
outlet thermal power, 22, 100
oxygen, xi, 3, 10, 12, 13, 18-20, 23, 119, 129-132, 138, 145, 147-152, 163, 170
oxygen carrier, 18-20, 23
oxygen carrier process, 20
oxygen enriched air, 148, 151
oxygen enrichment, 13, 145, 147, 148, 150, 151, 163, 170
oxygen enrichment of combustion air, 145, 148, 150, 151, 170
oxygen permeation rate, 147
oxygen production, 151
oxygen-enriched air, 147, 148, 150-152

P

Pareto optimum, 156
permselective membranes, 13, 145, 151
physical enthalpy, 5
physical exergy, ix, 5, 6, 33, 36, 59, 61, 66, 67, 82, 83, 85, 87, 161
physical processes, 153
pinch point problem, 110, 111, 114
Pitot tube, 82
pollution, 15, 30, 45, 47, 57, 117, 119, 126, 133, 135, 162
pressure exergy, 65, 71, 73, 75, 76, 79, 80, 162
production-consumption system, 154
pseudocycles, 8

pusher-type furnaces, 15, 141
pusher-type reheat furnaces, 138

Q

quasi-static states, 2

R

radial turbines, 74
radiation, 29, 49-51, 121-123, 126
radioactive wastes, 155
Rankine cycle, 103
recirculating system, 136
recovered energy(ies), 44, 52, 62, 106, 111, 114, 120, 124, 132, 138, 162
recovered exergy, 7, 36, 44, 67, 68, 114
recovered steam pressure, 62
recovered thermal energy, 40, 119
recovery boilers, 135
recovery system, 9, 40, 110-114, 120, 133, 141
recovery turbine, 73, 76, 162
recuperative heating, 10, 12
recuperator effectiveness, 93-98
reference entropy production, xi, 7, 66, 76-78, 80, 91
reference substances, 4
regasification, 59
regenerator system, 9
relative entropy production(s), xi, xii, 7, 66, 67, 71, 76, 78-80, 83, 89, 91, 93
restricted equilibrium, 5
reversibility, 2
reversible expansion, 146
room conditioning, 3

S

saturated vapor, 110
saw-tooth blast temperature, 9
scrubber-turbine system, 76
second law analysis, 20, 28, 82, 89, 99, 161, 162, 170
second law analysis exploitation, 20
second law of thermodynamics, 113
second-law effect, 11-14
setpoints, 126
Siemens-Martin furnaces, 136
Siemens-Martin open-hearth furnace, 137, 139
silicate slags, 48
silicone rubber, 147
sinter cooler, 108, 110-113
sinter energy recovery, 107

sinter(ing) plant, 15, 18, 103, 105, 106, 112-114, 159, 166, 167, 169, 170
sintering system, 105
slag accretion, 126
slag dry-granulation process, 57
slag energy, 49, 50
slag melting, 122
solar energy, 85
solar radiation, 3
solar satellites, 158
sole effect external, 1
sole effect internal, 1
specific enthalpy, x, 35, 66, 87, 117
specific entropy, xi, 35, 36, 64, 65, 86, 87
specific exergy, 33, 34, 66, 107, 108
specific volume flow rate, x, 33, 36-39, 46
steam enthalpy, 34, 62
steam power station, 137
steam pressure, 36-39, 46, 72, 107
steam production, 44, 106, 128, 135, 136, 138, 141
steam/gas combined cycle plants, 28
steam-water mixture, 128, 129, 136, 141
steelmaking, 9, 113, 117, 118, 159, 164
stove adiabatic combustion temperature, 20
stove combustion air, 10, 12
stove combustion gas, 10
stove waste gas, 11, 12
subcooled boiling, 119, 123
Sulzer design, 30
superheater, 108, 136, 137
superheating values, 107-109
system energy, 2, 86, 93
system energy efficiency, 93
system equilibrium states, xiii
system pressurization, 98
system state of unrestricted equilibrium, 5

T

thermal conductivity, x, 48, 99, 122, 124
thermal diffusivity, 31
thermal efficiency, xi, 53, 98, 100
thermal energy, x, xi, 9, 14, 15, 18, 19, 24, 29-31, 33, 39, 40, 44, 46, 48, 59, 63, 65, 82, 86, 100, 103, 106-108, 110-112, 114, 118, 132, 136, 141, 148-150, 157, 161
thermal energy recovery, 46
thermal enthalpy, 34, 39, 105
thermal exergy, 34, 77, 78, 81, 82
thermal fluxes, 128
thermal irreversibilities, 5, 6
thermal phenomena, 1
thermal power, x, 17, 20, 22, 23, 26, 28, 93, 99, 124

thermodynamic analysis, 71, 87, 89, 103
thermodynamic cycles, 98, 103
thermodynamic efficiency, 157
thermodynamic equilibrium, 2, 4, 154
thermodynamic optima, 158
thermodynamic optimization, 132, 158
thermodynamic optimum solution, 67
thermodynamics, 148, 156, 162
throttling valve, 8, 59, 62-65, 67, 71, 104, 105, 140
top gas, 9, 65, 73-78, 81-83, 89
top gas temperature, 74-78, 83
top gas turbine cycle, 89
total gas consumption, xii, 13, 14, 151
transmembrane pressure, 147, 152
turbine blade cooling techniques, 98
turbine combustion chamber, 18, 20
turbine efficiency, 93, 146
turbine inlet, 74, 81, 96, 98, 111, 112
turbine outlet, 65, 67, 74, 78, 82, 86, 112
turbine waste gas, 18, 19, 20
turbocompressors, 62
turbogenerator, 17, 22, 23, 28, 112
turbogenerator electrical power, 22, 23, 28
two laws of thermodynamics, 5, 6, 71

U

UHP electric-arc furnace(s), 118, 128, 129, 131, 159, 161
UHP furnaces, 118, 119, 133
ultra high power (UHP), v, 117-119, 128, 129, 131-133, 159, 161, 162
ultrathin membranes, 147
uncoupled (hot-blast stove – open-cycle gas turbine) process, 21
uncoupled process(es), ix, x, 22-24, 26-28
unrestricted equilibrium, 2, 5
usable exergy, ix, x, xii, 11, 13-15, 20, 22-28, 41, 44, 45, 53-56, 68, 145, 146, 151, 152, 156
usable exergy consumption, 15
usable exergy flow(s), x, 22, 24, 25, 28, 53-56
usable exergy losses, 13, 54, 55, 151
usable exergy saving(s), 11, 26, 27, 45
utilitarianism, 154
utilizing recovered energy, 29

V

vaporization, 85, 86, 89, 103, 111
vent steam, 62, 63, 140, 170
volume flow rate, x, 36, 54, 124, 128, 145, 150
volumetric displacement work, 5

Index

W

Wairas-Cassel allocation model, 154
walking beam furnace, 141, 142
warm cooling, 120, 124, 129, 132, 133, 135, 138
warm cooling plant, 135, 138
waste energy, 30, 47, 51, 63, 82, 89, 99, 114, 135, 143
waste energy potential, 47
waste gas(es), ix, x, 12-15, 18, 19, 29, 30, 34, 44-46, 86, 89, 106, 119, 120, 128-131, 133, 135, 137, 138, 141, 145, 146, 148, 151, 152
waste gas heat recovery, 145
waste gas pressure, 146
waste heat boiler, 138, 141
waste heat hot water generator, 110
waste heat recovery, 17, 159, 166, 167
waste products, 4
waste residuals, 155
waste thermal energy, 15, 18, 65, 82, 99, 148
waste-energy plants, 143
waste-gas heat exchanger, 100
waste-gas temperatures, 146
water flow rate, 81, 82
water heating, 15
water outlet temperature, 123, 124, 127
water quenching, 47
water-steam system, 120, 135
weathering products, 4
wet cleaning plant, 76, 77, 82
wet cleaning system, 76-78